LEGAL ASPECTS

OF

MEDICAL RECORDS

Legal Aspects of
Medical Records

BY

EMANUEL HAYT, LL.B. 1899-

Adjunct Associate Professor of Administrative Medicine,
Columbia University;

Counsel, Hospital Association of New York State,
Hospital Educational and Research Fund,
American Association of Nurse Anesthetists;

Fellow (Hon.) of American College of Hospital Administrators;

Fellow of American Academy of Forensic Sciences;

Member of the New York Bar

JONATHAN HAYT, B.A., LL.B.

Lecturer in Public Health and Administrative Medicine,
Columbia University;

Associate Counsel, Hospital Association of New York State,
Hospital Educational and Research Fund;

Member of the New York Bar

HAYT and HAYT, Counsel
Greater New York Hospital Association

1 9 6 4

PHYSICIANS' RECORD COMPANY

BERWYN, ILLINOIS

© Physicians' Record Company 1964

Copyright 1964

in the U.S. and Canada

by

Physicians' Record Company

———

Second Printing 1971

Printed in the United States of America by

Physicians' Record Company, Berwyn, Illinois

Dedicated to

the Memory of

LILLIAN R. HAYT, M.A., J.D.

who co-authored:

Legal Aspects of Hospital Practice, 1938,
  HAYT & HAYT

Legal Guide for American Hospitals, 1940,
  HAYT & HAYT

Law of Hospital, Physician & Patient, 1947 (1st Edition)
  HAYT & HAYT

Law of Hospital, Physician & Patient, 1952 (2nd Edition)
  HAYT, HAYT & GROESCHEL

Law of Hospital and Nurse, 1958
  HAYT, GROESCHEL & McMULLAN

FOREWORD

TODAY, hospitals and physicians are increasingly subject to tort claims and lawsuits. The best protection against an unjustified lawsuit is a complete, accurate medical record.

The modern practice of medicine emphasizes treatment of the patient as a whole. It brings into play all the skills and techniques of physicians, nurses and technicians. Proper management of the care of the patient requires prompt and accurate recording in the record by each member of the clinical team. The only reliable way to make sure that everyone concerned is fully and currently informed is by means of the written record. The good medical record contributes to the professional care of the patient and also reflects on the quality of this professional care. When either of these items are questioned, the medical record that has been written becomes the very keystone in the impending legal process.

This book should prove of inestimable value to the medical record librarian. If she has any question as to her responsibilities or course of conduct concerning the medical record she can find it in this text. Hospital trustees, administrators and physicians have available at their fingertips in this book the proper facts and references to guide them in their search for what is right and what their responsibilities are in regard to medical records.

Roscoe Pound, lecturing at Harvard University said, "Law is intended to serve the community, protect individual rights, provide equal treatment and be exact." The authors of this book, with its splendid educational and legal text and reference guide, have done this admirably for us.

KENNETH B. BABCOCK, M.D., F.A.C.S.,
F.A.C.H.A., *Director, Joint Commission
on Accreditation of Hospitals*

FOREWORD

ANYONE who has spent a lifetime in the field of Medical Records is appreciative of the diverse problems which may arise, and often do arise as the result of use and occasionally misuse of information within the records. From ethical and legal standpoints, the burden of secrecy placed upon those who have access to medical records is great. Medical Record Librarians and those who must regard with special care the custodial factor of privileged information have need for a textbook which will deal adequately with these important aspects of medical records. Such a book is now at hand in LEGAL ASPECTS OF MEDICAL RECORDS by Emanuel Hayt and Jonathan Hayt, both of whom have practiced law in medical and hospital fields over a period of years. This text is the outcome of their extensive knowledge and experience.

The text is clearly, concisely and understandably written. Its assertions are well documented by actual cases illustrative of litigation and the application of the law. It covers a wide variety of topics and becomes a handy reference for the answer to basic and principal problems which daily plague the librarian. The reader of this work will be better able thereafter to offer intelligent advice when the legal aspects of medical records are brought to question — this fact applies not only to the medical record librarian, the hospital administrator, the physician, the student, but as well to the rising legal practitioner.

(MRS.) JE HARNED BUFKIN, R.R.L.
Associate Professor in Medical Record Library Science
Director, Department of Medical Records
Duke University Medical Center
Durham, North Carolina

PREFACE

IN AN article published in *Medical Record News* in October 1963 by Willard Bartlett, M.D., F.A.C.S., the author states that he is "thankful that neither my duties nor my personal experiences have qualified me to speak more than briefly of the hospital record as a document whose contents may be reviewed in a court of law, or to sustain or deny a charge of negligence. During my earliest training I was indoctrinated with the principle that the physician's entries in the chart should be both sufficiently clear and complete that there could be no doubt as to what he thought and did about the situation in point." Dr. Bartlett advises that "the hospital record should receive more searching scrutiny within the hospital itself than it will in court."

One of the purposes of this textbook is to provide a means, to the extent possible, of permitting the medical record librarian, as well as the attending physician, to avoid scrutiny of medical records based on negligence or malpractice within the hospital. The medical record more frequently is used, however, not to establish carelessness within the hospital, but to prove the patient's injuries in cases in which he is suing a defendant for damages arising out of an accident. No matter what the need may be for the medicolegal use of the record, both in and out of court, the first "scrutiny" of its contents should be within the hospital itself. Here the medical record librarian serves as the reviewer of the record to assure its quality in accordance with recognized standards.

Although the contents of the medical record are prescribed by the Joint Commission on Accreditation of Hospitals and are reviewed by a hospital medical records committee of physicians, it is the trained professional — the medical record librarian — who is responsible for the final seal of approval of the record's contents and completeness, in the sense, at least, that she is a technical expert. The measurement of patient care, on the other hand, and the physician's contribution to the record, are the concern chiefly of the medical staff. It is after the hospital's personnel have recorded their entries as admission or consultation notes, progress notes, operative dictation and a discharge summary that the record assumes the status of a legal document.

It should be noted, however, that this record of treatment does not constitute the entire record of the hospital, since various consents are needed before the patient may be subjected to certain procedures. The importance of these various forms of consent which are published in this book and their legal significance should be a matter of concern to every medical record librarian, for without such consent the physician and the hospital may become involved in litigation. Scrutiny of the chart by the medical record librarian for proper forms should be one of her tasks.

The importance of legal knowledge for medical record librarians is recognized by the professional curriculum for medical record librarians under the *Essentials for an Acceptable School,* which includes in its required courses the subject of "Legal Aspects of Medical Record Science." It is one of the courses "very important to the students' understanding and confidence in their ability to carry out professional responsibilities."

It is hoped that the new guide book on legal problems will be of everyday use to the medical record librarian in her duties at the hospital, although the book is not intended as a substitute for competent legal advice in specific situations.

The authors are grateful for the gracious and expert advice and assistance of Mrs. Edna K. Huffman, medical records consultant for the Physicians' Record Company, who reviewed the manuscript and gave the benefit of her long experience in the field. Her participation has helped to assure that the technical aspects relating to the practice of medical records science are accurate. Mrs. Huffman was of particular assistance in pointing out the legal areas of interest to medical record librarians.

Some of the related material from previous works by the authors, including the late Lillian R. Hayt, M.A., J.D., August H. Groeschel, M.D., and Dorothy McMullan, R.N., has been revised and included in this expanded book on medical records. The untimely passing of Mrs. Hayt after the completion of the manuscript of the present text has deprived her of the satisfaction of seeing the results of her contribution, which is acknowledged with gratitude by the undersigned.

EMANUEL HAYT
JONATHAN HAYT

TABLE OF CONTENTS

Chapter   *Page*

I. The Patient's Record.. **1**

Standards for Medical Records.. 1
The Joint Commission on Accreditation of
    Hospitals... 2
Medical Record Standards of Joint Commission   3
Early Medical Records... 4
Contents of a Modern Medical Record..................... 5
Medical Record Science as a Profession................ 7
The Medical Record Librarian... 8
The Medical Record Librarian as Custodian..... 9
Duty to Maintain Confidential Status..................... 10
Patient's History in the Record..................................... 10
The Doctor's Order Sheet.. 16
The Nurses' Notes... 18
Authentication by Attending Physician................ 20
Reports of Specialists.. 25
Signatures of Physicians... 30
Procedure for Corrections... 32
Use of Medical Record Forms.. 32
Summary of the Medical Record................................... 35

II. Completion of Medical Records.................................. **36**

Problem of Incomplete Medical Records................ 36
Time Limit for Completing Records......................... 37
Importance of Adequate Medical Records........ 38
Functions of Medical Records Committee.......... 38
Signing the Record... 42
Survey by Joint Commission... 43
Removal of Records from Hospital............................. 44
Effect of Delay in Recording... 45

Chapter   *Page*

III. Preservation of Medical Records and X-Rays............ **47**

    The Record Control Program......................... 48
    Abstracting the Record.............................. 50
    Use of Microfilm.................................... 51
    AHA Statement on Medical Records
        Retention.. 52
    Guide to Retention of Hospital Records.............. 54
    Retention of Nurses' Notes.......................... 56
    Records of Deceased Physicians...................... 57
    Preservation of X-ray Films......................... 58
    Ownership of Films.................................. 59
    Policy on Ownership................................. 60
    The Storage Problem................................. 62
    Reasons for Preservation............................ 62
    Length of Time for Preservation..................... 64
    Methods of Preservation............................. 65
    Effect of Statutes of Limitations................... 66
    Limitations in Malpractice Cases.................... 67
    Malpractice Based on Alleged Contract............... 68
    Breach of Contract Limitations...................... 68
    The Husband's Cause for Action...................... 69
    Cases of Fraudulent Concealment..................... 69
    Postponement of the Statute......................... 70
    Causes of Action in Favor of Minors................. 71

IV. Confidential Communications........................... **73**

    Doctrine of Confidential Communications............. 74
    Purpose of Confidential Relationship................ 75
    Essential Elements of Privileged
        Communications................................... 75
    Application to Other Medical and Allied
        Practitioners.................................... 77

Chapter   *Page*

Partners of Physicians and Hospital
  Personnel.. 78
Inclusion of Professional Nurses Within
  Privilege.. 79
Confidentiality of Incident Reports................... 80
Confidential Information in Tax Cases.............. 82

V. Release of Medical Information........................ **84**

General Policies for Release of Information........ 84
Private Attending Physician's Approval not
  Controlling.. 86
Requirement for Signed Authorization of
  Patient.. 87
Furnishing Abstracts of the Record.................... 90
Preparing Photostatic Copies of Record............. 91
Disclosure of Names of Physicians...................... 92
Medical Information on Mental Patients............. 92
Information for Which no Authorization is
  Needed... 93
Use by Hospital Medical Staff for Study and
  Research... 93
Reports Required by Law...................................... 94
Medical Reports by Physicians............................ 94
Examination by Attorneys Representing
  Patients.. 95
Inspections by Defendants or Their Attorneys.. 96
Insurance Company Forms.................................... 97
Examination of Record by Patient or Family
  Undesirable.. 100
Inquiries from Employers...................................... 102
Abstracts for Other Hospitals.............................. 103
Information for Physicians.................................... 103
Authority of Governmental Agencies.................. 104
Information for Social Agencies............................ 104

Chapter   *Page*

VI. Courts and Jurisdiction.. **105**

The Federal Judicial System............................... 106
United States District Courts.............................. 106
United States Supreme Court............................. 107
Federal Administrative Agencies........................ 107
State Judicial System....................................... 108
Municipal, District or Justices Courts................. 108
County and Circuit Courts................................. 108
Justice of the Peace Courts.............................. 109
Surrogates Courts.. 109
Supreme Courts or Courts of Appeal................. 109
State Administrative Agencies............................ 110

VII. Legal Proceedings Before Trial......................... **111**

Disposition of Claims and Suits......................... 112
Breaches of Contract and Torts Distinguished.. 112
Parties and Pleadings...................................... 113
Service of the Summons................................... 114
The Complaint... 114
The Answer... 115
The Counterclaim and Reply............................. 115
The Bill of Particulars...................................... 115
Hearing of Motions... 116
Examination Before Trial.................................. 116
Interrogatories and Commissions....................... 117
Demanding Admission of Facts......................... 118
Notice of Trial... 118
Memorandum of Law....................................... 119

VIII. Subpoena of Witnesses and Records.................. **120**

The Power to Subpoena.................................... 120
Service of the Subpoena................................... 121
Compelling Attendance of Witness...................... 122

Chapter   *Page*

Payment of Fees and Mileage........................ 122

Subpoena of Records................................ 123

Power to Subpoena Hospital Records................. 123

Who May Be Subpoenaed.............................. 125

Disobedience of the Subpoena....................... 125

Subpoena for Medical Witness....................... 126

Records of Mental Patients......................... 127

IX. The Law of Evidence................................ **129**

Direct Evidence.................................... 129

Indirect or Circumstantial Evidence................ 129

Real or Demonstrative Evidence..................... 130

The Judicial Notice Rule........................... 131

Presumptions of Law................................ 131

Doctrine of *Res Ipsa Loquitur*.................... 132

Admissibility of Evidence.......................... 132

The Burden of Proof................................ 133

Nature of Hearsay Evidence......................... 134

Competency, Relevancy and Materiality of
    Evidence....................................... 135

The *Res Gestae* Rule.............................. 135

Dying Declarations................................. 136

Self-Serving Declarations.......................... 136

X. Documentary Evidence............................... **138**

The Best Evidence Rule............................. 138

Proof by Secondary Evidence........................ 139

The Parol (Oral) Evidence Rule..................... 139

Public Documents as Evidence....................... 140

Authentication of Private Documents................ 140

Use of Photographs................................. 141

Medical Books as Evidence.......................... 141

Chapter   *Page*

XI. **Tissue Committee Reports As Evidence** 143

Functions of the Tissue Committee 144
The Utilization Committee 146
The Work Sheet 147
Retention of Tissue Committee Reports 149
Use for Medicolegal Purposes 151
Records as Privileged Communications 153
Statutes on Tissue Committee Records 156

XII. **X-Rays, Microfilms, and Photographs As Evidence** 159

Marking Films for Identification 160
When Identification is Unnecessary 160
Admissibility of Copies of X-rays 161
Admission of Photostatic Copies of Records 161
Reproductions from Microfilm 162
Photographs as Evidence 164

XIII. **Hospital Records in Court** 165

The Business Entries Rule 165
Preliminary Proof Required for Admissibility 167
The Medical Record Librarian as a Witness 168
The Hearsay Rule and Admissibility 169
Records and Notes Must Be Relevant 171
Narrative Statements Must Be Those of
   Patient 172
Effect of Privileged Doctrine on Admissibility 173
Self-Serving Declarations Not Admissible 174
Admissions Against Interest 175
Admissibility of Diagnoses and Medical
   Observations 175
Admissibility of Psychiatric Opinions 177
Reports of Laboratory Tests 178
Nurses' Notes as Evidence 179

Chapter   *Page*

Records of Public Hospitals............................. 180
Admission of Financial Records.................... 181
Correspondence and Social Service Records........ 182
Private Medical Records of Physician................ 182

XIV. Trial Procedure.. **185**

Right to Trial by Jury................................. 185
Qualifications of Jurors.............................. 186
Questions of Fact Are for Jury...................... 186
Credibility of Witnesses is for the Jury............. 187
Questions of Law Are for the Court................. 188
Some Questions of Fact Are for Determination of
    Court... 188
Amount of Verdict is Fixed by Jury................. 188
Findings of Fact by Court........................... 189
Selection of the Jury............................... 189
Opening Address to the Jury....................... 189
Preliminary Motions................................ 190
Direct Examination of Witnesses................... 190
Cross-Examination of Plaintiff's Witness........... 191
Motion to Dismiss at End of Plaintiff's Case...... 191
Testimony of Defendant's Witnesses................ 192
Use of Exhibits in Evidence........................ 192
Motion at Close of Entire Case.................... 192
"Summing Up" to the Jury......................... 192
Instructions to the Jury............................ 193
The Verdict of the Jury............................ 194

XV. The Patient's Privacy.................................... **195**

Right of Privacy................................... 195
States in Which the Right Exists................... 196
Public Personages in Hospitals..................... 196
Death Ends Right of Privacy....................... 197
Newspaper Publicity of Patients.................... 197

Chapter   *Page*

Press, Radio and Television Relations 199
Patient's Privacy in Medical Teaching 200
Private Patients for Clinical Instruction 200
Intrusion on Patients by Laymen 201
Visitors to the Patient in Hospital 202
Rules for Visits by Attorneys 203
Rules on Seeking Legal Business 208

XVI. **Photographs of Patients** **209**

Pictures of Public Figures 209
Photographs of News Interest 210
Legal Consent to Photograph 211
Clinical Photography 212
Use of Postmortem Photographs 213
Publication of Photographs in Medical
   Journals 214
Patient's Authorization for Demonstration 215
Television Demonstrations 216
Exhibition of Patient in Motion Pictures 216
Ownership of Medical Photographs and
   Negatives 216

XVII. **Patients' Property Records** **218**

Delivery is Contract of Bailment 218
Hospital is Not Insurer 219
Preparation of Clothes List 219
Handling Cash and Valuables 220
Responsibility for Dentures 220
Deposits of Cash 222
Property of Helpless Patients 223
Property of Deceased Patients 223
Liability for Misdelivery of Property 224
Lost, Abandoned and Mislaid Property 224
Crime to Keep Found Articles 226

Chapter   *Page*

XVIII. Consents for Treatment **227**

    Identification of Patient 228
    Form and Necessity of Consent 229
    Oral Consent is Valid if Proved 229
    Consent by Telephone 230
    Consent by Telegram 230
    Witnessing the Consent 231
    Procedures Requiring Consent 231
    Informing the Patient 232

XIX. Authorizations for Minors **236**

    Legal Principles in Cases of Minors 236
    Consent is Implied in Emergencies 237
    Ratification of Unauthorized Operation 238
    Siblings Have No Authority to Consent 238
    Consents of Mature Minors 238
    Emancipated Minors 239
    Authorization of Emancipated Minors 239
    Consent of Married Minors 240
    Court Orders May Grant Consent 240

XX. Operations Without Consent **242**

    Damages for Operation Without Consent 242
    Fraudulent Consent is Invalid 243
    Lack of Consent of Husband 244
    Auxiliary Operations Without Consent 244
    Emergencies as Implied Consent 244
    Cesarean Sections as Emergencies 245

XXI. Consent for Blood Transfusions **247**

    Homologous Serum Jaundice 248
    State Not Liable as Distributor 248
    Transfusion is Not Sale of Blood 249
    Express Warranty of Fitness 251

Chapter   *Page*

Administering Wrong Type of Blood................ 252
Transfusion of the Wrong Patient.................... 254
Injuries to Blood Donors.................................. 255
Jehovah's Witnesses and Blood Transfusions...... 256
Objections of Parents on Religious Grounds........ 258
Elective Procedures....................................... 261
Statement of American Hospital Association...... 261

XXII. **Records of Abortions**... **267**

Recording History and Opinions.................... 267
The Consultation Record............................... 268
Confidential Communications Concerning
    Abortions... 269
Abortion Defined Medically.......................... 269
Abortion Defined Legally.............................. 269
Unlawful Inducing of Abortions..................... 270
Therapeutic Abortions................................. 270
Legal and Medical Indications for Therapeutic
    Abortions... 272
Religious Viewpoints.................................. 273

XXIII. **Consent for Sterilization and
    Artificial Insemination**................................. **275**

Legal Considerations.................................. 275
Criminal Liabilities.................................... 276
Reasons for Sterilization Operations............... 276
Legal Control of Nontherapeutic Sterilization.... 278
Prevention of Procreation of the Unfit
    (Eugenic).. 279
Conditions for Valid Consent....................... 280
Consent of Husband for Operation on Wife........ 280
Therapeutic Sterilization of the Husband.......... 281
Religious Attitudes on Sterilization............... 282
Civil Actions for Sterilization Operations........ 282

Chapter   *Page*

Consent for Artificial Insemination................ 284
Legal Decisions on Artificial Insemination......... 284

XXIV. **Autopsy Consents**................................. **286**

Who May Pronounce the Patient Dead.............. 287
The Death Certificate............................. 287
Rights in Dead Bodies............................. 288
Damages for Unlawful Autopsies................... 288
Securing Permission for Autopsy.................. 289
Administrative Responsibility for Autopsy........ 289
Use of Telegraph or Telephone Consent............ 290
Limitations on Autopsies.......................... 291
Religious Objections to Autopsies................ 292
Persons to Give Consent for Autopsy.............. 293
Separation by Abandonment of Spouse............. 294
Separation by Agreement of Spouses.............. 295
Effects of Judicial Separation................... 295
When Spouses Have Been Divorced.................. 296
Adult Children of Deceased Parent................ 296
Minor Children of Deceased....................... 297
Rights of Mother of Deceased Child............... 297
When Father Has Preference....................... 297
Parent May Forfeit Right......................... 297
Brother and Sisters of Deceased.................. 298
Executors and Administrators as Such Have
    No Control................................... 298
Authorization by Statute......................... 298
Autopsies in Insurance Cases..................... 299
Medical Examiner's and Coroner's Cases........... 300
Hospital Cases for Coroners or Medical
    Examiners................................... 301
Transplantation of Tissues and Organs............ 302
Legal Control of Transplantations............... 304

Chapter   *Page*

XXV. Medical Staff Organization........................... **307**

    Responsibilities of Governing Board................ 307

    Exclusion of Unqualified Practitioners............ 308

    Rights of Physicians.............................. 309

    Trustees' Liability for Acts of Medical Staff..... 311

    Appointments in Public Hospitals.................. 311

    Denial of Reappointment........................... 312

    Hearings for Disciplinary Action.................. 313

    Committees of Medical Staff....................... 314

XXVI. Operating Room Responsibility...................... **316**

    Records Before Surgery............................ 317

    Responsibility for Negligence..................... 318

    Duties of Nursing Personnel....................... 320

    Operating Room Nurses............................. 320

    Control Exercised Over Nurse...................... 321

    Relationship of Intern and Resident............... 321

    Liability of Attending Surgeon.................... 322

    Accounting for Sponges............................ 323

    Reliance on Nurses' Count......................... 324

    Removal of Drains and Tubes....................... 325

    Broken Surgical or Hypodermic Needles............. 325

XXVII. Medical Malpractice............................... **327**

    Duties of the Physician........................... 328

    Malpractice Defined............................... 328

    Failure to Cure is Not Malpractice................ 329

    Doctrine of *Res Ipsa Loquitur*................... 330

    Responsibility for Unexpected Drug
        Reactions..................................... 332

    Use of Experimental Treatments and Drugs.......... 333

    The Drug Amendments of 1962....................... 335

    Skill and Care Required of Specialists............ 336

Chapter   *Page*

Proof to Establish Malpractice 336
Defenses by the Physician 337
"Good Samaritan" Statutes 339

XXVIII. Hospital Liability **340**

Theories for Exemption 341
Evolution of Liability of Charitable Hospitals 342
Status of Exemptions and Liabilities 343
Decisions on Charitable Hospital Liability 344
Federal Tort Claims Act 349
Application to Servicemen and Dependents 351
Negligence of Public Hospitals 352
Liability of Proprietary Hospitals 353

LIST OF CHAPTERS

Page

1. The Patient's Record 1
2. Completion of Medical Records 36
3. Preservation of Medical Records and X-rays 47
4. Confidential Communications 73
5. Release of Medical Information 84
6. Courts and Jurisdiction 105
7. Legal Proceedings Before Trial 111
8. Subpoena of Witnesses and Records 120
9. The Law of Evidence 129
10. Documentary Evidence 138
11. Tissue Committee Reports as Evidence 143
12. X-Rays, Microfilms, and Photographs as Evidence ... 159
13. Hospital Records in Court 165
14. Trial Procedure 185
15. The Patient's Privacy 195
16. Photographs of Patients 209
17. Patients' Property Records 218
18. Consents for Treatment 227
19. Authorizations for Minors 236
20. Operations Without Consent 242
21. Consent for Blood Transfusions 247
22. Records of Abortions 267
23. Consent for Sterilization and Artificial Insemination ... 275
24. Autopsy Consents 286
25. Medical Staff Organization 307
26. Operating Room Responsibility 316
27. Medical Malpractice 327
28. Hospital Liability 340

LIST OF ILLUSTRATIONS

Figure   *Page*

1. Emergency Room Record 12
2. Authorization for Emergency Treatment and
   Release of Information 13
3. History 14
4. Physical Examination 15
5. Physician's Orders 16
6. Nurses' Bedside Record 17
7. Graphic Chart and Nurses' Notes 20
8. Nurses' Notes 21
9. Discharge Summary 22
10. Progress Notes 23
11. X-Ray Report 24
12. Report of Consultation 25
13. Tissue Report 26
14. Report of Operation 27
15. Anesthesia Record 28
16. Anesthesia Record (Back) 29
17. Summary Sheet 31
18. Short Stay Record 33
19. Graphic Chart—Nurses' Bedside Record 34
20. Analysis of Hospital Service 40
21. Comparative Report of Professional Performance 41
22. Incident Report 81
23. Authorization for Medical and/or Surgical
    Treatment and Release of Information 85
24. Patient's Clothes List 88
25. Authorization for Review of Medical Records 89
26. Authorization for Release of Information 89
27. Individual Hospital Insurance Form 98
28. Group Hospital Insurance Form 99

Figure   *Page*

29. Receipt for Hospital Record Produced in Court................ 124
30. Medical Audit Work Sheet.................................... 144
31. Medical Audit Findings..................................... 145
32. Physicians' Index.. 145
33. Tissue Committee (Daily Analysis) 148
34. Report of Tissue Committee................................ 150
35. Patient's Request to be Visited by an Attorney.............. 204
36. Authorization for Visit by an Attorney..................... 205
37. Consent to Photograph...................................... 211
38. Authorization for Surgeon to Operate....................... 212
39. Valuables Envelope... 221
40. Waiver of Responsibility................................... 222
41. Notice to Patient to Pick up Valuables..................... 225
42. Authorization for Medical and/or
        Surgical Treatment..................................... 227
43. Transfusion Record... 255
44. Refusal to Permit Blood Transfusion........................ 262
45. Agreement for Blood Transfusion............................ 263
46. Transfusion Reaction Report................................ 264
47. Investigation of Transfusion Reaction...................... 265
48. Release from Responsibility for Abortion................... 268
49. Therapeutic Abortion....................................... 271
50. Sterilization Permit....................................... 281
51. Authorization for Autopsy.................................. 292
52. Donor's Authorization for Removal of Organ................. 303
53. Authorization for Kidney Transplant (Adult) 304
54. Authorization for Kidney Transplant (Infant).............. 305
55. Authorization for Treatment with Drug under
        Clinical Investigation................................. 334

chapter 1

THE PATIENT'S RECORD

A RECORD has been defined as something set down in writing or otherwise recorded for the purpose of preserving memory; specifically, a register, an authentic or official copy of any writing; an account book of any facts or proceedings, usually entered in a book for preservation.

A medical record is the compilation of the pertinent facts of the patient's life history, his illness, and treatment. In a larger sense the medical record is a compilation of scientific data derived from many sources, coordinated into a document and available for various uses, personal and impersonal, to serve the patient, the physician, the institution in which the patient was treated, the science of medicine, and society as a whole.

Standards For Medical Records

Medical records are an important tool in the practice of medicine. They serve as a basis for planning patient care; they provide a means of communication between the physician and other professional groups contributing to the patient's care; they furnish documentary evidence of the course of the patient's illness and treatment, and they serve as a basis for review, study, and evaluation of the medical care rendered to the patient.

During the course of treatment there is no more important record than the patient's chart. It contains all pertinent information on his past and present medical history, his condition and treatment based on reports made by the x-ray department, pathology, operating room, consultants, attending physicians, house staff and nurses. The nurse's notes must be an accurate and purely factual report of her observations of the patient and the care he has received.

The Joint Commission on Accreditation of Hospitals

The Joint Commission on Accreditation of Hospitals is sponsored by four organizations: the American Medical Association, the American College of Surgeons, the American College of Physicians and the American Hospital Association. It is an independent, voluntary, nonprofit corporation, the main purpose of which is to improve the quality of care rendered to patients in hospitals. Its method of achieving this goal is to establish minimum standards of quality of patient care and then to invite all member hospitals to meet or surpass those standards.

All standards for accreditation are based on requirements which include:

1. A physical plant and administration providing x-ray, laboratory and other facilities for the adequate nursing care, feeding and housing of patients with proper protection from fire, explosion and other hazards.

2. Restriction of the hospital's medical staff to physicians and surgeons who are graduates of approved medical schools, legally licensed, competent in their fields and ethical in conduct.

3. Maintenance of complete medical records on each patient, so that not only the physician but all concerned in the present or future may know what was found and what was done.

4. A well-organized staff of physicians and surgeons permitted to practice in the hospital according to written rules and regulations, subject to the ultimate authority of the hospital governing board.

5. Medical supervision of the staff to assure that each member is restricted to performing duties only within his competence and to enable each member individually and all collectively to increase diagnostic accuracy and good results of treatment.

The fact that a hospital is licensed or otherwise authorized by the state does not mean it is "accredited," for licensure and accreditation are different: licensing connotes meeting the least of standards, while accrediting signifies positive achievement of high standards.[1]

Medical Record Standards of Joint Commission

The medical record department of a hospital is said to be a mirror of medical progress in the institution; here errors of omission and commission are revealed; here facts are stored for future use, whether for clinical, research or medicolegal purposes. This department in an approved hospital is one of the bases for accreditation by the Joint Commission on Accreditation of Hospitals.

Since medical records reflect patient care, the Commission evaluates a medical record on the basis of whether or not it contains sufficient recorded information to justify the diagnosis and warrant the treatment and end results. In agreement with this principle, the Commission has established certain standards of record keeping which it thinks are essential for good patient care.

The minimum requirements are: accurate and complete medical records be written for all patients and filed in an accessible place in the hospital, a complete medical record being one which includes identification and sociological data; personal and family history; history of present illness; physical examination; special examinations such as consultations, clinical laboratory, x-ray and other examinations; provisional or

---

[1] *Knecht* v. *Medical Service Association*, Court of Common Pleas, Lehigh County, Pa. (1957).

working diagnosis; medical or surgical treatment; gross and microscopical pathological findings; progress notes; final diagnosis; condition on discharge; follow-up; and autopsy findings.

Early Medical Records

Early hospitals kept no organized case records. Typical of the evolution in record keeping is that of The New York Hospital from 1793 to the present. The earliest document was a large book of admissions with fourteen headings across the page to include: Number, Names of Pay Patients, "Pays" per Week, Securities' Names for Pay Patients, Names of Pauper Patients, Occupation, Age, When Admitted, Names of Visiting Committee by Whose Orders Patients Were Admitted, Physicians or Surgeons, Diseases, Time Discharged, and In What State and on What Account, Died, Remarks.

In 1797 a numbering scheme was added; commencing in 1808 a Surgical Register of interesting cases was maintained. As a companion piece to the Surgical Register a Medical Register was kept, and also a record of the Lying-in Ward. By 1840 a bylaw required that records be kept of all admitted patients as well as a memorandum book in which facts were to be noted as to treatment and progress of the case. A third volume, a discharge book, was also required.

In time, new techniques and medications had their influence. By 1867 a "Urine Record" sheet was inserted; temperature readings were noted under the heading of "Record of Vital Signs." A few years later the family history and physical examination were included as a routine matter. By the turn of the century the history number replaced the old admission number; special record sheets were used for the record in place of writing notes into a book. As inventions and new techniques appeared, additional sheets were added to the record for roentgenologic reports, laboratory findings, and electrocardiograms.

It was not until the development of the hospital standardization program of the American College of Surgeons, around 1918, that the practice of maintaining medical records became prevalent. The purpose of the College was to raise the quality of surgery.

Hospitals that kept medical records had only sketchy reports; the records lacked uniformity. A standard set of medical records was suggested by the College as evidence of the medical work done in the hospital and with the objective of aiding accreditation of the institution. This development gave birth also to the profession of medical record library science and brought about another paramedical professional health group.

Contents of a Modern Medical Record

Medical records should contain the following information:

1. Identification Data
2. Provisional Diagnosis

    There should be a provisional or admitting diagnosis made on every patient at the time of admission. If a patient requires hospitalization, the hospital staff deserves this information to proceed intelligently.

3. Chief Complaint
4. Present Illness
5. History and Physical Examination
6. Consultations

    Consultations imply an examination of the patient and the patient's record. The consultation note should be recorded and either signed or authenticated by the consultant.

7. Clinical Laboratory Reports

    The original signed laboratory report is entered in the patient's record. Duplicates are filed in the laboratory.

Reports from laboratories outside the hospital are acceptable, in lieu of tests performed in the hospital, if the following safeguards are maintained:

a. Work is done in a laboratory approved by the city or state. Laboratory work performed in a physician's office by a technician, nurse, or office assistant is not acceptable. Since the hospital is held responsible for the quality of laboratory work reported in the medical record, it must limit outside laboratory work to approved laboratories.

b. The test is recent enough to be pertinent to the individual case. For example, a serological test for syphilis or an Rh determination done any time during the prenatal period would be acceptable. A urinalysis done prior to 48 hours of admission would not.

c. The original laboratory report is made part of the medical record.

8. X-ray Reports

The original signed radiological report should be entered in the patient's record. Duplicates are filed in the department.

9. Tissue Report

Since all tissues removed in surgery are sent to the laboratory, at least an acknowledgment that the tissue has been received and a gross description should be made part of the record. If a microscopic examination is done, a description of the findings should be made a part of the record. Whether or not a microscopic examination is done should be determined by the medical staff and the pathologist according to the rules and regulations of the hospital.

10. Treatment — Medical and Surgical

All treatment procedures should be documented in the medical record. Except in cases of grave emergency, the patient should receive a complete diagnostic work-up before surgery. Operative notes should be dictated immediately after surgery and should contain both a description of the findings and a detailed account of the technique used and tissues removed.

11. Progress Notes

Progress notes are important in that they give a chronological picture and analysis of the clinical course of the patient. The frequency with which they are made is determined by the condition of the patient.

12. Final Diagnosis

A definitive final diagnosis based on the terms specified in the *Standard Nomenclature of Diseases and Operations* should be written.

13. Summary

A summary of the patient's condition on discharge and course in the hospital is valuable as a recapitulation of the patient's hospitalization.

14. Autopsy Findings

When an autopsy is performed a complete protocol of the findings should be made part of the record.

Medical Record Science As A Profession

Medical Record Science is a profession responsible for planning, organizing, and managing the medical record department, including securing the patient's record, filing and cataloging records, diseases, and operations, making records available for use to the hospital staff and responsible agencies, and preparing reports and studies.

There are two levels of medical record personnel. The medical record librarian heads a department. She must be an individual interested in working with responsible hospital personnel for the welfare of the patient. She needs a large measure of ability in human relations in addition to mastery of techniques of medical record practice.

The medical record technician carries on the technical tasks of medical record work under the supervision of a medical record librarian or the medical record committee of the medical staff.

Until January 1, 1965 any person is eligible for registration, as a registered medical record librarian, who:

1. Is an active or associate member of the American Association of Medical Record Librarians;

2. Is a graduate of a school for medical record librarians approved by the designated accrediting authority, provided that the qualifications of such school at the time of the candidate's graduation would have met with the requirements of the current designated accrediting authority for an approved school, or be a graduate of a school for medical record librarians approved by a foreign association with which there is an agreement of reciprocity;

3. Passes the examination provided by the Education and Registration Committee.

Any person is eligible for accreditation, as an accredited medical record technician, who:

1. Is an active or associate member in good standing of the American Association of Medical Record Librarians;

2. Is a graduate of a school for medical record technicians approved by the designated accrediting authority; or has successfully completed the American Association of Medical Record Librarian's Correspondence Course for Medical Record Personnel.

3. Passes an examination provided by the Education and Registration Committee.

The Medical Record Librarian

The medical record librarian may be included among the

learned professions, for her education is that of a professional person. She is "the guardian of the books and records, who must make them available at a moment's notice as directed by law and by hospital rule; also, she must be knowledgeable about their essential character and purpose and must be called in as an indispensable member of a mixed professional team, which employs learning of any kind that can be helpful in solving the problems of health, in relation to disease."[2]

The record librarian is required to have a knowledge of basic legal principles applicable to her work. The Council on Medical Education and Hospitals of the American Medical Association, in collaboration with the Committee on Education and Registration of the American Association of Medical Record Librarians, establishes standards for medical record science education, which include 36 clock hours of "a study of principles of law and their applications in the health field, with particular reference to all phases of medical record practice."

The Medical Record Librarian As Custodian

The medical record librarian of the hospital is the custodian of records which contain professional secrets concerning patients. Such confidences have been respected both by civil and natural law since the time of the ancients. Hippocrates in his oath, dated about 450 B.C., pledges the physician to keep professional secrets inviolate. A modification of his oath is embodied in the pledge of the American Association of Medical Record Librarians, which states: "I pledge myself to give out no information concerning a patient from any clinical record placed in my charge, or from any other source, to any person whatsoever, except upon order from the chief executive officer of the institution which I may be serving; and to avoid all commercialization of my work."

Moreover, the *Code of Ethics for the Practice of Medical*

---

[2] BLUESTONE, E. M., M.D., "The Medical Record Librarian Among the Learned Professions," *JAAMRL*, 29:5, February 1958.

Record Science provides that a member should: "(2) Preserve and protect the medical records in his custody and hold inviolate the privileged contents of the records and any other information of a confidential nature obtained in his official capacity, taking due account of applicable statutes and of regulations and policies of his employer."

Duty to Maintain Confidential Status

The fact that there is, or is not, a medical record librarian in a hospital does not alter the basic obligations existing with reference to records among the patient, the physician, and the hospital. In many states, the privacy of the record is protected by a privileged communications statute. Even where there is no statute, the patient has the right to insist that his medical record be kept confidential. In the absence of a waiver by the patient, the hospital has a definite duty to enforce such right. As a corollary, this right survives the patient's decease.

In hospitals, it is universally accepted as "standing orders" that the medical record librarian will furnish confidential information only on written authority of the patient, his guardian if he is a minor, his committee if he is insane, or the representative of his estate if he is deceased. In cases where the patient is unconscious, delirious, or seriously ill and cannot give permission for inspection of the record, and such information is essential to treatment or to procure some immediate benefit, the proper officer of the hospital may assume responsibility for the release. In such an emergency the law presumes implied authority.

Patient's History in the Record

Hospital records are an important and sometimes neglected source of information in personal injury cases; they can be employed often for medical fact-finding purposes or to corroborate or dispute other medical contentions. Lawyers as well as insurance carriers have a special interest in reviewing such records.

Lawyers find it important in negligence cases, in order to evaluate a client's injuries properly, to inspect the complete hospital record thoroughly before trial. An abstract of a record is generally inadequate. Arrangements can be made with many hospitals to secure a photostatic copy, although this is not too widespread a practice.

The patient's lawyer prefers to go over the hospital records, with one or more of the attending physicians, to learn the true significance of the various tests and findings. Hospital physicians generally are disinterested in the medicolegal aspects in treating the patient; some physicians have a great aversion to testifying in court. Nevertheless, the patient's lawyer has an obligation to the client to prepare the medical evidence to the best advantage to the patient, for often personal injury cases are proven or corroborated by unusual and abnormal findings in the medical record.

The admission sheet may show whether the patient was unemployed or had no occupation, so as to attack an alleged loss of earnings. The patient is likely to tell the truth to the admitting officer as to whether or not he was gainfully employed.

If the admitting diagnosis is different from the final diagnosis, the comparison may call for some investigation, although it is not unusual for the provisional diagnosis to be modified at the time of discharge.

One of the important facts, for which both sides to the litigation may look, is the history of the accident (Figs. 1-2, pp. 12 and 13) to determine whether the manner of the happening of the accident is contradicted or corroborated by the patient's later claims. This aspect of the record is very important to the suit and requires a complete history (Fig. 3, p. 14) and physical examination (Fig. 4, p. 15) given at the time of admission.

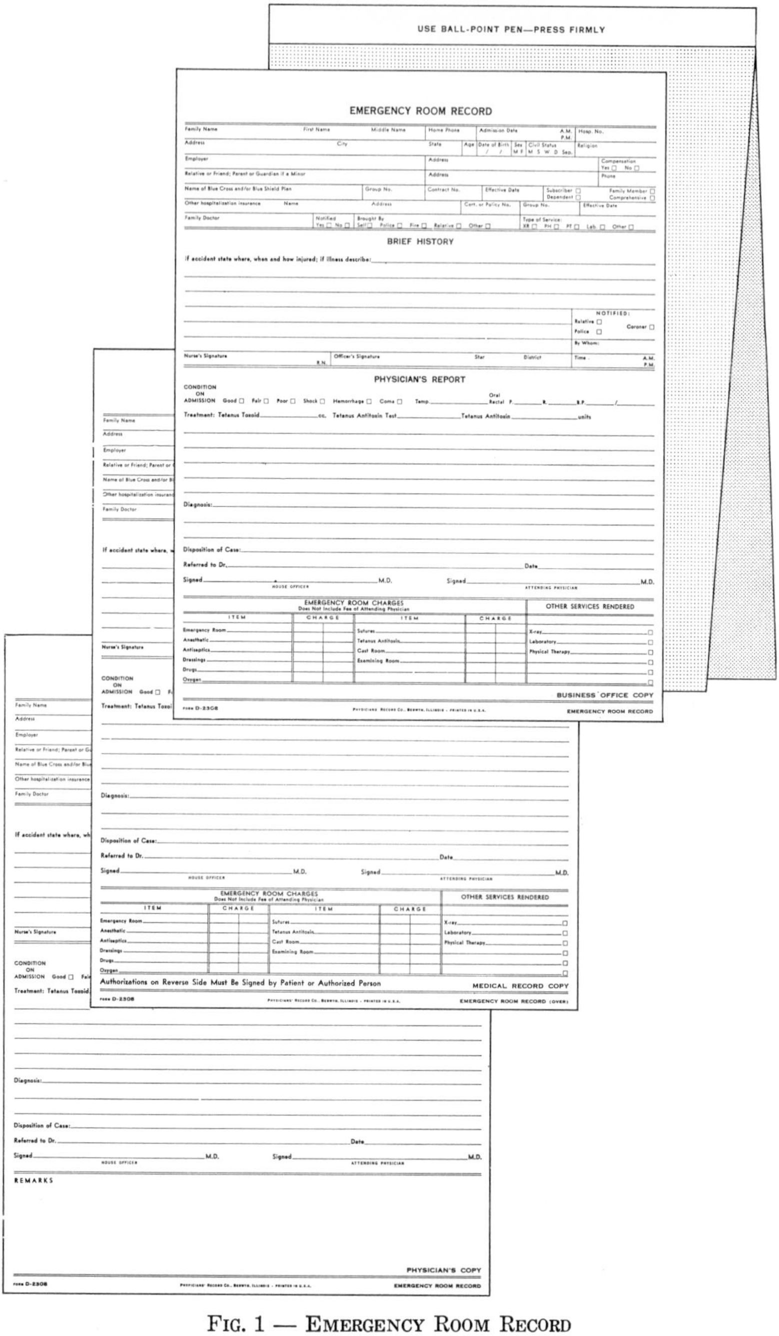

USE BALL-POINT PEN—PRESS FIRMLY

EMERGENCY ROOM RECORD

Family Name | First Name | Middle Name | Home Phone | Admission Date A.M. P.M. | Hosp. No.
Address | City | State | Age | Date of Birth | Sex M F | Civil Status M S W D Sep. | Religion
Employer | Address | Compensation Yes ☐ No ☐
Relative or Friend; Parent or Guardian if a Minor | Address | Phone
Name of Blue Cross and/or Blue Shield Plan | Group No. | Contract No. | Effective Date | Subscriber ☐ Dependent ☐ | Family Member ☐ Comprehensive ☐
Other hospitalization insurance | Name | Address | Cert. or Policy No. | Group No. | Effective Date
Family Doctor | Notified Yes ☐ No ☐ | Brought By Self ☐ Police ☐ Fire ☐ Relative ☐ Other ☐ | Type of Service: XR ☐ PH ☐ PT ☐ Lab ☐ Other ☐

BRIEF HISTORY

If accident state where, when and how injured; if illness describe:

NOTIFIED: Relative ☐ Police ☐ Coroner ☐ By Whom:

Nurse's Signature R.N. | Officer's Signature | Star | District | Time A.M. P.M.

PHYSICIAN'S REPORT

CONDITION ON ADMISSION Good ☐ Fair ☐ Poor ☐ Shock ☐ Hemorrhage ☐ Coma ☐ Temp. Oral Rectal F. R. B.P. /

Treatment: Tetanus Toxoid cc. Tetanus Antitoxin Test Tetanus Antitoxin units

Diagnosis:

Disposition of Case:

Referred to Dr. Date

Signed M.D. (HOUSE OFFICER) Signed M.D. (ATTENDING PHYSICIAN)

EMERGENCY ROOM CHARGES Does Not Include Fee of Attending Physician | OTHER SERVICES RENDERED

ITEM	CHARGE	ITEM	CHARGE	OTHER SERVICES RENDERED
Emergency Room		Sutures		X-ray ☐
Anesthetic		Tetanus Antitoxin		Laboratory ☐
Antiseptics		Cast Room		Physical Therapy ☐
Dressings		Examining Room		☐
Drugs				☐
Oxygen				☐

BUSINESS OFFICE COPY

FORM D-2308 PHYSICIANS' RECORD CO., BERWYN, ILLINOIS - PRINTED IN U.S.A. EMERGENCY ROOM RECORD

Authorizations on Reverse Side Must Be Signed by Patient or Authorized Person

MEDICAL RECORD COPY

FORM D-2308 EMERGENCY ROOM RECORD (OVER)

REMARKS

PHYSICIAN'S COPY

FORM D-2308 EMERGENCY ROOM RECORD

Fig. 1 — Emergency Room Record

Of considerable significance may be the patient's previous medical history, for it may reveal that a prior condition or disability existed before the accident, or it may justify a claim

AUTHORIZATION FOR EMERGENCY TREATMENT

The undersigned has been informed of the emergency treatment considered necessary for the patient whose name appears on the reverse hereof and that the treatment and procedures will be performed by physicians, members of the house staff and employees of the hospital. Authorization is hereby granted for such treatment and procedures.

The undersigned understands that a personal physician is to be selected by or on behalf of the patient within 24 hours if hospitalization or further treatment is required, or immediately if complications arise.

The undersigned has read the above authorization and understands the same and certifies that no guarantee or assurance has been made as to the results that may be obtained.

Date_____Time_____ A.M. P.M.   Signed_____
                                                                        PATIENT

Witness_____   Or_____
                                                                   AUTHORIZED PERSON

                                                  Relationship to Patient_____

> Both authorizations must be signed by the patient, or by an authorized person in the case of a minor or when patient is physically or mentally incompetent.

AUTHORIZATION FOR RELEASE OF INFORMATION

Authorization is hereby granted to release to the_____
                                                        NAME OF INSURANCE COMPANY OR COMPANIES
such information as may be necessary for the completion of my hospitalization claims.

Date_____   Signed_____
                                                        PATIENT

                                        Or_____
                                                   AUTHORIZED PERSON

                                        Relationship to Patient_____

(D-7308 BACK)

FIG. 2 — AUTHORIZATION FOR EMERGENCY TREATMENT
AND RELEASE OF INFORMATION

of aggravation of a previous injury or disability. The medical history may also show that the patient was addicted to alcohol or habit-forming drugs, which fact may have a bearing on

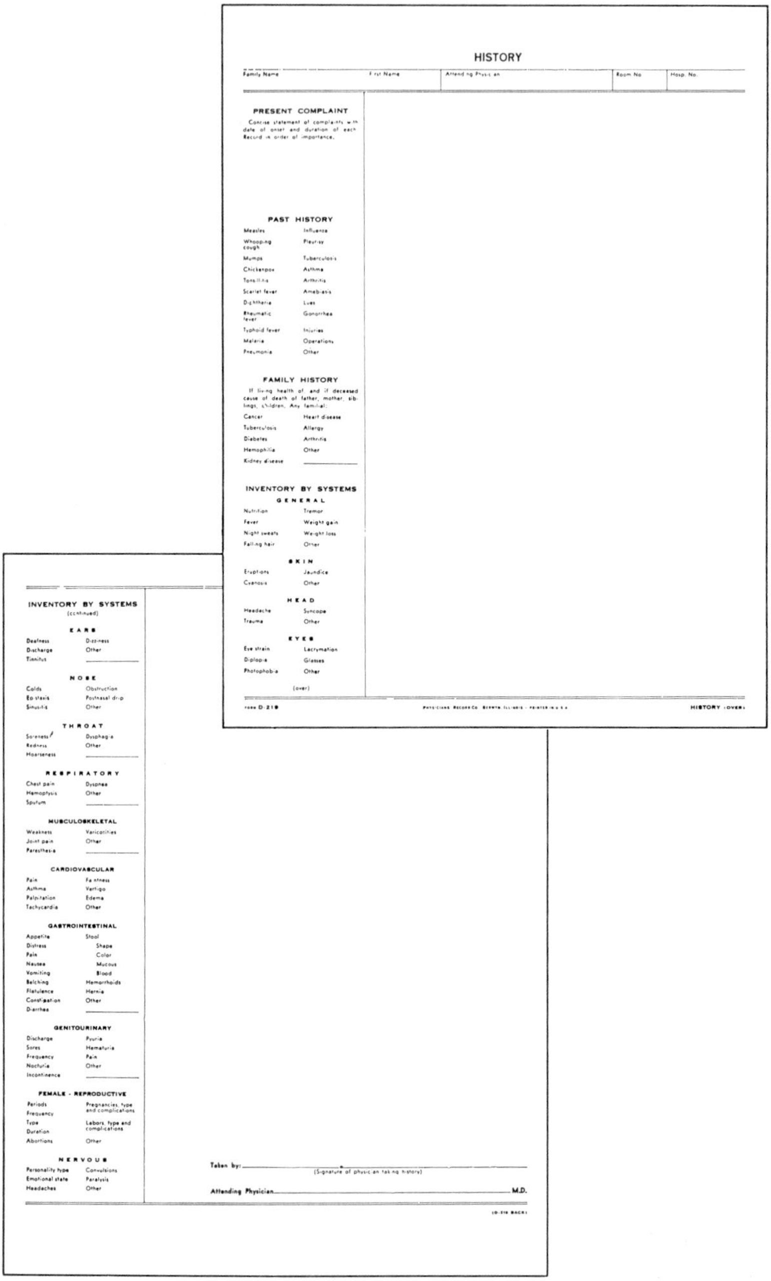

HISTORY

Family Name | First Name | Attending Physician | Room No. | Hosp. No.

PRESENT COMPLAINT

Concise statement of complaints with date of onset and duration of each. Record in order of importance.

PAST HISTORY

Measles	Influenza
Whooping cough	Pleurisy
Mumps	Tuberculosis
Chickenpox	Asthma
Tonsillitis	Arthritis
Scarlet fever	Amebiasis
Diphtheria	Lues
Rheumatic fever	Gonorrhea
Typhoid fever	Injuries
Malaria	Operations
Pneumonia	Other

FAMILY HISTORY

If living health of, and if deceased cause of death of father, mother, siblings, children. Any familial:

Cancer	Heart disease
Tuberculosis	Allergy
Diabetes	Arthritis
Hemophilia	Other
Kidney disease	

INVENTORY BY SYSTEMS

GENERAL

Nutrition	Tremor
Fever	Weight gain
Night sweats	Weight loss
Falling hair	Other

SKIN

Eruptions	Jaundice
Cyanosis	Other

HEAD

Headache	Syncope
Trauma	Other

EYES

Eye strain	Lacrymation
Diplopia	Glasses
Photophobia	Other

(over)

FORM D-219 HISTORY (OVER)

INVENTORY BY SYSTEMS (continued)

EARS

Deafness	Dizziness
Discharge	Other
Tinnitus	

NOSE

Colds	Obstruction
Epistaxis	Postnasal drip
Sinusitis	Other

THROAT

Soreness	Dysphagia
Redness	Other
Hoarseness	

RESPIRATORY

Chest pain	Dyspnea
Hemoptysis	Other
Sputum	

MUSCULOSKELETAL

Weakness	Varicosities
Joint pain	Other
Paresthesia	

CARDIOVASCULAR

Pain	Faintness
Asthma	Vertigo
Palpitation	Edema
Tachycardia	Other

GASTROINTESTINAL

Appetite	Stool
Distress	Shape
Pain	Color
Nausea	Mucous
Vomiting	Blood
Belching	Hemorrhoids
Flatulence	Hernia
Constipation	Other
Diarrhea	

GENITOURINARY

Discharge	Pyuria
Sores	Hematuria
Frequency	Pain
Nocturia	Other
Incontinence	

FEMALE - REPRODUCTIVE

Periods	Pregnancies, type and complications
Frequency	
Type	Labors, type and complications
Duration	
Abortions	Other

NERVOUS

Personality type	Convulsions
Emotional state	Paralysis
Headaches	Other

Taken by: ____________________ (Signature of physician taking history)

Attending Physician ____________________ M.D.

(D-219 BACK)

FIG. 3 — HISTORY

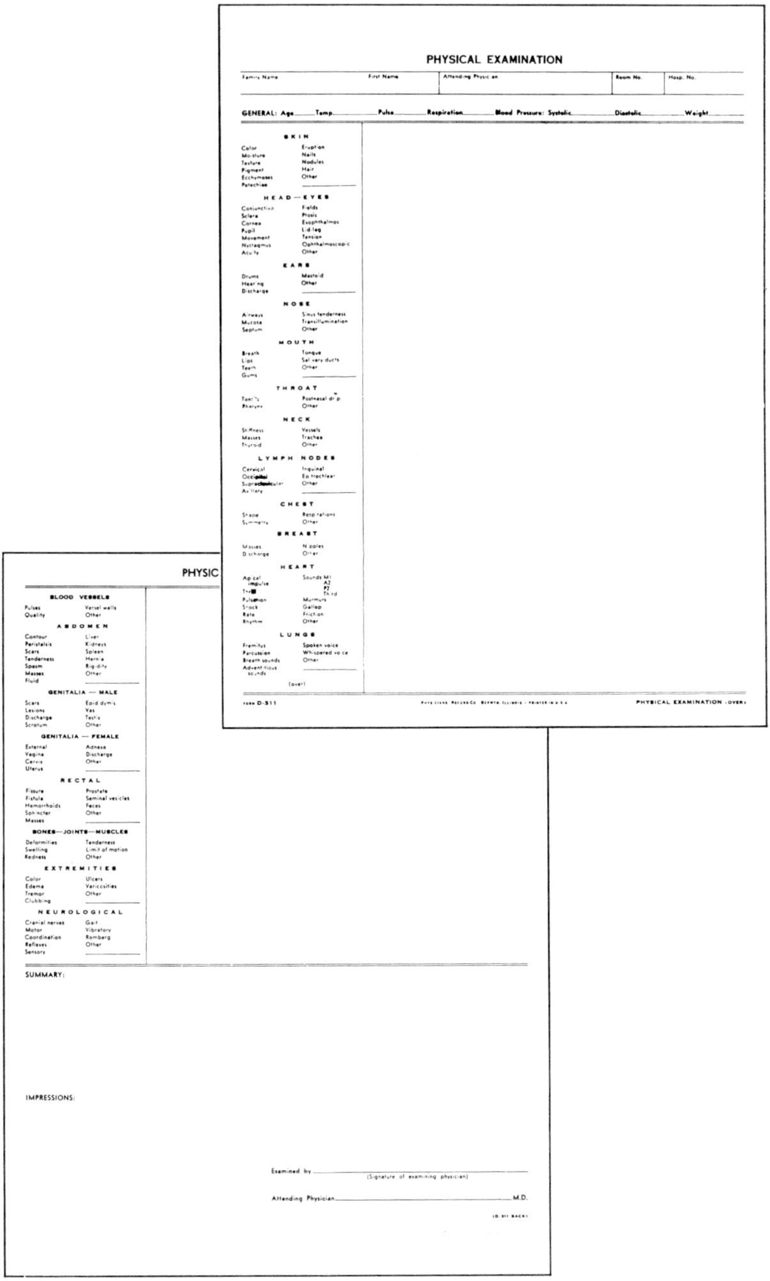

FIG. 4 — PHYSICAL EXAMINATION

the question of contributory negligence resulting from an excess of alcohol or sedative drugs and which may have caused mental or muscular incoordination.

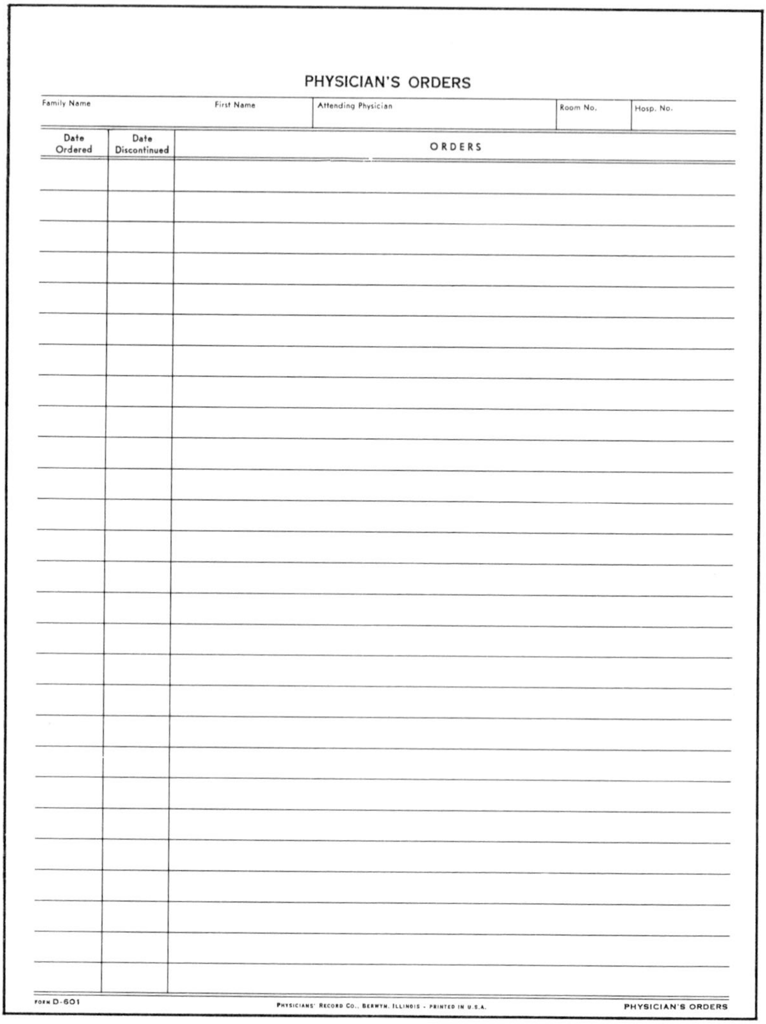

PHYSICIAN'S ORDERS

Family Name	First Name	Attending Physician	Room No.	Hosp. No.

Date Ordered	Date Discontinued	ORDERS

FORM D-601 PHYSICIANS' RECORD CO., BERWYN, ILLINOIS - PRINTED IN U.S.A. PHYSICIAN'S ORDERS

FIG. 5 — PHYSICIAN'S ORDERS

The Doctor's Order Sheet

The doctor's order sheet (Fig. 5, above) may indicate the extent of the patient's pain and suffering, which is an element in the proof of damages. Where mild analgesics, like aspirin or phenobarbital, are prescribed, it is possibly evidence that the pain and suffering were mild. More powerful drugs and

NURSES' BEDSIDE RECORD

Family Name	First Name	Attending Physician	Room No.	Hosp. No.

Hour	Medication and Diet	NOTES	Signature of Nurse

FORM D-801 PHYSICIANS' RECORD CO., BERWYN, ILLINOIS - PRINTED IN U.S.A. NURSES' BEDSIDE RECORD

FIG. 6 — NURSES' BEDSIDE RECORD

sedatives, like demerol or morphine, would imply more severe pain and suffering.

Comparison of the order sheet with the nurses' notes (Fig. 6, above) would show whether the drugs were actually administered and how frequently. When the drugs were commenced and when they were discontinued would help corroborate the length of time the patient suffered. Drugs administered a number of times a day over a specific number of days would be of greater importance than isolated doses during the hospitalization. Bathroom privileges and the nature of diet may have significance.

The orders of the physician therefore should be in writing. If an order is telephoned, the physician should sign the order on his next visit. Where the nurse is in doubt, as a precautionary measure, she should request a resident physician to examine the order to assure that the prescription is not inconsistent with the patient's requirements. Should a discrepancy appear, the resident or nurse should verify with the prescribing physician and note such fact.

Telephone orders may be given to the director of nurses, any resident or intern, the night supervisor, a floor supervisor, senior nurse or a private duty nurse. The person receiving the order should sign the name of the physician per his or her own name, pending the physician's next visit. Neglect of the physician to sign the orders may place responsibility on him for errors.

The nurse should act only on written orders where the law requires it, as in dispensing narcotics.

The Nurses' Notes

The Joint Commission has no requirements concerning nurses' notes. It is the responsibility of the hospital's medical and nursing staffs to develop policies concerning the type and extent of nurses' notes to be kept.

The nurses' notes may be used as evidence in a legal proceeding. Traumatic cases in particular, many of which eventually involve claims for damages, make imperative an accurate word picture of treatment and convalescence. Factors regarding the general condition of the patient, such as complaints, sleep and activity, may be essential information to prove his case.[3]

Although the doctors record their own observations of the patient's condition, they may neglect to record brief visits made on morning rounds. The judge and jury may seek this information in the nurses' notes. Whenever a nurse is aware that the doctor has visited a patient, she should record this fact in the nurses' notes.

Careful notation of the removal of foreign substances from the patient such as drains and the like, particularly the number thereof, is of the utmost importance, for one or more may come out with the dressings and later be unaccounted for. The absence of a record of the coming away of a drain with a dressing may be presumptive proof that the drain was left in the wound.

Other observations which contribute to the usefulness of the record are: (1) correct spelling of the name of patient and attending physician; (2) method of admission or arrival, i.e., by wheelchair, ambulance or ambulatory; (3) complete description of condition of patient on admission and on discharge, noting particularly any mark, bruise, burn, rash or irritation; (4) admission temperature, pulse and respiration; (5) routine and special procedures; (6) medication, dosage and manner of administration; (7) objective signs and subjective symptoms; (8) changes in appearance and mental condition; (9) complaints; (10) signature of nurse who renders the service.

In recent years the nurses' notes in hospital records many times do not reflect as much information on personal injury cases as they did before the nursing shortage became acute (Figs. 7-8, pp. 20 and 21). Nevertheless, the significance of the nurses' notes may be explored prior to a trial, for these notes may often dramatically show complaints of pain, periods of un-

---

[3] *Joseph* v. *W. H. Groves Latter Day Saints Hospital, et al.*, 318 P. 2d 330 (Utah) (1957).

consciousness, irrationality or emotional disturbance.

Authentication by Attending Physician

Authentication by the attending physician or a third, fourth or fifth year licensed resident of the history and physical ex-

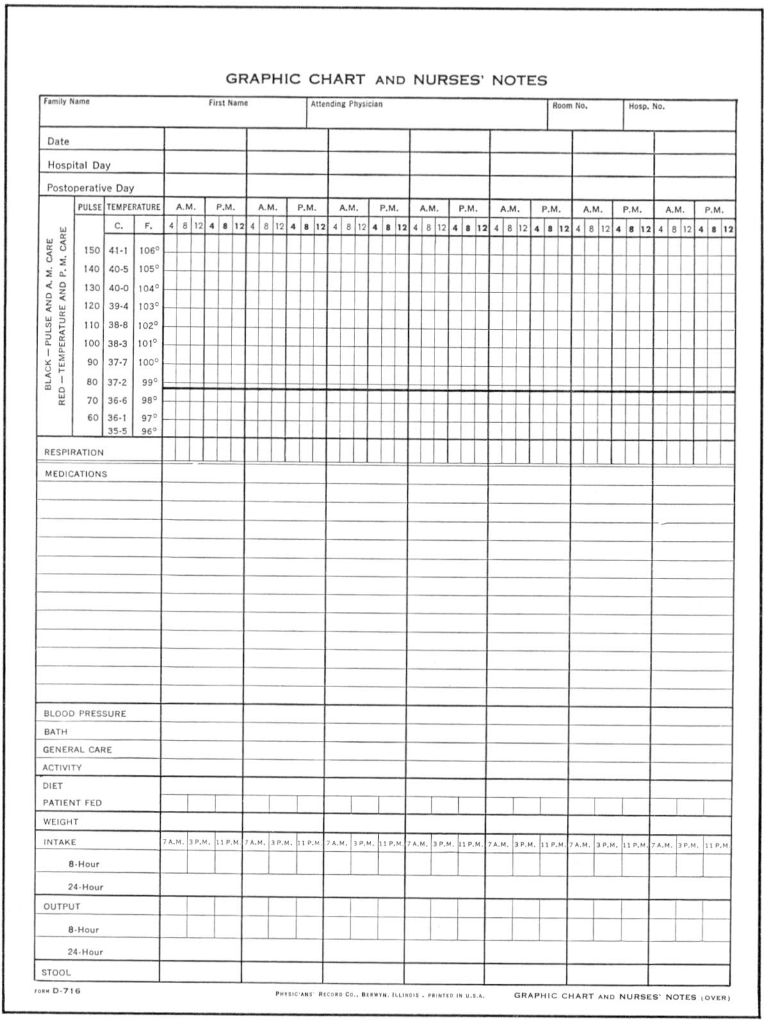
GRAPHIC CHART AND NURSES' NOTES

Family Name | First Name | Attending Physician | Room No. | Hosp. No.

Date

Hospital Day

Postoperative Day

PULSE | TEMPERATURE C. | F. | A.M. 4 8 12 | P.M. 4 8 12

BLACK — PULSE AND A. M. CARE

RED — TEMPERATURE AND P. M. CARE

150 | 41-1 | 106°
140 | 40-5 | 105°
130 | 40-0 | 104°
120 | 39-4 | 103°
110 | 38-8 | 102°
100 | 38-3 | 101°
90 | 37-7 | 100°
80 | 37-2 | 99°
70 | 36-6 | 98°
60 | 36-1 | 97°
35-5 | 96°

RESPIRATION

MEDICATIONS

BLOOD PRESSURE

BATH

GENERAL CARE

ACTIVITY

DIET

PATIENT FED

WEIGHT

INTAKE | 7 A.M. | 3 P.M. | 11 P.M.

8-Hour

24-Hour

OUTPUT

8-Hour

24-Hour

STOOL

FORM D-716 PHYSICIANS' RECORD CO., BERWYN, ILLINOIS . PRINTED IN U.S.A. GRAPHIC CHART AND NURSES' NOTES (OVER)

FIG. 7 — GRAPHIC CHART AND NURSES' NOTES

amination and the discharge summary (Fig. 9, p. 22) written by the house officer is important for several reasons: It informs the young doctor of the accuracy of his workup and his diagnosis and, in case of disagreement between his observations and those of the attending physician, it affords an oppor-

NURSES' NOTES

DATE	A. M.	REMARKS	P. M.	REMARKS

(D-716 BACK)

FIG. 8 — NURSES' NOTES

tunity for discussion and correction of the discrepancies. Second, the making of an accurate record is important to that patient's future care in the event of subsequent admissions to the hospital. Third, countersigning of an accurate history and physical examination and discharge summary indicates that the attending physician has read and accepted these as true.

DISCHARGE SUMMARY

Family Name		Room No.	Hosp. No.
Attending Physician		Date of Admission	Date of Discharge

Provisional Diagnosis:

Final Diagnosis:

Operation:

Brief History and Essential Physical Findings:

Significant Laboratory, X-ray and Consultation Findings:

Course in Hospital with Complications, if any:

Condition, Treatment, Final Disposition on Discharge and Prognosis:

Date_____   Signed_____M.D.

FORM D-103   PHYSICIANS' RECORD CO., BERWYN, ILLINOIS - PRINTED IN U.S.A.   DISCHARGE SUMMARY

FIG. 9 — DISCHARGE SUMMARY

This may be added legal protection for the physician and the hospital. On the other hand, if the house officer's record is inaccurate, or if the discrepancy cannot be resolved, the at-

tending physician should state in the record the facts as he
sees them and should sign this entry; otherwise, he may be

PROGRESS NOTES

| Family Name | First Name | Attending Physician | Room No. | Hosp. No. |

| Date | Notes Should Be Signed by Physician |

form D-501   PHYSICIANS' RECORD CO., BERWYN, ILLINOIS · PRINTED IN U.S.A.   PROGRESS NOTES

FIG. 10 — PROGRESS NOTES

held responsible for errors committed by the house officers.[4]

Progress notes (Fig. 10, above) are usually made by the

---

[4] MYERS, ROBERT S., "Physician's Signature Needed for Added Legal Protection," *Mod. Hosp.*, 94:126, March 1960.

attending doctor, resident or intern and generally contain objective findings upon which the physician bases his opinion.

FIG. 11 — X-RAY REPORT

These objective findings are important for subsequent expert opinions in or out of court. The progress notes serve their best purpose when they appear as a chronological narrative history of the progress and conduct of the case.

FIG. 12 — REPORT OF CONSULTATION

Reports of Specialists

The reports of various specialists who have participated in the care of the patient are of great interest to the examiner of the record. The interpretations of the radiologist (Fig. 11, p. 24) at the end of the report indicates whether there was a fracture or not. Negative for fracture does not preclude the

FIG. 13 — TISSUE REPORT

possibility of other injuries which may be equally severe without evidence of a fracture.

Whether the fracture is simple or compound is important;

also the position of alignment of the broken bones; whether the fracture is comminuted and impacted; anomalies of the bones.

Consultation reports (Fig. 12, p. 25) may be found in cases of relatively severe injury, which may show that certain con-

REPORT OF OPERATION

Family Name	First Name	Middle Name	Attending Physician	Room No.	Hosp. No.
		Resident	Intern	Date	

Preoperative Diagnosis:

Postoperative Diagnosis:

Surgeon: Assistants:

Operation:

Findings (including the condition of all organs examined) and Procedures (including incision, ligatures, sutures, drainage, sponge count and closure):

Wound primarily clean ☐   Wound primarily infected ☐

Healing of wound:—Clean—primary intention   Granulations:

Stitch abscess: Hematoma: Deep sepsis:

Dictated to: Date of Dictation:

Dictated by: _____ M.D.
                                        SIGNATURE OF SURGEON

FORM D-1101   PHYSICIANS' RECORD CO., BERWYN, ILLINOIS - PRINTED IN U.S.A.   REPORT OF OPERATION

FIG. 14 — REPORT OF OPERATION

ditions were precipitated by the accident or aggravated by the injury, and the prognosis or probable outcome of the case.

Pathology reports (Fig. 13, p. 26) may become relevant in cases of traumatic cancer, herniated disc and other conditions in which the role of trauma can be attributed or discounted

ANESTHESIA RECORD

NAME			AGE	DATE	CONSENT	PHYS. STATUS	ROOM NO.	HOSP. NO.

PREMEDICATION (DRUG, DOSE, TIME, EFFECT)   N.B.

Agents: N_2O / O_2

Fluids

Depth of Anes. — Stage: 1 2 3 4

B.P. ∨ / ∧ — Pulse — °C.: 240 220 200

Start Anes. X — 34 / 180

Start Op. ⊙ — 32 / 160, 30 / 140

End Anes. ⊖ — 120

Temp. △ — 100, 80

Suction S — 60

Rec. Room R — 40, 20

Resp. O: Spon. / Asst. / Cont. — 10

SYMBOLS

AGENTS	DOSAGE	TECHNIQUES	REMARKS (INDUCTION, MAINTENANCE, EMERGENCE)
A.			
B.			
C.			
D.			
E.			
F.			
G.			

FLUID SUMMARY
DEXTROSE – H_2O
GLUCOSE – SALINE
SALINE
PLASMA
BLOOD
OTHER

NASO/OROPHARYNGEAL AIRWAY
NASO/OROTRACHEAL – DIRECT – BLIND
CUFF – PACK – TUBE SIZE
UNDER MASK – DIRECT CONN.
TECHNICAL DIFFICULTY
ANESTHESIA TIME

OPERATION

LARYNGOSPASM – EXCESS MUCUS
RESP. DEPRESSION – O_2 WANT
BUCKING – VOMITING

HEMORRHAGE – ARRHYTHMIA
BRADY/TACHYCARDIA – SHOCK

SURGEON	ANESTHESIOLOGIST

FORM D-1014

APPROVED AS REVISED 1962 AMERICAN SOCIETY OF ANESTHESIOLOGISTS, INC.
PHYSICIANS' RECORD CO., BERWYN, ILLINOIS - PRINTED IN U.S.A.

ANESTHESIA RECORD (OVER)

FIG. 15 — ANESTHESIA RECORD

as a causal factor. Laboratory reports determine whether the findings were average or unusual; whether or not the abnormal findings are traumatic in origin.

Operating room reports (Fig. 14, p. 27) by the surgeon indicate how long the patient was in the operating room, the
nature and length of the operation, whether the procedure was

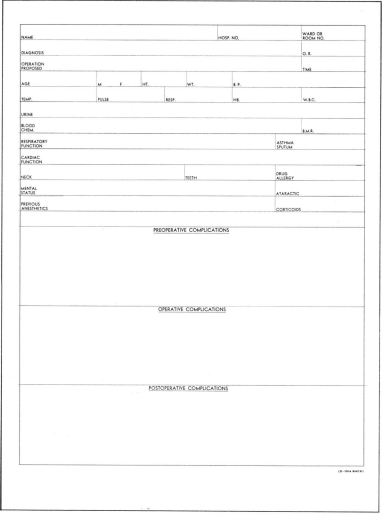

FIG. 16 — ANESTHESIA RECORD (back)

open or closed. All these facts have a bearing on the amount
of damages which can be proved by the patient.

The anesthesia report (Fig. 15, p. 28 and Fig. 16, above) indicates the type of anesthesia used, the duration of time the patient was under anesthesia. Whether transfusions or other intravenous procedures were used will be noted, as well as references to blood pressure, pulse and respiration, which are usually recorded by the anesthesiologist during the course of the operation. This information may be evidence of the seriousness of the operation or show the contrary.

From a legal standpoint, it is therefore essential that complete and detailed medical records with the various entries be kept. Anyone with experience in such matters knows the close scrutiny the medical record undergoes and realizes the importance attached by the courts to the documentation of the events of the patient's diagnosis and treatment.

Signatures of Physicians

In hospitals without house officers, the attending physician should separately sign the history (Fig. 3, p. 14), physical examination (Fig. 4, p. 15), operative report (Fig. 14, p. 27), progress notes (Fig. 10, p. 23), drug and other orders (Fig. 5, p. 16), and the summary (Fig. 9, p. 22). Standing orders should be reproduced on the record and signed by the physician.

In hospitals with house officers, the attending physician should countersign at least the history (Fig. 3, p. 14), physical examination (Fig. 4, p. 15), and summary (Fig. 9, p. 22), written by the house officer. It is not considered necessary to countersign progress notes or drug and treatment orders written by house officers. In all instances a physician should sign clinical entries which he himself makes. A single signature of the physician on the face sheet of the medical record (Fig. 17, p. 31) does not suffice to authenticate the entire content of the record.

The use of rubber stamp signatures is acceptable under the following strict conditions:

a. The physician whose signature the rubber stamp represents is the only one who has possession of the stamp and is the only one who uses it.

b. The physician places in the administrative offices of the

SUMMARY SHEET

Family Name	First Name	Middle Name	Home Phone	Room No.	Hosp. No.

Address	City	Zone	State	Sex M F	Civil Status M S W D Sep.	Religion

Age—Yrs.	Birth Mo. Day Year Date	Birthplace	Nationality	How Many Years in City County State U.S.	Ever in Military Service	Soc. Sec. No.

Occupation	Employer or Employer of Spouse	Address of Employer—Phone

Name of Husband or Maiden Name of Wife	Address if Other Than Above	Birthplace

Notify in Case of Emergency	Relationship	Address	Phone

Name of Father	Birthplace	Maiden Name of Mother	Birthplace

Name of Blue Cross and/or Blue Shield Plan	Group No.	Contract No.	Effective Date	Subscriber ☐ Dependent ☐	Family Member ☐ Comprehensive Coverage ☐

Other hospitalization insurance Name	Address	Cert. or Policy No.	Group No.	Effective Date

Attending Physician	Date of Last Admission	Admission Date A.M. P.M.	Discharge Date A.M. P.M.

Provisional Diagnosis (to be completed within 24 hours after admission):

On admission, patient or qualified person must sign authorization for Medical and/or Surgical Treatment on reverse side

Final Diagnosis: Code No.

Secondary Diagnosis or Complications:

Operation:

Discharged Alive: ☐   Died: ☐ Under 48 hours ☐ Over 48 hours   Autopsy: ☐ Yes   ☐ No

_____M.D., Attending Physician

FORM A-145   PHYSICIANS' RECORD CO., BERWYN, ILLINOIS - PRINTED IN U.S.A.   SUMMARY SHEET (OVER)

FIG. 17 — SUMMARY SHEET

hospital a signed statement to the effect that he is the only one who has the stamp and is the only one who will use it.

Initials in place of a full signature are acceptable provided that the initials can be recognized as having been placed there by a particular physician who can be identified by those initials. The physician should be consistent and not sign his full name one time and initial the next time.

A rubber stamp is most commonly used by a pathologist or radiologist for signature purposes. The use of the rubber stamp for the physician by his office nurse or secretary is not condoned, and its promiscuous use is to be questioned.

As a matter of sound hospital policy, however, the use of a rubber stamp should be discouraged, unless there is some valid reason why the physician cannot sign the documents in his own handwriting.

Procedure for Corrections

At times it becomes necessary for a physician, nurse, or laboratory technician to make appropriate corrections in the record during or after a patient's hospitalization. Erasures may create curiosity, if not suspicion, as to the reasons for the change. It is better practice therefore to make no erasures, but rather to line out the incorrect data with a single line in ink. The date of the lining out, the signature of the person doing it, and the correct information should be added.

Sometimes a request to alter a record is complied with, not by actually changing the record, but by adding a notation at the end of the chart that the patient called at the hospital on a certain date and asked to have the record amended in certain particulars. Any explanation for the change in the facts will then fall upon the patient instead of the hospital.

A physician who participates in improperly altering a patient's record may be deemed guilty of unprofessional conduct and be subject to disciplinary action or suspension of license.

Use of Medical Record Forms

The Joint Commission on Accreditation of Hospitals recommends no specific medical record forms. Records are evaluated on the basis of content and whatever forms the hospital finds most useful are acceptable. It is common experience that check-

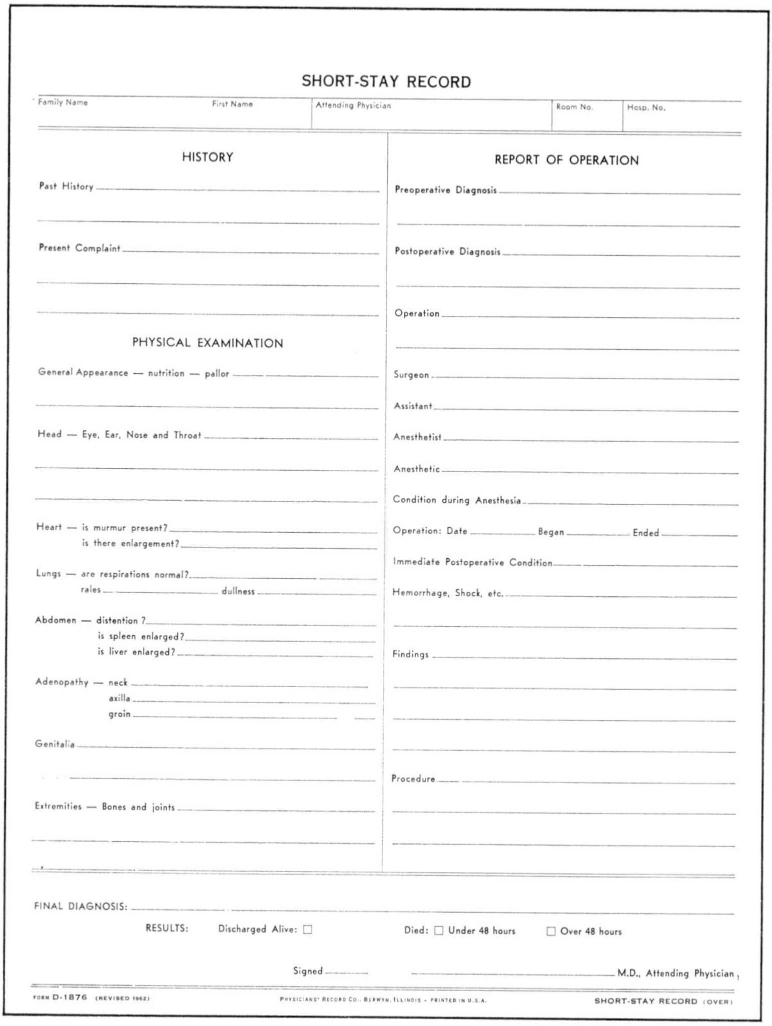
SHORT-STAY RECORD

Family Name | First Name | Attending Physician | Room No. | Hosp. No.

HISTORY

Past History

Present Complaint

PHYSICAL EXAMINATION

General Appearance — nutrition — pallor

Head — Eye, Ear, Nose and Throat

Heart — is murmur present?
is there enlargement?

Lungs — are respirations normal?
rales dullness

Abdomen — distention ?
is spleen enlarged?
is liver enlarged?

Adenopathy — neck
axilla
groin

Genitalia

Extremities — Bones and joints

REPORT OF OPERATION

Preoperative Diagnosis

Postoperative Diagnosis

Operation

Surgeon

Assistant

Anesthetist

Anesthetic

Condition during Anesthesia

Operation: Date Began Ended

Immediate Postoperative Condition

Hemorrhage, Shock, etc.

Findings

Procedure

FINAL DIAGNOSIS:

RESULTS: Discharged Alive: ☐ Died: ☐ Under 48 hours ☐ Over 48 hours

Signed M.D., Attending Physician

FORM D-1876 (REVISED 1962) PHYSICIANS' RECORD CO., BERWYN, ILLINOIS - PRINTED IN U.S.A. SHORT-STAY RECORD (OVER)

Fig. 18 — Short-Stay Record

off lists do not adequately provide sufficient information to substantiate the diagnosis and treatment. A short form medical record is acceptable in certain treatment and diagnostic cases of a minor nature which require less than 48-hours hospitalization (Fig. 18, p. 33 and Fig. 19, below). Short forms may be appropriate for such conditions as tonsillectomies, cystos-

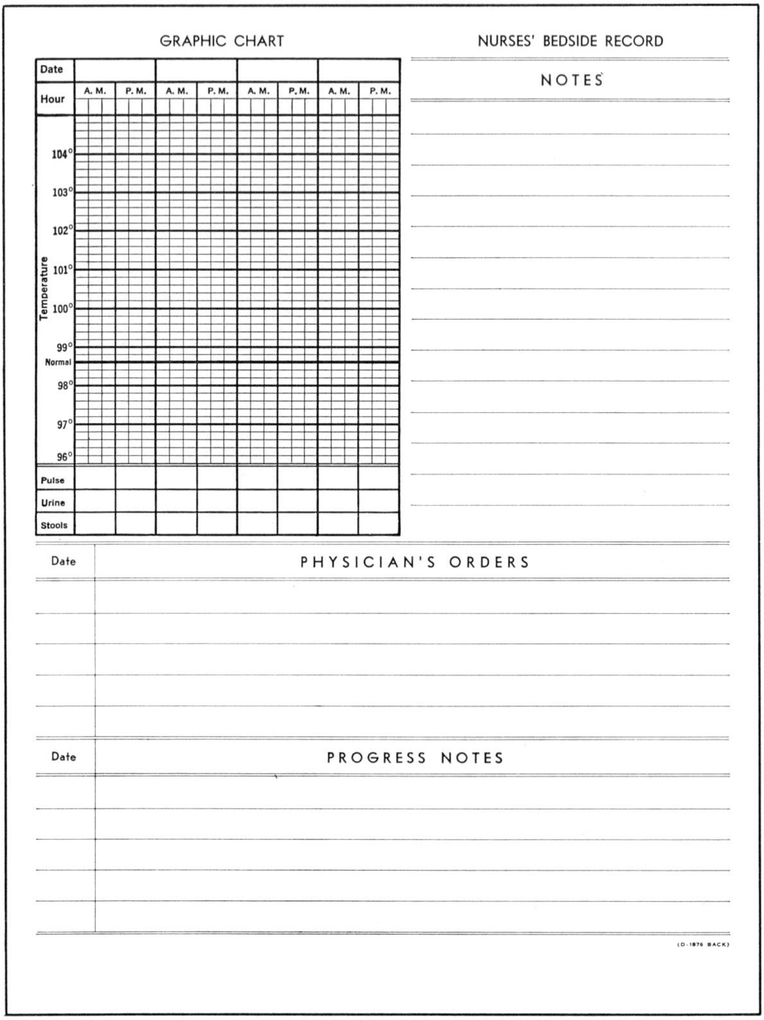
GRAPHIC CHART

NURSES' BEDSIDE RECORD

Date								
Hour	A. M.	P. M.	A. M.	P. M.	A. M.	P. M.	A. M.	P. M.
Temperature 104°								
103°								
102°								
101°								
100°								
99°								
Normal								
98°								
97°								
96°								
Pulse								
Urine								
Stools								

NOTES

Date	PHYSICIAN'S ORDERS

Date	PROGRESS NOTES

(D-1876 BACK)

FIG. 19 — GRAPHIC CHART — NURSES' BEDSIDE RECORD

copies, lacerations, plaster casts, removal of superficial growths, and accident cases held for observation. The short form should at least include identification data, a description of the patient's condition, pertinent physical findings, an account of the treatment given and data necessary to justify the diagnosis and treatment. The record should be signed by the physician.

Summary of the Medical Record

A summary of the patient's condition on discharge and course in the hospital (Fig. 9, p. 22) is valuable as a recapitulation of the patient's hospitalization.

The Joint Commission requires a summary on all medical charts except for minor cases of less than 48 hours' stay in the hospital. Short-stay forms (Fig. 18, p. 33) may be used for these latter cases.

The summary may be written in either one of these two ways:

1. The completion of a discharge summary (Fig. 9, p. 22). This summary should contain patient identification, a very brief résumé of the course of the case while in the hospital, any pertinent laboratory or x-ray findings. If the patient has been operated on, give the operation, any complications, prognosis and signature. If the summary is written by a house officer, it should be authenticated by the attending physician.

2. A narrative discharge summary of several paragraphs in length as a final progress note (Fig. 10, p. 23).[5]

---

[5] BABCOCK, B. B., "Accreditation Problems," *Hosp.*, 33:38, Jan. 16, 1959.

chapter 2

COMPLETION OF MEDICAL RECORDS

PRIOR to the beginning of and early in this century, when medical practice and the care of the patient were very simple, the attending physician could carry most of his knowledge and impressions of the patient in his head or in a small pocket notebook. But with the rapidly advancing science of medicine and its complexities, it is utterly impossible for the physician to do accurate, careful and scientific work in caring for the sick and injured without the medical record or case study. Today it is essential that each patient in the hospital have an accurate and adequate medical record, one that contains sufficient data to justify the diagnosis and warrant the treatment and end results.

The trustees of a hospital also have a great responsibility to see that the medical record is promptly and properly written on every patient admitted to the hospital. These are the production records of the institution which show how the patient has been cared for and the results of the expenditure of the budget for which the trustees are responsible. The trustees must be assured that the patient is receiving the best of care. This can never be known without adequate medical records.

Problem of Incomplete Medical Records

The attending physician is responsible for seeing that the medical record is written promptly and accurately. Unfortunately, he sometimes neglects this duty, feeling he is too busy to do it and puts it off. This is one of the greatest problems in hospitals—getting members of the medical staff to write medical records as they should be written.

Many hospital administrators have a difficult time in getting members of the medical staff to write their medical records or to make their medical records of scientific value. In certain instances, as already stated, members of the medical staff are delinquent and will not write records as they should be written. Not infrequently patients go to operation without an adequate medical record. This is dangerous. The regulation or policy of no operation proceeding without the medical record being completed and accompanying the patient should not be overlooked except, of course, in extreme emergency.[1]

One of the greatest problems in having records completed is in keeping track of incomplete charts, since there are many places where the records may be. Incomplete records may be (1) in doctors' incomplete file; (2) in interns' file; (3) in the death file; (4) in the tissue committee file; (5) in the records committee file; (6) signed out to student nurses for study; (7) in the autopsy secretary's file; (8) on the floor for current reference; (9) in one of the transcription baskets; (10) signed out to the doctor's office in some cases; (11) signed out to the administrator; (12) in the insurance clerk's basket; (13) in the coding specialist's basket.

Time Limit for Completing Records

Medical records should be dictated within 24 hours of the admission of the patient and should be completed within 48 hours of his discharge. In exceptional cases where a pathological report or special examination is not returned within 48 hours, it may be excusable to delay the final completion of the record until such report or reports are returned. It should be

---

[1] MacEachern, M. T., "Medical Records—a Vital Trustee Responsibility," *Trustee*, 5:1, Oct. 1952.

rare, however, that such reports are not completed by seven days after discharge of the patient and it should be expected that a week's delay is the maximal allowable period for completion of a discharged patient's record. It is becoming common hospital operating procedure for the medical staff to insist that all medical records should be completed within seven days after discharge of the patient.

Importance of Adequate Medical Records

Consistently adequate medical records highlight important information that is readily understandable by the board of trustees. The board can be assured that each physician will give the most careful thought to a diagnosis that is to become part of the written history of the patient; a diagnosis that will be preserved in the hospital annals for many years, and one that is subject to review by his colleagues. This is also true of the treatment prescribed for each patient.

Should the physician, through carelessness or lack of competence or for any other reason, err in the treatment ordered for a patient, the properly kept medical record will bring this fact to light when it is examined by his colleagues. On the other hand, the physician who practices the highest quality of medicine will want his records to be adequate as an indication of his skill and as protection should someone err in caring for his patient.

Without adequate medical records, the medical board cannot judge the performance of the medical staff properly. Medical records thus are an indispensable part of the hospital's service to patients and are primarily the responsibility of the medical staff. A medical records committee, as provided in the bylaws, specifically prescribing its functions, can aid greatly in the maintenance of good records.

Functions of Medical Records Committee

Under the medical staff bylaws, the medical records committee has the duty to see that proper medical records are maintained. Although there is little likelihood that the board of trustees would be held liable in damages for the failure of the medical staff to keep adequate records, such responsibility might be imposed if it were shown that the board had knowledge of these deficiencies and took no steps to remedy them, and that damages resulted to the patient.

Both procedure and penalty for disciplinary action against a staff member whose records are incomplete should be in the bylaws. The bylaws may provide that if a second notice to the physician to complete his record remains unheeded, the medical records committee should report the delinquent physician to the medical board. If the notice to complete, now coupled with warning, is unheeded, the medical board should recommend his suspension to the governing board.

In one hospital, a records committee meets once a month in open forum, just before the staff meeting. The record librarian, interns, residents and occasionally directors of nursing are invited. The previous month's records as to discharges, wound infections, deaths and unusual cases are discussed.

At the regular staff meeting the records committee reports on autopsy percentages, consultations, deaths, infections and other items of unusual interest (Figs. 20-21, pp. 40 and 41). A list of those members of the staff whose records are incomplete is posted or read. Staff members who fail to cooperate in completing records are notified that the privilege of practicing in the hospital is suspended. The admitting office is notified, and beds made unavailable to such doctors.

The following procedure has been issued by a hospital to its medical staff in order to facilitate the prompt completion of medical records:

1. A list of all doctors having incomplete charts will be posted in the ambulance entrance to the hospital.

2. If a record is not completed within two weeks from date

of discharge of the patient, the doctor will be notified that he has an additional two weeks to complete it before his admission privileges are suspended.

ANALYSIS OF HOSPITAL SERVICE Month of

CLASSIFICATION or SERVICE (List each patient once only)	Number of Patients	Hospital Days	CONSULTATIONS			Infections	DEATHS			AUTOPSIES	
			Total	Rendered	Recorded		Total	Post-oper.	Anesthetic	Total	Over 48 hrs.
Medicine											
Surgery											
Obstetrics											
Delivered in Hospital											
Admitted After Delivery											
Aborted											
Not Delivered											
Newborn											
Term, Born Alive											
Immature, Born Alive											
Gynecology											
Ophthalmology											
Otorhinolaryngology											
Urology											
Orthopedics											
Dermatology											
Pediatrics											
Neurology											
Neurosurgery											
Psychiatry											
Thoracic Surgery											
Total Discharges											

RECAPITULATION OF PATIENTS IN HOSPITAL		
Patients in hospital midnight last day previous month		
Patients admitted during month (exclude newborn)		
Newborn this month		
Total patients treated this month		
Patients discharged this month (exclude deaths)		
Deaths this month		
Total patients in hospital last day this month		

RESULTS (List each patient once only)	Number of Patients
Discharged Alive	
Deaths - under 48 hours	
over 48 hours	
Total Discharges and Deaths	
Late Fetal Deaths (stillbirths)	

DEATHS

(List additional deaths on a separate sheet)

FORM C-619 PHYSICIANS RECORD CO., BERWYN, ILLINOIS - PRINTED IN U.S.A. (OVER)

FIG. 20 — ANALYSIS OF HOSPITAL SERVICE

A red clip will be placed by his name on the bulletin board as an additional reminder.

3. If the record is still incomplete two weeks from date of

this notice, or one month from date of discharge, admission privileges will automatically be suspended until it is completed.

4. If the record remains incomplete for three months after

FIG. 21 — COMPARATIVE REPORT OF PROFESSIONAL PERFORMANCE

admission privileges have been suspended, the doctor will be notified that unless it is completed within one week the face sheet of the chart will be stamped, "FILED INCOMPLETE.

DOCTOR REFUSES TO COOPERATE," and the chart filed in the permanent file.

Signing the Record

There are three reasons why the attending physician should sign the history, physical, and summary of a patient's medical record.

The patient should be protected. A poorly written history and physical seen by another doctor called into the case could be misleading and unfair to the patient. If this patient returned in five years' time and an inadequate or poor history and physical had been written, it could lead to irreparable harm to the patient.

The legal significance of having signed the history and physical would be of help to the physician if the case came to court. If he had not signed it and the contents were contrary to his own findings, then it would be his hearsay evidence or memory against the written word, and he would be in trouble. The quotation has often been made — "one line of faded blue ink is worth 1000 memories."

The American Medical Association has stated in its brochures, *Essentials of An Approved Internship* and *Essentials of an Approved Residency* that it is the duty and responsibility of the attending physician on any case to read and correct and amend and criticize the history and physical of the house officers writing this document. If they do not do this then it is exploitation of the house officers. What good is their history and physical if it is not read by the physician on the case, and handled in the way spelled out? If the physician does not like the history and physical he should say so, and put in any corrections which he deems necessary to make it an adequate history and physical. Only when the history and physical with his additions or amendments have been completed, should he sign it. For the protection of the patient, if he countersigns it, it means that he agrees in substance with it, and if he does not agree, he should so state, both for the protection of the patient and his own protection.

Survey by Joint Commission

The Joint Commission on Accreditation of Hospitals conducts a survey of hospital medical record departments according to a definite, established procedure. The standards upon which the surveyor bases his opinion are outlined in the *Standards for Hospital Accreditation.*

The director of the Joint Commission notifies the hospital of the date of the surveyor's visit to the hospital. With the notice, he also encloses a detailed questionnaire for completion by the hospital. The completed questionnaire is presented to the surveyor upon his arrival at the hospital. These questions may include the following with regard to the medical records:

1. Is the medical record department under the supervision of a qualified medical record librarian?

2. If no one is available, are medical record technicians employed?

3. Are the minimum standards for medical records enforced?

4. Are the medical records kept up to date at all times?

5. Is there a deadline as to the completion of records?

6. Are the delinquent records reported to the medical staff by the medical record committee?

7. Is there any method of disciplining doctors who refuse to cooperate in the completion of records?

8. Are hospital privileges suspended temporarily if a doctor does not complete his records before the agreed deadline?

9. If a physician refuses to complete his records, are they filed as such?

10. Are records taken away without the permission of the doctor, patient, and hospital?

11. Are physicians allowed to take the whole record or any part of it to their offices for completion of information?

12. Is the backlog of incomplete records more than one-third of the current hospital discharges?

13. Are clerks, nurses, and librarians allowed to take part of or the whole history of patients?

14. Is there an active record committee of the medical staff?

15. Do they have authority to review samples of medical records and report to the medical staff on their quality?

16. Do they cooperate with the medical record librarian?

17. Are all histories and physical examinations written or dictated within 48 hours of admission?

18. Is the provisional diagnosis invariably recorded on admission?

The second most common reason for the failure of hospitals to receive accreditation is incomplete medical records. The Joint Commission considers the quality of a hospital's medical records of the utmost importance, because good medical records correlate very highly with good medical care. Since the medical record reflects the care of the patient, the Commission evaluates the record, and judges whether or not it contains sufficient recorded material to justify the diagnosis, therapy, and results.

Moreover, the Joint Commission puts great emphasis on the care and extent to which the medical staff reviews and evaluates its clinical practice. To live up to its responsibility of review and evaluation, the hospital staff must have good records.[2]

Removal of Records from Hospital

Medical records should never be removed from the hospital, not even for purposes of completion. The medical record is a potential legal document and should be treated as such. Therefore, it should be put away for safekeeping and should be preserved under the strictest possible rule so as to preserve its legal validity on behalf of the patient.

[2] MacEachern, M. T., "Medical Records—a Vital Trustee Responsibility." *Trustee,* 5:1, Oct. 1952.

The records should be completed at the hospital. If there is not room for the physician to complete his records, then the hospital should provide him with accommodations as soon as possible in the record room or elsewhere. All too frequently, the physician has to take medical records home because the hospital does not supply him with proper facilities for completing his medical records.

It has been held in one case that the complaint of a patient should not have been dismissed, but the evidence should have been submitted to the jury, which could have found that the failure of the doctor and the nurse to make a note of the doctor's direction to keep the patient for further observation, and that the discharge of the patient by the nurses contrary to hospital routine, were administrative acts of negligence on the part of defendant-hospital.[3]

Effect of Delay in Recording

The doctor must not only exercise a high quality of medical care, but he should also be able to prove that he has done so. His greatest aid, in this respect, is the clinical record. This should show what was done, when it was done, and should include a complete recording of all instructions given the patient together with the written history, the record of the results of physical examinations, and reports of laboratory examinations, and the progress notes. The physician cannot possibly recall all of these facts after a year or more, but the disgruntled patient is likely to remember (not always accurately) every detail and every word spoken.

It is a common human characteristic to remember only that which one wishes to remember and to remember what one has heard, not in context in which it was stated, but in the context of how one interpreted it. Moreover, the patient's vivid recollection of the circumstances as he remembers them is liable to sway the average judge or jury when there is a conflict be-

---

[3] *Adams* v. *City of New York*, 285 App. Div. 868 (N.Y.) (1955).

tween his and the physician's statements. Juries are also apt
to conclude, and perhaps justifiably, that the poor record reflects laxity on the part of the physician in his management of
the case.

Delay in making the notes may make the notations inadmissible at the trial. In an action involving an automobile accident,
a notation in the hospital record that there was an odor of
alcohol on the breath of the driver of the car was properly rejected. Although the intern testified he found the alcoholic
odor in the regular course of his business, he had made the
notation two days later.[4]

The effect of delay in making notes on the legal value of a
record is pointed out in a case involving the death of a patient.
An action was brought against a hospital and physician whose
alleged malpractice in failing to administer tetanus antitoxin
resulted in the death of the patient. The decedent had suffered
severe lacerations about the legs and fractured bones. A witness testified that she saw a nurse prepare a hypodermic which
was injected into the patient's arm; that it was morphine and
not tetanus antitoxin. There was no note in the chart that
antitetanus serum was administered, nor was there a charge
for the serum given to the bookkeeper by the nurse. The chart
was made up after the patient was carried out of the operating room to her private room, instead of as the treatment
progressed.

The operating room, remarked the court, was the proper
place in which to administer the serum, yet there was no record of what transpired there. "An account that does not purport to contain entries of records of a given transaction is not
competent to affirm or to negate what actually took place. In
the present case, the records were not correctly kept. That is
shown without contradiction." The records were refused as
evidence to prove the administration of the serum.[5]

---

[4] *Weller* v. *Fish Transport Co.*, 123 Conn. 49, 192A. 317 (1937).

[5] *Hembree* v. *Von Keller*, 119 P. 2d 74 (Okla.) (1941).

chapter 3

PRESERVATION OF MEDICAL
RECORDS AND X-RAYS

THE permanent preservation of all records routinely is an economic waste; some records, however, should be kept indefinitely because of their historical, research or teaching value. Records of adults may be needed within the period of the statute of limitations to collect hospital bills, or to defend the hospital or its personnel against malpractice or negligence claims within the one, two, or three year period of the statute, depending on the state.

The Joint Commission on Accreditation of Hospitals has no standards governing the preservation of medical records. The length of time a medical record is to be preserved is a matter which should be determined by the local hospital and local laws. Methods of preservation by microfilming or other means of storage is a decision for the individual hospital to make. However, no records should be destroyed from one examination by the Commission to the next.

The American Hospital Association in 1960 adopted a resolution recommending that medical records should be retained for clinical and scientific purposes for 25 years, but in hospitals with limited clinical and scientific programs, retention should be for ten years. These standards have been approved by the American Association of Medical Record Librarians.

With regard to roentgenograms, the American College of

Radiology recommends that films in the average hospital should be maintained for at least five years, except that apparently negative chest films of adults should be preserved, if practical, for ten years. Films of an unusual nature or of teaching value should be kept indefinitely.

The prime factors in the retention of records are law and usage. The medical record department of the hospital, as well as the other departments, should check on the frequency of referral to old records; a tabulation as to such requests would be useful to a committee which studies usage and the desirability of a retention schedule.

What records to retain or to destroy and the period of preservation differs with the type and size of the hospital. Hospitals with teaching and research facilities may be interested in retaining certain records for educational, statistical or other purposes. The fact that a medical record is no longer "active" is not necessarily the criterion of whether it is to be disposed of. By the same token, an "inactive" record need not be preserved by microfilming or otherwise, unless it is anticipated that there is a reasonable likelihood the record may be needed in the foreseeable future. The microfilming of a record which can have no possible value in the future merely preserves a useless record at a cost to the hospital. The primary consideration should be the benefit to the hospital alone of retaining the record in some form, whether as the original or by microfilm or otherwise. Such consideration naturally involves the requirements of applicable federal and state laws.

The Record Control Program

Record control programs have been created with several objectives in mind, and it is important that these objectives be carefully defined. Many programs received the initial impetus from a storage space problem.

Control of this increasing avalanche of paper is an economic necessity, and responsibilities are neglected when the problem is ignored. Uncontrolled retention of records costs money and adds to the patient's bill. Failure to keep necessary records, however, can also add to the patient's bill. Adequate factual data are essential to: (1) the receipt of just payments in behalf of patients from third party payers; (2) protection in the event of court action; (3) analysis of hospital managerial skills and resultant benefit to the patient in the development of operating economies.

The ultimate success which can be expected from a records management program is dependent on the support of the top manager of the organization and the interest and enthusiasm of the appointed records manager. The committee approach to record retention scheduling is common, and a small group with the authority to enforce the schedules can be successful.

Such a committee can be composed of the assistant administrator, the controller, the director of medical records and the chief x-ray technician. The objectives of the group should be (1) to serve in an advisory capacity to the administrator and board of trustees for the development of record policies, (2) to suggest patterns for the storage of records, (3) to suggest policies for retention schedules, (4) to schedule orderly disposition of records, and (5) to enforce record policies.

The program should consist of examining available publications outlining applicable general regulations, along with studies of other approaches; listing by type, the records maintained by each department of the hospital, in order to know what records are actually being kept; developing tentative policies of disposition and retention based on the knowledge of members of the group and discussions with the departments concerned; reviewing tentative recommendations with the hospital attorney to clarify legal requirements; marking existing records for destruction or storing them with future destruction dates; setting up destruction lists and schedules of periodic inventories; final review and recommendations to the administrator for adoption of policies developed; notifying hospital departments of approved policies.[1]

A card index record should be kept of the papers destroyed both to eliminate the need for a fruitless search and to account for the absence of such records.

Abstracting the Record

Medical records may be disposed of by being destroyed, summarized on index cards or microfilmed. Which procedure to follow would depend on whether the records are sufficiently accurate to be of use and whether the cost of summarizing or microfilming is offset by their value to patients, house staff, research workers or the medical staff. A careful study of a representative number of records by the medical record librarian and the medical records committee of the medical staff can determine the value of keeping the records in some condensed form.

Certain old records may be abstracted before destruction if they are not of sufficient value for microfilming. Where they are of little research value, and are used occasionally to establish date of birth or to check childhood conditions that reflect on adult illness, they should be briefed. The patient's name, hospital number, diagnosis, operation, x-ray verification, death, physician's name, admission and discharge dates make up the abstract.

The advantages of card summaries are: low cost of materials; small storage space is required; it is easily placed on the new chart if there is a readmission; the summary may be indexed according to disease; it is easy to read by the physician; it eliminates difficulty of reading the physician's handwriting or misinterpreting abbreviations; the unit system may be retained with less difficulty than in microfilming.

---

[1] TURNER, W. T., "Record Retention: There Has to be a System," *Hosp.*, 34:44, Aug. 16, 1960.

On the other hand, there are certain disadvantages: the space on a small card may limit the information to a bare minimum; small cards may be lost during the handling of chart; cards deteriorate with much handling; the cards may not be admissible in evidence in court as a copy or summary of the original.

Use of Microfilm

The use of microfilm for the preservation of records has increased to a marked extent since the termination of World War II. The need to conserve space and the economy of the microfilm method of copying papers are the forces which motivate the use of microfilm. In a limited sense there are many beneficial factors from the use of microfilming, but one fundamental objection to the use of the device is the fact that the use of microfilm destroys the availability of the record.

In hospitals, the shorter stay, improved record keeping, and increased attention to the completeness of records increases the number of charts and the volume of the individual record.

Industry or business can well afford to spend taxable profits in research and the administrative study to review and condense their records into smaller units to conserve space, but the limited budgets of hospitals require consideration of various methods of solving medical record problems and must even consider the possibility of discarding superfluous data to conserve space.

Microfilmed records represent a 98 per cent saving in storage space. Such records cannot be misfiled; they are on a certain spot on the film, and are alteration-proof. Photo copies can be made at small cost, and with no possibility of error. Film manufactured according to the U.S. Bureau of Standards requirements is non-explosive, fire-resistant, and will last almost indefinitely.

Physicians and house officers are not too enthusiastic about microfilmed records. Instead of having the previous record of admission delivered to the floor, they must use the film reader in the record room. Requests are made for the installation of film readers in the outpatient department and on all floors. Physicians accustomed to having original records available selectively through an index of diseases or operations object to reviewing records for research in a film reader. The costs of microfilming and multiple film readers may not justify the system when it is used for the preservation of records no longer useful.

That microfilm saves space cannot be disputed. Whether the process is really necessary or the expense justified should be considered before undertaking the procedure. The hospital should review its experience with demands for obsolete records. For instance, how many records more than ten years old have been needed during the past year? How many records more than five years old have been required? What was the nature of the requests, and could not the information have been supplied from other sources, such as the patient's index card, x-ray department records, etc.? Is the hospital planning to microfilm its useless records merely because others are doing so, or because a definite study has convinced the hospital authorities of the advantages over any other system?

AHA Statement on Medical Records Retention

Following is the statement on preservation of medical records of hospital inpatients adopted by the Board of Trustees of the American Hospital Association at its meetings in Chicago, May 19-20, 1960:

WHEREAS Medical records are the property of the hospital; and

WHEREAS Hospitals retain such records for varying periods of time because of clinical, scientific and legal considerations; and

WHEREAS In most jurisdictions the hospital is not required by law to preserve its records for any given length of time; and

WHEREAS In most states the Statute of Limitations is less than twenty-five (25) years for torts and for contracts; and

WHEREAS In most states the Statute of Limitations requires that the right of suit for personal injuries sustained during the period of minority be exercised within a few years after becoming of age; and

WHEREAS It is deemed unnecessary to preserve medical records in the hospital for any given time as proof of birth or age, verification of residence, proof of citizenship, or verification of family relationship, in view of the existence of official records for these purposes; and

WHEREAS Hospitals, in general, are seldom called upon to produce medical records older than twenty-five (25) years, either for clinical, scientific or legal purposes; and

WHEREAS Generally, it is deemed unnecessary to retain the original record in cases older than twenty-five (25) years and it is ordinarily sufficient to retain basic information (such as dates of admission and discharge, name of responsible physician, and record of diagnoses and operations) in an index or register on summary cards in cases older than twenty-five (25) years; therefore be it

RESOLVED That the medical records of hospital inpatients usually should be retained for clinical and scientific purposes, either in the original or reproduced form, for a period of twenty-five (25) years after discharge or death. After this period such records may be eligible for destruction except as may be specifically prohibited by statute, ordinance, regulation or law, and be it further

RESOLVED That, in institutions in which use of medical records for scientific purposes is limited and the rate of readmissions low, and where the needs of the medical staff and

the interests of the patients would be adequately met and
protected by the retention of medical records (either in
the original or reproduced form) for a period of substantially less than twenty-five (25) years, then a ten (10)
year retention period is considered a desirable minimum,
after which the records may be destroyed except as may
be specifically prohibited by statute, ordinance, regulation
or law, or as may be required for legal purposes, provided
that:

1. Records of minors should be retained until after the
   expiration of the period of election following achievement of majority as prescribed by statute in the individual states.
2. The hospital retains in an index or register or on summary cards certain basic information (such as dates
   of admission and discharge, name of responsible physician, and record of diagnoses and operations) for all
   records so destroyed.

Guide to Retention of Hospital Records

Hospital records are not restricted to records relating only
to the medical care of patients. There are numerous other records consisting of business transactions, reports required to be
kept by law, personnel records, administrative records, etc.,
which should be reviewed from time to time to determine
whether they should be disposed of and after what period of
time.

A "Guide" prepared by the Greater New York Hospital Association has been found useful by member hospitals in orient-
ing them as to the disposition of such records, by classifying
the type of records and periods of retention as follows:

Records to be Retained for One (1) Year

Type of Records

Statistical data; admissions, discharges, etc.

Services — medical, surgical, etc., quarterly and semi-annual
    reports. Visiting Physicians' register

Ward personnel assignment slips

Daily admission and discharge sheets

Obsolete book records, patients' baths, temperatures. Day and
    night report books.

Records to be Retained for Two Years

Employee time sheets or time cards

Leaves of absence, vacations, etc.

Personnel charges, interdepartmental Division Summary of
    Absences, etc.

Copies of payroll

Pharmacy regular and special requisitions.

Manifold books — all requisitions except those for Department
    of Purchase

Individual reports of receipts

Certain monthly reports

Engineering reports of institutions

Ward inventories

Special Nurses register

Form 673 (non-revenue collections)

Collection records non-revenue producing

X-ray request cards for other than employees

Laboratory reports

Blood Bank requests and donor cards.

Records to be Retained for Five (5) Years

Ward Narcotic Records

Pharmacy Narcotic Prescriptions

Student Nurses Accounts

Vouchers (payment vouchers)

Records to be Retained for Seven (7) Years

General Correspondence (exclude general orders and blue
    prints, etc.)

Ambulance Slips

Accident Reports (patients and visitors)

Student Nurse Accounts

Patients; duplicate receipt books

Patients' clothing and property books

Patients' S.R. 1204 Ledger Sheet

Special (city and privately paid) nurses

Agreement book

Payees receipt book

Cash disbursements book #11,256

Department of Purchase Requisitions

X-ray film (other than employees)

Records to be Retained for Ten (10) Years

Compensation and Liability Records (exclude those reopened
    in this ten year period)

Inpatient chart records (from last contact with patient) (do
    not destroy records of minor until he or she has attained
    the age of 22 years)

Outpatient chart records (from last contact with patient)

Division of Collections records, (exclude those reopened dur-
    ing the ten year period) and no Revenue

Records to be Retained Permanently

Accident reports of employees

X-ray of employees

Engineering forms — fuel records, plans, etc.

Institutional forms — employee personnel records, health, etc.

Birth Book or Birth Certificates

Death Book or Death Certificates.

Retention of Nurses' Notes

In most cases there is no need for retaining nurses' notes
for as long a time as the remainder of the record. Some hospitals remove the nurses' notes from the record and destroy

these sheets two or three years after the patient's discharge, unless a malpractice or negligence action has been brought.

There are cases where it would appear advisable that such notes be retained for a longer period, as where patients have threatened suicide, been noticeably disgruntled, threatened legal action or have suffered an accident in the hospital. Should a nurse or other hospital employee be involved in an accident to the patient, it is suggested that the nurses' notes be retained with the record or microfilmed.

Practices in the preservation of nurses' notes differ. At one large hospital the notes are removed from the record at the discharge of the patient, filed numerically according to hospital number in a separate file and kept for six years. In special cases they are kept for longer periods of time. If it is shown that they should be retained indefinitely, the record librarian will have them bound permanently with the medical chart.

Records of Deceased Physicians

There are no recorded court decisions or statutes dealing specifically with the retention of medical records when a physician dies. The practice of a physician dies with him, and so does the physical value of his medical records. The records cannot be sold because the information they contain is confidential. Therefore, they should not be inventoried as "property" in the estate of the physician.

Generally, it is recommended that the following disposition be made of the records of a deceased doctor:

Records which might be pertinent to any litigation in which a patient may be involved should not be destroyed without prior notice to the patient.

Records which may be of value to the estate in defending any existing or potential malpractice claim against the estate should be retained until the expiration of the applicable statute of limitations.

In those instances where patients of the deceased physician have requested in writing that their records be forwarded to another physician of their choice, this should be done.

Records of adult patients who have not visited the physician for more than three years should be destroyed.

Records which should be retained for a reasonable time should be entrusted to the care of a physician who was associated in practice with the deceased.

If the circumstances are such that the confidential nature of the records can only be preserved by destruction because there is no one to whom they may be entrusted in keeping with the above recommendations, then they should be destroyed.

Preservation of X-Ray Films

The possession of the roentgenograms and their availability for study is of the utmost value to the roentgenologist, since they add continuously to the sum total of his clinical experience and thereby are of added benefit to the patient. They are as important to the roentgenologist as a microscopic slide is to the pathologist or an electrocardiogram to a heart specialist.

Roentgenograms taken at a hospital are the property of the hospital and/or radiologist. At the hospital these roentgenograms are filed in the x-ray department as part of the hospital records. The roentgenograms and the roentgenologist's report, based on his study of these roentgenograms, constitute a hospital x-ray record; the original report is filed with the patient's chart and a copy kept in the Department of Radiology.

The preservation or destruction of x-ray films is a matter of choice for the hospital trustees. Each hospital must weigh the cost of storage against its duty to its patients, to its physicians, to the community that it serves and to itself. If x-ray films are to be destroyed, the medical staff should prepare instructions for the guidance of the radiologist and the total procedure for disposal should be reviewed by the hospital's legal counsel with approval by the governing board before being put into effect.

The radiologist is a consultant to the medical staff, giving reports of his examination or treatment to his colleagues. The report, signed by the roentgenologist assuming responsibility for its contents, is an integral part of the hospital record. As such, it is available to those who have a valid interest in the chart. Where the chart is admissible in evidence under the Uniform Business Records as Evidence Act, the x-ray readings which are part of the chart are admissible without the need of producing and identifying the films. X-ray readings which are not part of a hospital record are not admissible until the films have been identified and offered in evidence.

Ownership of Films

X-rays made at a private laboratory frequently are delivered to the patient, who takes them to his physician for interpretation. In such case, the patient pays for the x-rays and they then become his property. If the x-rays are later turned over to a physician or dentist, the patient still retains ownership.

Dental x-rays made by a dentist operating his own machine, for the purpose of treating his own patients, are his property and a part of his records. Likewise, where a private physician takes x-rays, the negatives are the physician's property in the absence of any contrary agreement, notwithstanding the cost was charged to the patient.

X-rays taken in the hospital laboratory are hospital property, retained on the same theory as the patient's temperature chart or other records of diagnosis or treatment.

The patient and his physician are entitled to the roentgenologist's opinion, but not to the plates. No report should be given to the patient except through the referring physician. In the event of a malpractice suit against a physician or surgeon, the negative may justify the treatment of the condition of which the patient complains.

Three x-ray pictures were taken of the patient's foot and lower limb. The x-ray specialist was paid for his services and he forwarded the films, together with his findings, to the referring physician, who sent his own report to the attorney for the patient. The plates were retained by the referring doctor. Another attorney, later substituted for the original lawyer, demanded the x-rays, but was refused. He thereupon brought suit against both doctors for possession of the films. The court dismissed the action, holding that the x-ray plates were the property of the roentgenologist. "The x-ray plate becomes the veritable foundation stone of the roentgenologist's diagnosis and report and it is essential that he retain it as a permanent record in support of his diagnosis, for should it be destroyed by unskillful handling or loss, the roentgenologist would have no means to justify the correctness of his diagnosis or findings in the event of challenge to his professional opinion."[2]

Policy on Ownership

The American College of Radiology has adopted the following statement of policy regarding ownership of radiograms, for the guidance of hospitals and physicians.

1. Roentgenograms should be used for the best interests of the patient.

2. The roentgenograms are the legal property of the radiologist or of the hospital in which they were made. It is advisable, but not necessary, to mark on each film the statement "Property of Dr. John Doe." Such a mark is particularly desirable if the radiologist delivers the films to the referring physician instead of filing them in his office or hospital department.

3. It should be the policy of the radiologist to make the films available for inspection by the physician who referred the patient for x-ray examination, along with a copy of the report of the radiologist. The best results are undoubtedly obtained when it is possible for the radiologist and the referring physician to confer personally when the latter views the films.

---

[2] *Spaulding* v. *Bierman and Sinberg*, Mun. Ct. of the City of New York, Small Claims part, Boro. of Man., November 23, 1945.

4. If the referring physician, or if the patient on behalf of the referring physician, wishes to take the films away from the office or the hospital, it should be clearly understood that the films are "on loan" and should be returned after the loan has served its purpose.

5. If the patient dismisses the referring physician and goes to another physician, the films and the report should be made as freely available to the second as they are to the first physician who originally referred the patient.

It is desirable that the patient notify the first physician of the change and it may be assumed that he has done so, but even if this notification has not been made, the obligation of the radiologist is unchanged. When the second physician wishes to examine the films it is assumed that he is doing so at the request of the patient.

6. If the referring physician objects to the submission of the films to the second physician or to giving to the latter a copy of the radiologist's report, the radiologist is obligated to do so in spite of this objection. If the referring physician has possession of the films and refuses to release them, the radiologist, whose legal property they are, has the right to take whatever action is necessary to get the films for the further benefit of the patient.

7. All films should be legibly and permanently marked so that the patient can be identified and the date on which they were taken can be determined. This is important because, under some conditions, a comparison of films just made with others made previously may be the crucial factor necessary to establish a diagnosis or to estimate the progress or regression of a disease.

8. When a medicolegal situation exists, the radiologist has a right to refuse to release the involved films if necessary for his own protection, except on a court order.

9. A liberal attitude regarding the release of films is more

desirable than strict insistence on one's legal rights. It is better to run the occasional risk of losing films than to engender the enmity of a patient or of a physician by strict adherence to the rule which in the past has led to attempts to make laws making the films the legal property of the patient.

The Storage Problem

Storage of films is a problem in almost every hospital. The demand for space for new procedures, diagnostic, therapeutic, teaching or research is seemingly without end and some hospitals may feel that the space used to store x-ray films could be employed more productively.

Some institutions have solved the problem of storage of x-ray films by making photographic reductions of the originals. These are generally satisfactory for most fracture work, but have not been found entirely adequate for detailed chest studies. This is equally true of microfilms and the drawback will probably continue until more refined methods of photographic reproduction are evolved. The contracted copy of the original x-ray film is unquestionably of less medical and legal value than the original. Even so, it may represent a compromise between the need for medical and legal protection and the hospital's need for the space that is occupied by the x-ray films.

Reasons for Preservation

The most important reason for preserving the x-ray film is its use in the future care of the patient. To destroy the original x-ray film and to rely entirely on the report of the radiologist is to reduce by that much the patient's chances of getting an accurate diagnosis. Even x-ray films that purport to show nothing but a normal portion of the anatomy may contain some undetected disease in its incipient stages. Radiologists are not infallible and early lesions may be missed.

As a teaching aid, the x-ray film speaks for itself. The development of any particular lesion may be traced from its inception to autopsy. Combined with the actual anatomy, either living or dead, the x-ray film is a graphic demonstration that is not easily forgotten. Films of unusual conditions can be preserved indefinitely for demonstration to students and physicians. A good collection of teaching films of any particular disease is worth many hours of illustrationless lecturing, even by the most facile speaker.

Another reason for preserving film is for the patient's welfare. The preservation of the x-ray film is a protection of his civil rights in a law court. The x-ray film itself is the best evidence that the patient can present to prove the truth of his allegations. The report of the radiologist, no matter how well or how carefully made, is not as valuable as the actual film itself. On the other hand, it is extremely difficult to alter a film without detection. Its authenticity is therefore easy to establish. A report can be changed or substituted, but the x-ray film does not lend itself easily to such chicanery. To destroy the x-ray film of the patient's condition is to deprive him of his best chance of obtaining justice before the law.

In addition to the patient, two other parties are concerned in the preservation of x-ray records, namely, the hospital and the physicians who were involved in the care of the patient. In an action for damages by a patient against a hospital or its radiologist, for example, the radiologist's unsupported testimony on his own or the hospital's behalf cannot be expected to carry conclusive weight with an impartial jury. When the x-ray film is presented in court, the evidence, properly identified, is there for all to see. It is open to inspection by experts appointed by the court or by either of the litigants. Though the jury may be confused by medical language, it can be made to understand the meaning of certain shadows on the x-ray film.

Another compelling reason for the preservation of x-ray

films is the identification of bodies that are impossible to recognize by other standard means.[3]

The rule that x-ray films are part of the patient's record and should remain the property of the hospital and of the radiologist who took them has been tested and reaffirmed in various court decisions.[4] Yet the enforcement of this rule meets with many difficulties. The patient does not understand that something for which he paid and that he believes is the material proof of his sickness or his accident, should not be given to him. He cannot see that it is "not the film itself but the interpretation by the trained observer" for which he paid, and he is frequently supported by his physician, who under similar conception requests the films be delivered to his office. It might be that the case requires prolonged care or is of particular interest to the physician. In the end, invariably these films are lost, misplaced, or returned in unrecognizable form.

The interpretation of the rule by which the film should remain with the radiologist and his institution is not uniformly handled. There are institutions that by their central and authoritative character can easily enforce the regulation that films cannot be released but can be inspected in their film-viewing room. Others release the films upon the request of the referring physician with a form letter asking that they be returned after inspection. Even more important the patient frequently does not remember where and when he deposited his x-ray films after he changed domicile, physician, or hospital.[5]

Length of Time for Preservation

How long should x-ray films be kept? Twenty years ago, there was much controversy over the value of preserving x-ray films. In those days, there was another good reason for getting

[3] LETOURNEAU, C. U., "The Preservation of X-ray Films—Five Pertinent Reasons", *Hosp.*, 26:136, April 1952.

[4] *McGarry* v. *Mercier*, 262 N.W. 296, 72 Mich. 501 (1931).

[5] *J.A.M.A.*, 157:1332, April 9, 1955.

rid of them besides the need for space. Made of cellulose nitrate (celluloid) they were a fire hazard and had been responsible for more than a few deaths. The cellulose acetate film had not yet been developed to its present high standard of accuracy. Today, however, safety film has eliminated danger from fire. There is but one good argument against preservation of x-ray films, and that is cost of storage space.

There is no law that obliges a hospital to preserve x-ray films for any given period of time. Nor has there been any official pronouncement by any body in the medical or associated fields on the preservation of x-ray films, other than by the American College of Radiology.

Some may contend that x-ray films should be kept only as long as the statute of limitations preserves the right of action. Up to a point this is correct, but it must always be remembered that the statute of limitations sometimes does not begin to run until the damage has been discovered, and the damage may not be discovered for several years. It should also be recalled that the statute of limitations does not operate against minors and only begins to run when they come of legal age. It is suggested by some that films of minors be kept until one year after they come of age. In litigation cases which involve x-ray films, the films should be retained for at least ten years. Films suitable for teaching and research should be kept indefinitely.

Methods of Preservation

Several methods of preserving reduced copies of x-ray films are in use in hospitals. One method is a simple contraction of the original film and filing in the x-ray department. Some hospitals prefer to extract films which have a particular medical, legal or research interest, retaining these originals indefinitely and reducing the remainder. In such cases, the radiologist, the attending physician or a committee composed of both, may review the films and indicate which originals are to be retained.

In another method, x-ray films are microfilmed in chronological order and stored in the x-ray department on a roll of film. The obvious drawback to this method is the necessity of reviewing much of the microfilm roll before the desired film is located. Review of a patient's x-ray films may involve the examination of several rolls so that the loss in man-hours may well exceed the gain from increased availability of storage space. Comparative film studies are difficult with this method.

A third method is to include the microfilmed original negatives with the microfilmed record of the patient's illnesses and to file these away as a complete record in the medical records department. This method makes it virtually impossible for the radiologist to examine several films simultaneously. Comparison is thus made difficult though not impossible.

Another suggested practice is to retain the microfilmed negative of the original film in the x-ray department and to attach a positive print of the microfilm to the patient's medical documents. This practice is useful only in the most obvious diagnoses. Physicians are accustomed to reading negative x-ray plates and the conversion from positive to negative may lead to occasional errors. It should be added, moreover, that the microfilming of the patient's records would present a difficulty if it were proposed to microfilm the reduced positive print, because the x-ray picture would be almost unrecognizable.[6]

Effect of Statutes of Limitations

One of the factors to be considered in connection with the preservation of records is the statute of limitations of the state. In general, it is felt that medical records should be retained in some form for use in litigation or for other legal purposes.

Such records may prove useful also in establishing dates of births, marriages, age for social security purposes, previous

---

[6] LETOURNEAU, C. U., "The Preservation of X-ray Films — Five Pertinent Reasons," *Hosp.*, 26:138, April 1952.

illnesses, etc. All these possibilities of inquiry influence hospital personnel in their decisions on record retention policies. The length of time to retain particular types of records may depend on the state statute of limitations. The greatest concern, however, seems to be with records involving malpractice or negligence cases against physicians or hospitals, especially in the case of minors.

Statutes of limitations fix the time within which a lawsuit may be brought. The policy behind the limitation period is to make claimants prosecute their causes of action promptly, a protection for defendants who would otherwise be indefinitely subject to liability. After the time fixed in the statute the lapse may be pleaded as a defense. The statutory time for bringing actions varies in the states, as does the time for the different types of lawsuits.

One of the variations in determining when the cause of action accrues depends on the interpretations of the statutes by the courts. The courts of the various states have given conflicting answers as to when the cause of action accrues or the statute of limitations begins to run. The date may be when (1) the physician terminated his treatment; (2) the wrongful act was done; (3) the injurious consequences become known; (4) the patient reasonably should have discovered the injury; (5) the contract between the physician and patient ended; (6) when the "continuous" malpractice ended.

Occasionally, the same facts may give rise to an action for tort (personal injury) and for breach of contract. The statute may bar one action, but not the other.

Limitations in Malpractice Cases

Malpractice is predicated upon the failure to exercise requisite medical skill and is tortious in nature. The damages recoverable in malpractice are for personal injuries, including the pain and suffering which naturally flow from the tortious act.

The statutes on malpractice limitations in the various states require the action to be brought from one year to not more than three years after the negligent act, except for South Carolina where the period is six years.

Malpractice Based on Alleged Contract

The relationship of physician and patient arises out of a contract, expressed or implied. In the event that the physician breaches his contract, the patient has a cause of action for damages. However, the failure of a physician to cure the patient or even to accomplish a specific result cannot be the basis of an action for breach of contract unless there was a specific warranty or agreement to accomplish a particular result. Improper treatment or malpractice is a tort and cannot by itself constitute a ground for a breach of contract action.

While it may be unusual for a physician to enter into a special contract to cure rather than to undertake only to render his best judgment and skill, since the practice of medicine is not an exact science, it cannot be doubted that there are occasions when such contracts are made. A doctor and his patient are at liberty, of course, to contract for a particular result and, if that result be not attained, a cause of action for breach of contract arises which is entirely separate from one for malpractice, although both may accrue from the same transaction. The action in contract is based upon a failure to perform a special agreement.[7] In the contract action the damages are restricted to expenditures for nurses and medicines or other damages that flow from the breach thereof.[8]

Breach of Contract Limitations

Breach of contract limitations may range from three years to fifteen years if the contract is in writing; in the case of oral contracts, from one year in Tennessee to ten years in Louisi-

---

[7] *Baum* v. *Turel*, 206 F. Supp. 490 (D.C.N.Y.) (1962).

[8] *Robins* v. *Finestone*, 308 N.Y. 543; Anno., 74 A.L.R. 1256, 1260 (1955).

ana. In some states there is no difference in the time period between actions for tort or in contract, as in Arkansas, Colorado, Massachusetts, Minnesota, and South Dakota.

In the cause of action framed in breach of contract, the allegations must be for other than the personal injury, otherwise it is classified as one in malpractice. The allegations must have the essentials of a cause of action for breach of contract.[9] In one case, the plaintiff and her husband brought an action in contract in which she alleged the physician left a needle in her body after delivering her child. The court held that this was an action in malpractice and that both causes of action were subject to the statute of limitations for malpractice actions.[10]

The Husband's Cause for Action

If the wife's action is barred by the statute, the husband's action for damages resulting from injuries to the wife may also be outlawed.[11] The two liabilities, however, are distinct: that of the wife is for injuries sustained by her personally; the husband's action is for loss of her services and companionship and for any reasonable medical expenses incurred arising out of her injuries. In some jurisdictions, the fact that the statute of limitations has run against the wife's cause of action will not necessarily prevent the husband from prosecuting his action.[12]

Cases of Fraudulent Concealment

As a matter of equity, some jurisdictions will stay the statute of limitations where there has been a deliberate concealment from the patient of facts of which the patient should have been informed by the physician, or a false assurance had been given to the patient as to his real condition.[13] "Fraudu-

---

[9] *Calabrese* v. *Bickley*, 143 N.Y.S. 2d 846 (1955).

[10] *Hertgen* v. *Weintraub*, 215 N.Y.S. 2d 379 (1961).

[11] *Rex* v. *Hunter*, 140 A. 2d 753, 26 N.J. 489 (1957).

[12] *Milde* v. *Leigh*, 28 N.W. 2d 530 (N.D.) (1947).

[13] *Hinkle* v. *Hargens*, 81 N.W. 2d 888, 76 S.D. 20 (1957).

lent concealment" means the employment of artifice planned to prevent inquiry, to mislead or to hinder the acquiring of information disclosing a right to a cause of action.[14]

Failure to exercise due care is negligence, but negligence is not fraudulent concealment. In the case of a foreign substance left in the patient, where its presence was deliberately concealed by the operating surgeon, the statute of limitations may not begin to run until such fact becomes known to the patient. A fraudulent concealment includes first, actual knowledge that the object was left in the patient's body, and second, an intentional concealment of the wrong from the patient.[15]

Postponement of the Statute

The statute of limitations is supposed to prevent recovery of damages on stale claims and is based on the presumption that one who has a well-founded claim will not delay enforcing it beyond a reasonable time if he has the right to proceed. On the other hand, if an injured party is wholly unaware of the nature of his injury or the cause of it, it is difficult to see how he may be charged with a lack of diligence or sleeping on his rights.

It is therefore held in some jurisdictions that the cause of action does not accrue until the patient discovered, or in the exercise of reasonable diligence should have discovered, that a foreign object had been left in his body.[16] The reason is predicated on the fact that since the patient usually does not know of the physician's negligent act until a long time after the act was performed, the statute of limitations should begin to run from the date the patient discovers or should discover that a cause of action exists. This delay or rule encourages greater care in surgical operations.[17]

---

[14] *Hall* v. *DeSaussure*, 297 S.W. 2d 81 (Tenn.) (1956).

[15] *Carroll* v. *Denton*, 157 S.W. 2d 878 (Tex.) (1942).

[16] *Spath* v. *Morrow*, 14 CCH Neg. Cases 2d 508 (Neb.) (1962).

[17] *Fernandi* v. *St. Joseph's Hospital*, 35 N.J. 434, 173 A. 2d 277 (1961).

In an Ohio case, it was held that the statute of limitations does not come into operation until the doctor-patient relationship comes to an end. The last treatment or consultation in such case would commence the running of the statute, where there has been "continuing negligence."[18]

Under some circumstances, the period may be extended for many years, as where the doctor who is to be the defendant was absent from the state, in which case the statute is suspended during the period of his departure. Where one is under a disability of insanity or imprisonment, the limitation is deferred by law until the disability is removed.

Causes of Action in Favor of Minors

The operation of the statute of limitations, in the case of infants, is suspended generally until the minor reaches at least the age of 21 years, although he may sue for personal injuries at any time during his minority.

The rule that the statute does not begin to run until the infant has reached his majority has been a perplexing problem to hospital administrators and other hospital personnel in relation to the retention of records. That there is a difference in certain respects between the records of adults and minors from a legal standpoint cannot be denied. However, that there is little practical difference may be difficult for some hospital people to accept.

When a child is injured, it is inconceivable that his parents will do nothing about consulting a lawyer until the minor reaches his majority. No conscientious lawyer would postpone instituting such an action merely because the statute of limitations is extended for a period of time beyond that applicable to adults. There is every incentive for a lawyer to commence the proceedings in behalf of the child at the earliest practical date. The average court case may not be reached for trial for

[18] *Pump* v. *Fox*, 13 CCH Neg. Cases 2d 838 (Ohio) (1961).

a considerable time after the action is instituted; witnesses may move or disappear; the memory of those familiar with the facts may become vague or less accurate; physicians in a position to testify may no longer be available; old records may fail to refresh the recollection of professional persons. A "stale case" is less likely to impress a jury; such tardiness gives rise to the suspicion that there is little merit to the case.

The lawyer himself who is interested in earning a fee and in protecting the interests of his client is well aware of the maxim that "Justice delayed is justice denied." Since lawyers are subject to malpractice actions arising out of undue delay in the prosecution of a client's case, it is unrealistic to expect that the lawyer will be less diligent in the prosecution of a child's case than that of an adult. The parents, too, are eager to secure compensation for the child and to recover their own expenses for medical attention and other damages. Thus there is every logical reason for proceeding with the child's case without abnormal delay.

Cognizance should also be taken of the fact that the attorney who is retained by the parents in behalf of the child will soon make his presence known in the case by requesting an abstract or a copy of the hospital record. The authorization from the parent generally indicates against whom the case is planned and the date of the injury. If there is nothing in the history which indicates an accident, further inquiry should be made of the lawyer as to the nature of the contemplated claim.

An interesting case is reported in which the two year statute of limitations under the Federal Tort Claims Act barred an action for personal injuries resulting to a woman and her unborn infant from an alleged negligent blood transfusion. At the time the transfusion was given the child had not been conceived.[19]

---

[19] *Morgan* v. *United States*, 143 F. Supp. 580 (USDC-N.J.) (1956).

chapter 4

CONFIDENTIAL
COMMUNICATIONS

A CONFIDENTIAL communication is information which is transmitted to a lawyer, physician, nurse or clergyman in confidence of the relation between him or her and the party making it, and under circumstances which imply that it shall remain undisclosed by the confidant. The communication may be the result of examination, treatment, observation or conversation relating to the confider.

The information which a lawyer secures from a client such as a hospital corporation would fall within the attorney-client privilege, because a corporation is entitled to the same treatment as any other client. If it seeks legal advice from an attorney, and in that relationship confidentially communicates information relating to advice sought, it may protect itself from disclosure, in the absence of a waiver thereof.[1]

The physician has a clear obligation to keep secret any information relating to a patient's illness which he obtains during the performance of his professional duties, unless the patient authorizes disclosure of the information or a competent court orders him to reveal it. This obligation is based first, on the ethics of the profession and second, upon legislative enactment in most states.

In a personal-injury suit arising out of an automobile accident, a court in Pennsylvania took the occasion to sternly re-

---

[1] *Radiant Burners Inc.* v. *American Gas Association,* 320 F. 2d 314 (C.A. 7) (1963).

buke a physician for giving a medical report on the condition of his patient to another physician employed by the attorneys who represented an opponent in the litigation without the patient's consent.[2]

Physicians are required by professional ethics, aside from any legal considerations, to maintain inviolate the secrets of their patients communicated to them or learned from observation, examination or conversation. The Hippocratic Oath, which is taken by physicians at the time of graduation from medical school, includes the following: "Whatever, in connection with my professional practice or not in connection with it, I see or hear, in the life of men, which ought not to be spoken of abroad, I will not divulge, as reckoning that all such should be kept secret." The sanctity of the oath has been recognized by both court decisions and by statutes in many states, which refer to the confidential information obtained by physicians in the course of practice as "privileged."

In addition to privileged communications arising directly out of the physician-patient relationship, certain reports and records which are required to be maintained by law are accorded a confidential status by statute and may not be divulged by the physician or hospital without a court order. Such records may include data and reports of birth, death, certain specified diseases and conditions, and fetal deaths.

Doctrine of Confidential Communications

Under the common law, no such doctrine of privileged or confidential communications existed. In England from whence our common law emanates, there is no privilege between physician and patient; the physician may protest to the court against any disclosure of professional secrets, but he is not considered guilty of a breach of ethics if he is compelled by law or by the courts to testify to confidential matters relating to his patient. Seventeen states still follow the English com-

---

[2] *Alexander* v. *Knight*, 177 A. 2d 142 (Pa.) (1962).

mon law of no privilege: Alabama, Connecticut, Delaware, Florida, Georgia, Illinois, Maine, Maryland, Massachusetts, New Hampshire, New Jersey, Rhode Island, South Carolina, Tennessee, Texas, Vermont and Virginia.

In Louisiana, a husband was held to have the right to obtain hospital records of his wife and to use them in a divorce proceeding. The wife was denied damages against the hospital for disclosure of confidential information. The court said that once a patient institutes a suit, in the prosecution or defense of which such communication or records are necessary and relevant, no privilege exists.[3]

Purpose of Confidential Relationship

The majority of the courts, in interpreting confidential communications statutes, have declared that the primary purpose of the statute is to encourage the utmost confidence between the patient and his physician so that the patient will frankly reveal to his physician all of the facts, circumstances and symptoms to enable proper diagnosis and treatment, without the fear that such information would be embarrassing if given general circulation. It has also been held that the purpose of the statutes is to protect the patient's right of privacy, to prevent humiliation, disgrace and in some instances, civil or criminal prosecution. The legal relationship of privilege, as distinguished from the ethical, exists only by statute and is subject to change by the state legislatures.

As the statutes of the various states are far from identical, it is advisable to examine the wording in the particular state. Some states make exceptions only in special medical situations, permitting disclosure in the interests of justice or the discretion of the trial court, except in matters of vital statistics.

Essential Elements of Privileged Communications

For the information to constitute a privileged communication, there must be (1) a physician-patient relationship: (2)

---

[3] *Pennison* v. *Provident Life and Accident Ins. Co.,* 154 So. 2d 617 (La.) (1963).

information acquired through such relationship; and (3) the need and propriety of the information to enable the physician to treat the patient professionally.[4]

Even if the patient has repudiated the physician, the relationship may still be implied. However, nothing prevents a physician from testifying as to information secured from, or by observation of, one who was at no time his patient. The privilege does not extend to facts acquired before the physician-patient relationship commences, or after it ceases. Information obtained from an examination not intended for the purpose of treatment is not privileged, even though made by the patient's physician.[5]

It is not necessary in order to create the relation of physician and patient that the doctor actually treat the patient; if he makes an examination with the patient's knowledge and consent, believed by the patient to be for the purpose of treatment, the relationship is created by implication, even though no treatment was rendered.

A pedestrian who had been struck by a taxicab was taken to a hospital, where a doctor examined her at the request of the taxicab owner, without explaining to the patient the circumstances which brought him there. During the trial of the action for personal injuries, the taxicab owner argued that there was no physician and patient relationship which would prevent this doctor from testifying as to the examination he made; that he did not acquire the information for the purpose of prescribing or treating her. With these contentions the court disagreed; the patient had believed him to be a member of the hospital staff, as indeed he was; unknown to her, he was not then acting in such capacity. A physician may not obtain information, declared the court, by trick or fraud and divulge it in violation of the confidential privilege.[6]

---

[4] *Massachusetts Mutual Life Ins. Co., v. Brei*, 311 F. 2d 463 (C.A. 2) (1962).

[5] *McGinty v. Brotherhood of Trainmen*, 164 N.W. 249 (Wis.) (1917).

[6] *Ballard v. Yellow Taxi Co.*, 145 P. 2d 1019 (Wash.) (1944).

The physician-patient relationship may exist without regard to the duration of treatment. A single examination or interview or even a few moments of professional care is enough.[7]

It is unnecessary that there be an agreement by the patient or others to compensate the physician in order to develop the relationship and even a charity patient in a hospital may assert the privilege with respect to records of his hospitalization.[8]

If the physician makes an examination of the patient for the employer or for the opposing party in a lawsuit and follows it with advice or treatment, the patient merely acquiescing, the physician-patient relationship is established so as to preclude the doctor from testifying.[9] However, if the examination is made for aiding the patient's attorney in preparation of a lawsuit or for the sole purpose of enabling the physician to serve as a medical witness at the trial, the physician-patient privilege is held not to exist.[10]

It is always necessary that the examination or consultation be, at least, in part, for the purpose of curative or remedial measures and treatment in order for the privilege to exist, although it is not necessary that the physician actually treat, advise, or prescribe for the patient.

The physician-patient relationship does not in any way depend upon whether the patient is conscious or aware of the treatment. But the report of an autopsy performed upon a dead body is not privileged since a dead body is not a patient.[11]

Application to Other Medical and Allied Practitioners

Where the statutory privilege exists, any licensed physician or surgeon falls within its scope whether he treats the patient

---

[7] *Grattan* v. *Metropolitan Life Ins. Co.*, 92 N.Y. 274 (1883); *Harvey* v. *Silber*, 300 Mich. 510, 2 N.W. 2d. 483 (1942).

[8] *Metropolitan Life Ins. Co.* v. *McSwain*, 149 Miss. 455, 115 So. 555 (1928).

[9] *Battis* v. *Chicago R.I. & P.R. Co.*, 100 N.W. 543 (Iowa) (1905).

[10] *San Francisco* v. *Superior Court*, 37 Cal. 2d. 227, 231 P. 2d. 26 (1951); *Taylor v. United States*, 222 F. 2d. 398 (1955).

[11] *Felska* v. *John Hancock Life Ins. Co.*, 144 Misc. 508 (N.Y.) (1932); *Travelers Ins. Co.* v. *Bergeron*, 25 F 2d. 680 (1928).

in a hospital or elsewhere.[12] Practitioners such as mental healers, chiropractors, psychoanalysts, veterinarians, and drugless healers are not within the privilege. In New York State dentists and nurses are within the relationship by law.

A pharmacist is not included and may be compelled to testify as to what medicines he has furnished to a person, for he is not "duly authorized to practice physic or surgery.[13] Dentists are not physicians or surgeons within the statute, except in New York State, and their testimony may be admitted in evidence. The terms "dentist" and "surgeon" are not interchangeable; a dentist is not a surgeon within the meaning of the law; although his business as a dentist is a branch of surgery, the statute relates to those whose business as a whole comes within the definition of "physician" or "surgeon."[14]

In New York State the privilege afforded to physicians has also been extended to registered psychologists.[15] A new Illinois law makes communications between psychiatrists and their patients legally privileged.

Partners of Physicians and Hospital Personnel

The privilege is held to extend also to information acquired by a partner of the physician attending the patient,[16] Assistant physicians and surgeons in a hospital are included, as well as interns.[17] The intern is a physician who is a graduate of a medical school, though not yet licensed to practice. Part of his duty is to get the medical history of the patient, and in other respects to relieve the attending physician of some professional duties. Moreover, in many instances he does the work of the physician and in other respects relieves the physician of pro-

---

[12] *S. S. Kress & Co.* v. *Sharp,* 155 Misc. 693 (N.Y.) (1930).

[13] *Deutschmann* v. *Third Ave. R. Co.,* 84 N.Y.S. 887 (1903).

[14] *People* v. *DeFrance,* 104 Mich. 563 (1895).

[15] Education Law §7611.

[16] *Aetna Life Ins. Co.,* v. *Deming,* 123 Ind. 324, 25 N.E. 86 (1890).

[17] *Smart* v. *Kansas City,* 208 Mo. 162, 105 S.W. 709 (1907).

fessional services which he would ordinarily perform.[18] A house physician and an assisting physician occupy a professional relationship to a hospitalized patient even though the patient has his private physician.[19] It is immaterial whether the assisting physician is called in by the patient or by the patient's physician.[20]

There are few legal decisions as to the application of the doctrine of confidential communications to medical students, attendants, technicians and non-medical employees of the hospital. They are bound to maintain secrecy by hospital or personal ethics, but few statutes include any of these persons.

Inclusion of Professional Nurses Within Privilege

Unless a statute or court decision specifically includes a nurse as within the privileged professions, she is not precluded from giving testimony as to confidential communications learned by her while present and assisting in the care of the patient.

There are some jurisdictions which hold that the nurse who assists in the treatment stands in the same position as the physician or surgeon and is hence included by implication. Another theory for inclusion is that a professional nurse assisting a physician is an agent of the physician and as such stands in the same relation of confidence to the patient as the physician himself.

She is not bound to secrecy if the information is not the result of her assistance to the doctor or if the information secured by her is in no way connected with the diagnosis of the patient's condition or his treatment. A nurse was permitted to tell of a conference at which she was present between the doctor and the patient's father, at which time the latter agreed to

[18] *Eureka-Maryland Assur. Co.* v. *Gray*, 121 F. 2d. 104 (D.C.) (1941).

[19] *Estate of Lucy W. James*, Surr. Ct., N.Y. County, N.Y.L.J., Nov. 4, 1938.

[20] *Munz* v. *Salt Lake RR.*, 70 P. 852 (Utah) (1902).

pay all the charges for an operation.[21] A nurse who is neither
"professional or registered" may properly give testimony of
conversations between the doctor, the patient, and herself, as
to the patient's condition and its cause.[22]

Confidentiality of Incident Reports

The American Hospital Association's Committee on Safety,
recognizing the need for a suitable form for reporting accidents sustained by patients, has cooperated with the National
Safety Council in developing an Accident Report form. This
form is adaptable to reporting of all accidents within the hospital including personnel as well as patients. There are specific
questions covering data to be recorded in the event of an accident to a patient. It is recommended that this report be filed in
the patient's record and a copy included in the administrator's
accident report file. These should be available to the hospital's
Safety Committee or a copy may be provided for the members
if the administrator wishes.

Hospitals which send incident reports (Fig. 22, p. 81) and
other notices to insurance carriers about happenings within
their premises must recognize that such documents probably
can be subpoenaed or otherwise subjected to examination by a
plaintiff in a law suit, if the document is relevant to the liti-
gated issues. Whether the contents can be used as evidence is
a matter for court decision.

A hospital administrator was required to produce for examination an "incident report" made by a nurse in relation to
an injury to a hospitalized patient. A trial court in Maryland
held that the report was subject to discovery as a record made
by the hospital in the ordinary course of its operations.

The discovery was permitted in a suit by a patient for damages suffered by him in falling from bed when side rails had

[21] *Cleveland* v. *Maddox*, 152 Ark. 538 (1922).

[22] *Hobbs* v. *Hullman*, 171 N.Y.S. 390 (1918).

not been raised. It was established that the hospital's *Manual of Nursing Procedure* required the preparation of an "incident report" in the case of any accident involving a patient, includ-

INCIDENT REPORT
(Record additional comments on reverse side)

| Family Name | First Name | Middle Name | Home Phone | Room No. | Hosp. No. |

| Address | City | Zone | State | Age | Sex M F | Civil Status M S W D Sep. | Religion |

Date of incident_____ Time_____ A.M. P.M. Place_____ Attending physician_____

Status of person involved: patient ☐ visitor ☐ employee ☐ other _____
(SPECIFY)

If other than patient, give name, address, phone number, occupation, and reason for presence at hospital_____

If patient, state cause for present hospitalization _____

Describe condition before incident: disoriented ☐ senile ☐ sedated ☐ normal ☐ other ☐ _____

Was height of bed adjustable? yes ☐ no ☐   Was bed up? yes ☐ no ☐   Was bed down? yes ☐ no ☐   Were bedrails ordered? yes ☐ no ☐
Were they present? yes ☐ no ☐   Were they up? yes ☐ no ☐   Were they down? yes ☐ no ☐

What caused incident?_____

Where did incident occur?_____

If person involved was injured, state part of body injured; if property or equipment was damaged, describe _____

Description of incident by person involved _____

Give names, addresses and phone numbers of any who witnessed incident_____

Was physician called? yes ☐ no ☐ Time_____ A.M. P.M. Who responded?_____ Time_____ A.M. P.M.
ATTENDING PHYSICIAN ☐   RESIDENT ☐   INTERN ☐

Statement of physician_____

Recommendations for prevention of similar occurrence _____

Date of report_____ Signed_____
SUPERVISOR ☐   GRADUATE NURSE ☐   STUDENT NURSE ☐   SPECIFY IF OTHER

FORM D-2310   PHYSICIANS' RECORD CO., BERWYN, ILLINOIS - PRINTED IN U.S.A.   INCIDENT REPORT

FIG. 22 — INCIDENT REPORT

ing falling from bed. In addition to holding the report discoverable as a report prepared in the usual course of business, the court ruled that it was not exempt from discovery as a report prepared in anticipation of litigation or in preparation for trial.[23]

Insurance companies do not enjoy a confidential privilege recognized by law, such as exists between a physician and patient or between an attorney and client. Nor are worksheets or reports given to the insurer a "work product" within the meaning of a federal court decision. To be used as evidence the document must be essential to the case.[24]

On the other hand, it has been held that records or reports which may have been made as the result of an investigation concerning the liability for any injury which the patient may have sustained while in the hospital will not be ordered for inspection as these constitute a "work product."[25] Nor is the patient entitled to examine the hospital before trial as to its private or departmental rules.[26] However, were it shown that hospitals of the community have established reasonably uniform rules and regulations with respect to the care of their patients, such rules and regulations might be admissible in a negligence action against the hospital.[27]

Confidential Information in Tax Cases

State laws prohibiting the use of "privileged communications" in court actions are not applicable to federal income tax investigations. The hospital would be required to divulge the names and addresses of patients of staff doctors to internal revenue authorities. Federal and not state law determines what evidence is admissible. However, medical information concerning the patient remains privileged and is governed by state law.

---

[23] *Hoff* v. *Rashad*, Super. Ct. of Baltimore City, No. 63251 (Md.) (Jan. 25, 1963).

[24] *Gottlieb* v. *Bresler*, 28 Law Week 2155 (D.C.D.C.) (1959).

[25] *Scott* v. *Memorial Hospital of Queens*, Stoddard, J. N.Y.L.J., March 12, 1953, p. 8, col. 7.

[26] *Kimmelman* v. *Beth Israel Hospital*, City Court, N.Y. Co., Sp. 1, Mulcahy, J., N.Y.L.J., Feb. 1, 1955, p. 8, col. 4.

[27] *Judd* v. *Park Avenue Hospital*, 235 N.Y.S. 2d 843, aff'd 235 N.Y.S. 2d 1023 (1962).

The public interest in the collection of taxes owing by a taxpayer outweighs the private interest of the patient to avoid embarrassment resulting from being required to give a revenue agent information as to fees paid the attending physician. Disclosure of the fact of hospitalization does not involve revealing the reason for the hospitalization.

The United States District Court for the Northern District of New York held that the Commissioner of Internal Revenue may examine hospital records to obtain the names and addresses of the patients of a certain physician admitted to the hospital and that the information sought by the Commissioner was not privileged. The case was decided on the basis of New York law.

The Court of Appeals for the Second Circuit agreed with the United States District Court and made it clear by its opinion that it did not intend to hold that the revenue agent could use the hospital records to learn the nature of the patient's illness, and pointed out that the District Court had done all it could to protect the patients from the disclosure of their treatment or the diagnosis of the illness.

The United States Supreme Court refused to review the ruling of the Second Circuit Court of Appeals that the names and addresses of a doctor's patients were not privileged under the New York Civil Practice Act.[28]

---

[28]*In re Albert Lindley Memorial Hospital*, 209 F. 2d 122, (2d Cir.) (1953), cert. denied, 347 U.S. 960 (1954).

chapter 5

RELEASE OF MEDICAL
INFORMATION

FTER the patient has been discharged from the hospital,
his medical record is carefully filed away where it can
be available for future reference for any proper purpose for
which it may be needed, whether in the patient's behalf or for
the benefit of those who are concerned with his care. By its
very nature, the patient's medical record is an instrument
which concerns not only the patient, but other persons as well.
It must therefore be accessible to all those who have a legitimate interest in its contents.

The information contained in hospital medical records is essential for the successful processing of some legal proceedings
and insurance claims. The record itself is the physical property
of the hospital and may be withheld from examination by out-
siders until a subpoena is issued. Of course, most hospitals
have developed rules for routine disclosure of medical record
information. Occasionally, a patient or his representative is
dissatisfied with the hospital's rules and seeks redress in court.

General Policies for Release of Information

All information leaving the hospital based on the contents
of the medical record should be controlled by a single person or
agency. In the small hospital this person may be the medical
record librarian. In the large institution, with the tremendous
increase in hospital and medical insurance and consequent re-

quests by third parties for information on which to determine the payment of insurance benefits, the issuance of medical in-

AUTHORIZATION FOR MEDICAL AND/OR SURGICAL TREATMENT

I, the undersigned, a patient in ________________ Hospital, hereby authorize

Dr. ________________ (and whomever he may designate as his assistants) to administer such treatment as is

necessary, and to perform the following operation ________________ .
NAME OF OPERATION

and such additional operations or procedures as are considered therapeutically necessary on the basis of findings during the course of said operation.

I also consent to the administration of such anesthetics as are necessary, with the exception of ________________ .
NONE, SPINAL ANESTHESIA, OR OTHER

Any tissues or parts surgically removed may be disposed of by the hospital in accordance with accustomed practice.

I hereby certify that I have read and fully understand the above **Authorization for Medical and/or Surgical Treatment**, the reasons why the above named surgery is considered necessary, its advantages and possible complications, if any, as well as possible alternative modes of treatment, which were explained to me by Dr. ________________ . I also certify that no guarantee or assurance has been made as to the results that may be obtained.

Date ________________ **Signed** ________________
PATIENT

Witness ________________ **Or** ________________
NEAREST RELATIVE

Relationship to Patient ________________

Both authorizations must be signed by the patient, or by the nearest relative in the case of a minor or when patient is physically or mentally incompetent.

AUTHORIZATION FOR RELEASE OF INFORMATION

Authorization is hereby granted to release to the ________________
NAME OF INSURANCE COMPANY OR COMPANIES

such information as may be necessary for the completion of my hospitalization claims.

Date ________________ **Signed** ________________
PATIENT

Or ________________
NEAREST RELATIVE

Relationship to Patient ________________

(A-145 BACK)

FIG. 23 — AUTHORIZATION FOR MEDICAL AND/OR SURGICAL TREATMENT AND RELEASE OF INFORMATION

formation should be centralized in a Medical Information Bureau, operated best as a subdepartment under the direction and control of the Director of the Record Department. Such an arrangement would facilitate not only the benefits payable to the patient, but also the payments due directly to the hospital through assignments or direct payment provisions in the policies.

It may be desirable for the hospital to incorporate in the admission record a form of consent (Fig. 23, p. 85) which will permit medical information to be forwarded to the employer or his insurance carrier, any physician, nursing service, welfare agency, or convalescent or nursing home, or hospital appearing to have a legitimate interest and making inquiry.

Private Attending Physician's Approval not Controlling

Hospital patient records fall into two groups: (1) those of service or ward patients, and (2) those of private and semi-private patients. In the case of private and semi-private cases, it is customary, at least in some hospitals, to obtain the approval of the attending physician for the release of information or for an examination of the record.

After a chart is filed, the attending physician has no legal right to determine who shall and who shall not see the record; his permission may be sought as a matter of courtesy. The attending physician of a private or semi-private patient should know of a request to view the chart of the patient by an insurance representative, an attorney, another physician now treating the patient, or other person properly authorized by the patient. If the attending physician declines to be concerned, the hospital should release the abstract even though there may be a claim contemplated or pending against another physician or the hospital.

The consent of the attending physician for release of medical information is technically not necessary since the privilege against disclosure belongs to the patient and not the treating physicians.

The record librarian would do well to let the final decision in controverted cases rest with the administrator. Ordinarily, the administrator can refuse permission to any person, whether authorized by the patient or not, to inspect the record at the hospital. Whether such an attitude is justified under the particular circumstances must remain a matter for the sound discretion of the administrator. He may be arbitrary if he wishes, until he or the custodian of the record is served with a subpoena *duces tecum* or order for the production of the record in court, or with some other valid legal process which relieves him of his discretionary authority in the case. In any event, the administrator need not act unless he is required to do so by competent legal direction.

Requirement for Signed Authorization of Patient

The hospital should procure a specimen signature of every patient before his discharge; his signature usually appears on the consent for operation (Fig. 23, p. 85), patient's clothes list (Fig. 24, p. 88) or some other form. An actual specimen signature will enable the hospital to make comparison with the signature presented on a request authorizing the bearer to view the hospital chart, or an authorization for a copy or abstract of the record.

There is no legal requirement that the authorization of the patient be witnessed either by a notary public or other person. Comparison with the sample signature, which should indicate that the signature is that of the same person, is sufficient. The presence of a notary's signature and stamp or seal gives additional assurance that the authorization is bona fide.

The authorization (Figs. 25-26, p. 89) should:

a. Be addressed to the hospital;

b. Contain the name of the person or company to whom the information is to be given;

c. Be dated;

d. Be signed by the patient;

    (1) If the patient is a minor, the authorization must be

PATIENT'S CLOTHES LIST

Family Name   First Name   Middle Name   Room No.   Hosp. No.

Address   Physician   Locker No.   Date

ARTICLES PLACED IN CUSTODY OF HOSPITAL

☐ Bathrobe	☐ Dress	☐ Hose	☐ Scarf	☐ Sweater	☐ _____	
☐ Bed jacket	☐ Earrings	☐ House coat	☐ Shirt	☐ T-shirt	☐ _____	
☐ Belt	☐ Galoshes	☐ Luggage	☐ Shoes	☐ Tie	☐ _____	
☐ Blouse	☐ Garters	☐ Negligee	☐ Shorts	☐ Trousers	☐ _____	
☐ Bra	☐ Girdle	☐ Nightgown	☐ Skirt	☐ Vest	☐ _____	
☐ Bracelet	☐ Gloves	☐ Pajamas	☐ Slip	☐ _____	☐ _____	
☐ Coat	☐ Handkerchiefs	☐ Panties	☐ Slippers	☐ _____	☐ _____	
☐ Collar	☐ Hat or cap	☐ Rubbers	☐ Suspenders	☐ _____	☐ _____	

VALUABLES FOR DEPOSIT IN HOSPITAL SAFE

☐ Valuables placed by me into Valuables Envelope No._____ as itemized on face of envelope.

ARTICLES RETAINED BY PATIENT

☐ Bible	☐ Dentures	☐ Earrings	☐ Money	☐ Rings	☐ _____	
☐ Bracelet	☐ Upper	☐ Glasses & Case	☐ Prayer book	☐ Rosary	☐ _____	
☐ Comb	☐ Lower	☐ Hair Brush	☐ Purse	☐ Scapular	☐ _____	
☐ _____	☐ Partial	☐ Make-up kit	☐ Radio	☐ Tooth Brush	☐ _____	
☐ _____	☐ _____	☐ Medals	☐ Razor	☐ Wallet	☐ _____	

The first group above is a correct list of my belongings which I hereby place in custody of the hospital. I take the full responsibility for retaining in my possession the articles listed immediately above and any others brought to me while a patient in the hospital.

Signed_____Patient

Checked by_____Nurse

If the patient is unable to sign the above record the nurse will record the reason as follows:_____

RECEIPT FOR PERSONAL ARTICLES

The articles placed in custody of the hospital were received by me in good condition on_____ 19 ____ Time____ a.m. p.m.

Signed_____ or _____
    (Patient)   (Nearest Relative)

Relationship to Patient_____

FORM D-3051   PHYSICIANS' RECORD CO., BERWYN, ILLINOIS - PRINTED IN U.S.A.   PATIENT'S CLOTHES LIST

Fig. 24 — Patient's Clothes List

signed by one of the parents or a legally appointed guardian. In certain instances, when the patient is a minor, married, or self-supporting and living apart from the parents' residence, he may sign his own authorization. In one case it has been held that a

AUTHORIZATION FOR REVIEW OF MEDICAL RECORDS

Hospital No.__________

To____________________Hospital ____________19____

____

You are hereby authorized to allow____________________

to review and make a copy of the ☐ complete record of my hospitalization
☐ record of my hospitalization from________19____ to________19____

Signed____________________
(Patient)

Signed____________________
(Nearest of kin)

Signed____________________ ____________________
(Attending Physician) (Relationship)

Authorization must be signed by the patient, or by the nearest relative in the case of a minor; or when patient is physically or mentally incompetent, and also by the attending physician.

FORM C-404 PHYSICIANS' RECORD CO., BERWYN, ILLINOIS PRINTED IN U.S.A.

FIG. 25 — AUTHORIZATION FOR REVIEW OF MEDICAL RECORDS

AUTHORIZATION FOR RELEASE OF INFORMATION

To____________________ Hospital Number__________
(NAME OF HOSPITAL)

You are hereby authorized to furnish such professional information, in accordance with the policy of your hospital, as may be necessary for the completion of my hospitalization claims by____________________
(NAME OF THIRD PARTY)

____________________ from the medical records compiled during my hospitalization
(NAME OF THIRD PARTY)

from__________19____ to__________19____ and are hereby released from all legal liability that may arise from the release of the information requested.

Date____________________ Signed____________________
(PATIENT OR NEAREST OF KIN)

Signed____________________ ____________________
(PARTY INSPECTING RECORD) (RELATIONSHIP IF SIGNED BY OTHER THAN PATIENT)

Date of inspection of record________19____ Signed____________________
(ATTENDING PHYSICIAN)

Authorization must be signed by the patient, or by the nearest relative in the case of a minor or when patient is physically or mentally incompetent.

FORM C-409 PHYSICIANS' RECORD CO., BERWYN, ILLINOIS PRINTED IN U.S.A.

FIG. 26 — AUTHORIZATION FOR RELEASE OF INFORMATION

child could object to testimony by the obstetrician who delivered him at birth which would tend to dis-

grace the memory of a deceased parent and which
might tend to reflect on the legitimacy of the child.[1]

(2) If the patient has died, the authorization must be
signed by the identified next of kin, or by the administrator or executor of the decedent's estate.

(3) In the event the patient is unable to sign the authorization by reason of physical or mental disability,
the authorization should be signed by the next of kin
or legally appointed guardian. If possible, verification of such disability should be obtained from a
physician.

Furnishing Abstracts of the Record

Attorneys and others having a legitimate interest in the
medical record of a patient may be provided with an abstract
or copy of the record upon presentation of the authorization of
the patient, or guardian in case of an infant, or the executor
or administrator of the estate in case the patient is deceased,
or committee or other legal representative of an incompetent,
and on payment of the hospital's customary charge for such
service. The hospital has the right to withhold such data as
has no reference to the specific hospitalization, but the authorized inquirer may be advised of the other dates of hospitalization or treatment, if any. No further information need be
given unless expressly authorized by the patient. In the case
of a mental patient, or where the hospital deems the information to be of extraordinary character, the hospital in its judgment may refuse such abstract.

Before information is released on any patient, a check may
be made with the accounting department to ascertain whether
the patient's bill has been paid. If any balance is still due, it
may be possible to arrange some form of security for payment,
where it is determined that money may be made payable to the
patient in connection with an insurance or other claim.

[1] *Jones* v. *Jones*, 144 N.Y.S. 2d 820 (1955).

The mere fact that the patient or his representative requests an abstract of the record does not, of itself, require the hospital to furnish the abstract, nor to release medical information.

Preparing Photostatic Copies of Record

When specifically authorized by the patient or his legal representative, such as his guardian or committee, the hospital may prepare or have prepared a photostatic copy of the record, the charge therefor to be paid to the hospital in advance, including a service fee if demanded. The person receiving the photostatic copy of the record should be requested to use it only for the purposes of litigation and not to permit its examination by the patient or those who are not concerned in the litigation.

Photostatic records may eliminate the need of the record librarian's appearance in court if both attorneys stipulate to the use of the photostatic copy in lieu of the original, or it may be used in evidence by statute. In New York, for example, a photographic reproduction, when properly certified by an officer of the hospital, may be admitted in evidence in the same manner as the original record; delivery of the photocopy to court, pursuant to subpoena, is deemed sufficient compliance, eliminating the necessity of a representative of the hospital to testify (C.P.L.R., Sec. 2306).

However, it is questionable whether a photostatic copy of a medical record should be available to persons not connected with the hospital; intimate details of the record may cause embarrassment to the patient, to physicians or nurses who have attended the patient, if given unrestricted circulation. Discretion should be used in each case to make certain that the information is not likely to be abused.

The court may issue an order directing that a record be produced and a photostatic copy be permitted to be made thereof as part of a record on appeal, in lieu of having the original subpoenaed on the argument of the appeal. No authorization of the patient is necessary, because the record is already in evidence, its admissibility having been passed upon at the trial. It is possible that the record was not admitted in evidence at the trial, but was marked merely as an exhibit for identification. In such case, the appellate court will probably pass upon the admissibility of the record. The court order must be complied with, irrespective of whether the record has been marked in evidence or for identification.

Disclosure of Names of Physicians

Disclosure of the names of physicians and house officers associated with the case, while technically not privileged, should be considered carefully; there is no legal compulsion to reveal the names except by court order, or in court. However, it is customary to disclose the names of attending physicians with their permission. Representatives of insurance carriers and attorneys for patients frequently are willing to pay the physician a fair fee for his time in court. The hospital can create good will by acting as an intermediary for the physician rather than as a barrier against making contact with him for legitimate purposes. In any event, the physician should be notified of the request, as he may desire to get in touch with the inquirer.

Medical Information on Mental Patients

A mental patient who has been judicially adjudged to be an incompetent is represented by a person appointed by the court as a "committee" or guardian. The committee acts in place and in behalf of the patient and is authorized to do what the patient himself, if sane, could do. The authorization of the committee for the release of information is entitled to the same consideration as that of the patient.

When the patient is confined to a mental institution or hospital, the superintendent may be the one who was appointed as the committee. There should be no hesitancy in releasing information to the medical director or other head of a mental institution since the data will be for the patient's benefit.

Information for Which No Authorization is Needed ✓

No authorization from a patient is necessary to disclose ordinary facts unrelated to treatment, such as the name of the attending physician, number of times and dates upon which the physician attended a patient, the name, age and address of the patient on admission, that the patient was ill and was operated upon, admission and discharge dates, name of relatives or friends given upon admission, whether the patient was sick, date of birth of a patient's child, and other facts which are obvious to anyone. However, discretion should be used and care taken to ascertain that the inquiry is a proper one.

Any other information regarding the nature and extent of the patient's injury or condition, symptoms, diagnosis or treatment, age, address on discharge, if to a sanitarium or state hospital, the service on which the patient was hospitalized and all professional information, particularly the diagnosis, should not be disclosed without proper authorization.

Use by Hospital Medical Staff for Study and Research

Members of the resident and attending medical staffs may freely consult such records as pertain to their work. Should there be any doubt in the mind of the medical records staff as to the purpose of viewing the record, access to the particular record may be refused, and the matter referred to the administration for decision.

In its discretion, the administration may permit use of medical records for research purposes. Except for the house and visiting staffs, persons asking this privilege should secure the written authorization of the administration. When the record is used for research, it is not regarded as that of any individual but as a report involving the study of a disease or group of diseases which may prove beneficial in future cases.

Consent of the patient is not necessary when the record is used in the hospital for the common good. Should the record be sought for research purposes by one outside the hospital, a photostatic copy may be loaned until the study is completed.

Copies of medical records should be made with the specific approval of the administration. No member of the resident medical staff should issue any verbal or written information to persons outside the hospital organization without the written approval of the administration, except in the discussion of the progress of the case with relatives or friends.

Reports Required by Law

Where reports are required by law, such as births, or communicable or industrial diseases, the law prescribes the procedure to be followed and what information is to be disclosed; by its force as a statute it protects the hospital or physician against liability for disclosures.

Medical Reports by Physicians

Physicians upon proper authorization should promptly furnish the attorney with a complete medical report, and should realize that delays in providing medical information may prejudice the opportunity of the patient either to settle his claim or suit, delay the trial of a case, or cause additional expense or the loss of important testimony.[2]

A medical report form has been prepared by the American Medical Association's Law Department as a guide to physicians furnishing comprehensive information in cases where litigation may arise.

Detailed medical reporting can frequently save a doctor time in court. Such comprehensive medical records tend to avoid litigation by outlining accurately the situation in each case.

[2] *National Inter-Professional Code.*

It is stressed that the new medical report form prepared by the AMA is principally a guide; the physician may wish to modify the form and compose his report in his own style.

The medical report may serve several purposes for the physician. It may be the final step he takes to assist his patient in obtaining compensation due him; it may be the physician's means of conveying his findings to the patient's attorney; it may be valuable to the doctor, if called to testify, for refreshing his memory.

For the attorney, the medical report furnishes information on the nature of his client's injuries and condition; it helps him plan his conduct of the case; and it is the beginning point in his legal and medical research in preparing himself for trial. The medical report may possibly be the most important factor during settlement negotiations.

Examination by Attorneys Representing Patients

Hospital records contain evidence which is important in litigation cases. In connection with the lawsuit, the attorney is required to prepare a bill of particulars which indicates to the opposing side what he intends to prove at the trial as to the patient's injuries; he is restricted in his proof in court to what has been specifically claimed in the bill.

The chief objection to examination of the record by the attorney is that the names of the attending physicians may be obtained, and the doctors subsequently subpoenaed to court. Other objections to showing the records are the possibility of alteration and the necessity of having someone present while the record is being examined. Some administrators or medical record librarians may sit down with the attorney and answer questions from the record.

If it appears that litigation is intended against the hospital, it is advisable to notify the liability insurance carrier and the hospital's attorney. If a specific physician is involved, he should be informed of the nature of the inquiry, as he may desire to report the matter to his insurance company. Whether to give out information under such circumstances should be left to the hospital's lawyer. When such information is refused, a subpoena or court order may require the hospital to produce the records for inspection.

Inspections by Defendants or Their Attorneys

In most states with hospital lien laws, the statutes permit persons or corporations responsible for the injury to examine the records of the hospital pertaining to the injured patient. Ordinarily, the hospital requires the patient's consent before the chart may be inspected, but some lien laws do not make the patient's authorization a prerequisite.

The Delaware, Illinois, Maryland, New Jersey, New York, North Dakota, Oregon and Texas statutes state that the person or corporation liable for the lien is entitled to examine the hospital records of treatment, care, and maintenance in reference to the injured person. In Illinois, the hospital is required within ten days after it receives a written request to furnish to a party to the claim, or to file with the clerk of the court in which the action is pending, a statement of the nature and extent of the injuries and the history of the accident. Failure to comply therewith makes the lien null and void.

In New York State, however, examinations are restricted to items relating to the charges for treatment, care and maintenance; the patient's clinical chart containing the history, diagnosis and opinions of the physicians usually is not shown without the patient's permission. New York decisions have held that the lien statute does not repeal or modify the privilege against disclosure of confidential communications, but enables one liable for damages to examine the records for the purpose of checking upon the correctness and reasonableness of the hospital charges. Although the language of the New York statute is particularly broad, it was not intended to require a hospital to reveal confidential communications, nor is it necessary in order to determine the reasonableness of the hospital's charges to examine records as to the diagnosis of the ailment or disease of the patient. The hospital should furnish information in respect to the treatment, care, and maintenance of the injured person without disclosure of confidential communications.

The hospital lien law of the District of Columbia, which has a privileged communications statute, does not permit an examination of the patient's medical chart, but allows examination of the ledger entries and similar records of the hospital for the purpose of ascertaining the basis of such lien.

Aside from any rights which may be given to attorneys for defendants or to insurance company representatives under the lien laws, there is no authority for the hospital to open the medical record of any patient to inspection, without the patient's permission.

Insurance Company Forms

Certain types of insurance policies are concerned with illness and injury to the person. These are accident and health policies, Blue Cross contracts, workmen's compensation insurance, products liability coverage, automobile and public liability, indemnity, hospital and medical malpractice protection, and others. To facilitate prompt payment of bills, such information should be made available as readily as possible. The authorization should direct the specific hospital to release the information, but a generally worded waiver attached to the insurance form or a photostatic copy thereof should be deemed sufficient.

It has been suggested that a code system be used in filling out certificates of proof of illness. *The International Statistical Classification of Diseases, Injuries and Causes of Deaths* was published in 1947, at Ottawa, as a project of the Interim Commission of the World Health Organization of the United Nations. Whether this classification or the "Standard Nomenclature" is used, a medical report in code, reaching only a medically trained person, would involve far less work to report

INDIVIDUAL HOSPITAL INSURANCE FORM IHF-1 (1961)

Spaced for Typewriter — Marks for Tabulator Appear on this Line

Hospital Complete and Furnish Copy To	Address
Name of Policyholder	Policy Number(s)

Address Street and Number	City	State or Province

Name of Patient (if other than policyholder)	Age

Date Admitted	Time Admitted AM PM	Date Discharged	Time Discharged AM PM

Other Insurance Indicated by Hospital Records. If YES name of Company
☐ NO ☐ YES

Complaint

Date of First Symptoms

Diagnosis from Records (if injury give date, place of accident)

Operations or Obstetrical Procedures Performed (Nature and Date)

HOSPITAL CHARGES (Complete this section or attach copy of itemized bill showing information below.)

ROOM AND BOARD	☐ Ward	Days at $	TOTAL	$
	☐ Semi-Private	Days at $	TOTAL	$
	☐ Private	Days at $	TOTAL	$
	☐ Other			$
OTHER CHARGES			OPERATING OR DELIVERY ROOM	
			ANESTHESIA	
			X-RAY	
			LABORATORY	
			EKG BMR	
			PHYSICAL THERAPY	
			AMBULANCE	
			MEDICAL AND SURGICAL SUPPLIES	
			PHARMACY (Except Take Home Drugs)	
			INHALATION THERAPY	
			INTRAVENOUS SOLUTION	
			TOTAL	$

TOTAL CHARGES $

$
$
$

THIS FORM APPROVED BY THE HEALTH INSURANCE COUNCIL AND ACCEPTED BY THE AMERICAN HOSPITAL ASSOCIATION FOR USE BY HOSPITALS (see explanatory instructions).

HEALTH · INSURANCE · COUNCIL

HOSPITAL	ADDRESS
TAKEN FROM RECORDS ON 19	SIGNED BY

AUTHORIZATION TO RELEASE INFORMATION: I hereby authorize the above named hospital to release information requested on this form.

Date __________, 19___ Signed __________
Patient (Parent if a Minor)

AUTHORIZATION TO PAY INSURANCE BENEFITS: I hereby authorize payment directly to the above named hospital of the Hospital benefits otherwise payable to me but not to exceed the hospital's regular charges for this period of hospitalization. I understand I am financially responsible to the hospital for charges not covered by this authorization.

Date __________, 19___ Signed __________
Policyholder

FORM C-645 PHYSICIANS' RECORD CO., BERWYN, ILLINOIS PRINTED IN U.S.A.

FIG. 27 — INDIVIDUAL HOSPITAL INSURANCE FORM

and would limit the spread of the confidential information.

Hospitals have had trouble with the multiplicity of questions on forms of various sizes and arrangements, and the inadequate space to answer questions. The American Hospital Association has recommended two general forms (Fig. 27, p. 98, and Fig. 28, below) for use in all hospitals. The first form,

GROUP HOSPITAL INSURANCE FORM *TO BE PRESENTED TO THE HOSPITAL IN DUPLICATE* HAP-4 (1961)

Spaced for Typewriter — Marks for Tabulator Appear on this Line

To ____ Hospital. This certifies that ____ is insured for the following Group Hospital Benefits (in behalf of his dependent ____ *(Name)* ____ *(Relationship)*) By ____ *(Name of Insurer)*

BENEFITS FOR OTHER THAN MATERNITY CASES	BENEFITS FOR MATERNITY CASES
A. HOSPITAL ROOM AND BOARD (INCLUDING GENERAL NURSING SERVICES) ACTUAL HOSPITAL CHARGES UP TO $ ____ FOR EACH DAY OF HOSPITALIZATION UP TO ____ DAYS.	HOSPITAL ROOM AND BOARD (INCLUDING GENERAL NURSING SERVICE) AND OTHER HOSPITAL SERVICES . . . ACTUAL CHARGES UP TO $ ____ OR 1. HOSPITAL ROOM AND BOARD (INCLUDING GENERAL NURSING SERVICES) $ ____ FOR EACH DAY OF HOSPITALIZATION UP TO ____ DAYS
B. OTHER HOSPITAL CHARGES FOR HOSPITAL CARE AND TREATMENT (EXCLUDING CHARGES FOR NURSES' AND PHYSICIANS' SERVICES AND TAKE HOME DRUGS) $ ____	2. OTHER HOSPITAL CHARGES FOR HOSPITAL CARE AND TREATMENT (EXCLUDING CHARGES FOR NURSES' AND PHYSICIANS' SERVICES AND TAKE HOME DRUGS) $ ____

THE MINIMUM HOUR HOSPITALIZATION REQUIREMENT WILL BE MET IF ____

GROUP POLICYHOLDER	ADDRESS	PHONE
BY *(Name and Title)*	ABOVE CERTIFICATION VALID FOR ONLY SEVEN DAYS FROM THIS DATE *(Exception — Maternity Cases)*	DATE

HOSPITAL COMPLETE FOLLOWING AND FURNISH COPY TO		ADDRESS		
NAME OF PATIENT	AGE	DATE ADMITTED	TIME ADMITTED AM PM	DATE DISCHARGED	TIME DISCHARGED AM PM
IF PATIENT HAD OTHER THAN SEMI-PRIVATE ROOM, INDICATE SEMI-PRIVATE DAILY RATE		$	OTHER INSURANCE INDICATED BY HOSPITAL RECORDS. IF YES, NAME OF COMPANY ☐ NO ☐ YES	

DIAGNOSIS FROM RECORDS *(If Injury, Give Date and Place of Accident)*

OPERATIONS OR OBSTETRICAL PROCEDURES PERFORMED *(Nature and Date)*

HOSPITAL CHARGES *(Complete This Section or Attach Copy of Itemized Bill Showing Information Below).*

ROOM AND BOARD	☐ WARD DAYS AT $ TOTAL	$	TOTAL CHARGES	$
	☐ SEMI-PRIVATE DAYS AT $ TOTAL	$		$
	☐ PRIVATE DAYS AT $ TOTAL	$		$
	☐ OTHERS	$		$
OTHER CHARGES	OPERATING OR DELIVERY ROOM			
	ANESTHESIA			
	X-RAY			
	LABORATORY			
	EKG BMR			
	PHYSICAL THERAPY			
	AMBULANCE			
	MEDICAL AND SURGICAL SUPPLIES		THIS FORM APPROVED BY THE HEALTH INSURANCE COUNCIL AND ACCEPTED BY THE AMERICAN HOSPITAL ASSOCIATION FOR USE BY HOSPITALS (see explanatory instructions).	HEALTH • INSURANCE • COUNCIL
	PHARMACY *(Except Take Home Drugs)*			
	INHALATION THERAPY			
	INTRAVENOUS SOLUTIONS			
	TOTAL	$		

HOSPITAL	ADDRESS
TAKEN FROM RECORDS ON 19	SIGNED BY

AUTHORIZATION TO RELEASE INFORMATION: I hereby authorize the above named hospital to release the information requested on this form.

Date ____, 19____ Signed ____ *Patient (Parent if a Minor)*

AUTHORIZATION TO PAY INSURANCE BENEFITS: I hereby authorize payment directly to the above named hospital of the Group Hospital Benefits herein specified and otherwise payable to me but not to exceed the hospital's regular charges for this period of hospitalization. I understand I am financially responsible to the hospital for charges not covered by this authorization.

Date ____, 19____ Signed ____ *(Insured)*

FORM C-655 PHYSICIANS' RECORD CO., BERWYN, ILLINOIS PRINTED IN U.S.A.

FIG. 28 — GROUP HOSPITAL INSURANCE FORM

approved by the Association's Board of Trustees in 1947, relates primarily to individually insured persons; the second, in 1949, to those covered by group insurance.

Examination of Record by Patient or
Family Undesirable

It is undesirable to allow a patient or his family to inspect his chart. He or they may find comments by nurses, interns, or other members of the professional staff which may be considered uncomplimentary or incorrect. The patient may then attempt to have the record changed, or cause annoyance to the administration or the professional staff. He may even bring a lawsuit for libel or some other fancied grievance. It is, therefore, advisable to have the abstract of the record omit characterizations or other remarks which may offend the patient.

In some states, as in Connecticut, a hospital, after the discharge of the patient, by statute must permit such patient or his physician or duly authorized attorney, upon request, to examine the hospital record, including the history, bedside notes, charts, pictures, and films kept in connection with the treatment of such patient, and permit copies of such history, bedside notes and charts to be made by such patient, his physician or duly authorized attorney.

An amendment to Wisconsin statutes in 1963 provides that upon receipt of written authorization and consent signed by a person who has been the subject of medical care or treatment, or in case of the death of such person, signed by his personal representative or by the beneficiary of an insurance policy of his life, the physician, surgeon or other persons having custody of medical or hospital reports, records, etc., concerning such care or treatment shall permit the person designated in such authorization to inspect and copy such records.

Nebraska has amended its privileged communications statute to provide that any person who institutes any action in any court to recover damages for personal injuries or in which his physical or mental condition is one of the issues involved in such action shall be deemed to have waived any legal privilege as to any physician or surgeon who is presently attending or who has attended such person for the physical or mental injuries or conditions involved in such action. This new statute also applies to any hospital records and is also binding upon the personal representative of a deceased person who institutes any legal action which involves injury to, or the death of, the deceased person, or in which the physical or mental condition of the deceased is an issue.

In some hospitals, when a former patient or a member of his family insists upon seeing the record, the following procedure is followed: the former patient (or his family) is advised that the record is the property of the hospital; that he has no right to it, except as to information which may be needed by his physician in treating him, or by his attorney in representing him, in which case the information will be given directly to the physician or attorney upon proper authorization. The patient himself is advised to consult his physician (private or staff) who took care of him for any information he may desire. If the physician is not available, the patient is given an appointment with a physician on the administrative staff of the hospital, who evaluates the inquiry and under proper and appropriate circumstances provides the desired information to the patient, together with a proper interpretation.

A bill introduced in the 1963 Legislature of New York State, but which did not pass, relating to the right of a patient to examine and obtain copies of medical reports and records, provided that:

"No person shall be denied the right to examine and make copies or extracts of their own medical records and reports, and/or upon the prepayment of the actual cost of any transcript or photographic reproductions shall receive a copy thereof from any person or corporation in possession of such medical record or report. Any person may by written authorization, duly acknowledged, permit or authorize another person to examine and/or upon the prepayment of actual cost of any transcript or photographic reproduction to receive a copy thereof from any person or corporation in possession of such medical report or record.

"Upon any person or corporation in custody of such medical records or reports refusing to comply with such request within five days, upon motion a party may obtain a court order directing such person or corporation to make available to the patient or the person given written authorization for examination, and/or upon the prepayment of actual cost of any transcript or photographic reproduction to receive a copy of such medical report or record.

"A guardian *ad litem* appointed for an infant shall have the same rights as the infant person to obtain medical records and reports of such infant. An executor or administrator shall have the same rights as decedent to obtain medical records and reports of such decedent."

It is natural for the patient and his family to be anxious about his condition. During the patient's stay in the hospital inquiries should be directed to the attending physicians; nurses should restrict their opinions to general statements concerning the patient's condition; no prognosis should be given except by the physicians.

After the patient has been discharged, his signed permission should accompany any request for information concerning his hospitalization to be sent to a third party. At the patient's own request, information should be forwarded to his physician.

A report of postmortem findings should not be sent directly to the patient's family; it should be forwarded to any physician requesting such information in behalf of the family. The findings are not considered confidential; however, they may be meaningless or confusing to a layman, and the information therefore should be in competent hands for interpretation.

Inquiries from Employers

The fact that an employer has arranged for the hospitalization or has agreed to pay the hospital charges does not act as a waiver of the confidential relationship between the patient and the physician. No matter who arranges for the hospitalization or the medical service, he is entitled to no information from the case record except the dates of admission and discharge, without the patient's authorization.

Industrial companies frequently employ their own physician or operate their own clinic. It is permissible to transmit information confidentially to a company physician caring for a patient after hospital discharge, but such information is not the property of the personnel department or company management.

Sending unauthorized reports to employers or insurance carriers in cases not involving an industrial injury or disease is not permissible; however, where the state workmen's compensation act or unemployment insurance law requires a report, the necessary information may be transmitted to the employer, insurance company, or labor department in accordance with legal requirements, without the consent of the patient.

Abstracts for Other Hospitals

Abstracts, copies, and summaries may be supplied to referring physicians, hospitals, veterans' bureaus, sanitaria, or similar institutions in charge of registered physicians, without an authorization from the patient. In case of transfer of a patient to any other hospital, sanitarium, nursing home, or other institution under the direct charge of a physician, the patient should be accompanied by a sealed copy of the summary. When another hospital requests an abstract, or a copy of the patient's history in whole or in part, the request may be deemed as coming from another attending physician.

Information for Physicians

Outside physicians who make inquiries concerning patients should be referred to the administration; merely because the applicant is a physician gives him no more right than a nonphysician to see a patient's record, unless he is treating the patient or has the patient's authorization. Access may be allowed to a second attending physician, even over the objections of the original physician, if in the opinion of the administration such examination would be to the patient's benefit.

Authority of Governmental Agencies

On request of a federal or state compensation commission, where it appears that a compensation claim is pending, information from the records may be supplied and reports made on forms submitted by such agency, without the patient's authorization. Unless such reports are required by law, a governmental agency is not entitled to medical information without a patient's consent. The fact that the request comes from some governmental unit does not constitute a waiver. If such agency desires to review the record, a subpoena should be served on the hospital; at the designated time and place the patient or his attorney can voice objections, if any. It is to be remembered that the prohibition is against the disclosure of confidential information and not ordinary facts such as the patient's name, address and the dates of admission and discharge.

Information for Social Agencies

Despite the fact that a social agency is one of recognized standing, it possesses no greater legal authority than any individual to demand medical information, without proper authorization. However, this rule is frequently ignored in the case of approved social agencies, where it is deemed for the welfare of the patient. Strictly speaking, the disclosure is not proper.

Verbal requests for information are to be discouraged in favor of written requests. The proper procedure is to write to the social service department of the hospital.

chapter 6

COURTS AND JURISDICTION

THE medical record librarian may find herself puzzled as to the various types of courts and the kind of cases which are heard in these courts. Sometimes the subpoena *duces tecum* calls for the production of records or for her appearance in a supreme or superior court, county court, district court, surrogate's court, circuit court, etc.

Basically, the court in which an action is brought is determined by one or more factors: the place of residence of one or the other party, the territorial limits of the court, the amount of money sued for, or the nature of the lawsuit.

There are also administrative agencies which hear certain controversies in place of regularly recognized courts. Records and witnesses may be subpoenaed to these agencies to provide evidence. Such agencies may be boards, commissions, bureaus, or other judicial or administrative bodies or officers. The particular matters which may come before such agencies are defined by law.

A court is defined as a place where justice is administered by a judge or group of judges, as authorized by state or federal law. The words "court" and "judge" are often used interchangeably and indiscriminately.

The "jurisdiction" of the tribunal is the right to determine the controversy between the parties; the court must have cognizance of the class of cases to which the dispute belongs; the parties to the action must be present or represented at the trial; the points to be adjudicated must be within the issue. Where the court lacks jurisdiction, its findings are invalid. Jurisdiction is to some extent determined by the amount of damages sought, as well as by the character of the relief demanded.

Two separate and distinct systems of courts exist in our country; they are the state and federal systems. Each system, in turn, has courts of original jurisdiction, wherein cases and special proceedings are tried, and courts of appellate jurisdiction, which hear appeals from the courts of original jurisdiction. A court may have both original and appellate jurisdiction; the latter may be termed the appellate division of the court.

The Federal Judicial System

The federal courts have jurisdiction over all cases involving federal questions arising under the Constitution of the United States, federal laws, treaties, and cases of admiralty or maritime jurisdiction. In addition, they hear cases involving as parties (1) ambassadors, ministers, and consuls, (2) the United States, (3) two or more states, (4) a state and the citizens of another state, (5) citizens of different states, (6) a state or its citizens on one side and foreign states or aliens on the other side.

Congress alone has the right to determine whether the United States may be sued and in what court suit may be brought. The United States Government is immune from suit, unless Congress has clearly authorized otherwise, as it has done under the Federal Tort Claims Act.

United States District Courts

These courts have original jurisdiction over cases in bankruptcy, postal and banking laws, admiralty cases, and crimes involving federal laws and those committed on the high seas. They also have jurisdiction where the amount involved is not over $3,000.00 and the question concerns the Federal Constitution, federal law, treaties, and controversies between citizens of different states, or between a state and the United States.

The Federal Tort Claims Act gives exclusive jurisdiction to the district court over civil actions involving damages for injury to an individual or to his property, due to the negligence of the United States through its servants, agents or employees.

United States Supreme Court

The cases in which the Supreme Court of the United States has original jurisdiction are those involving ambassadors, public ministers, and consuls, and those controversies in which a state is a party.

Most of the work of this court consists in hearing appeals from the decisions of the circuit court of appeals. Some cases may be heard directly from the United States district courts, as, for example, those concerning a constitutional question. Appeals from the state courts involving questions of federal law, or questions of the constitutionality of any law, state or federal, involving the United States Constitution, may be brought to the Supreme Court directly, on appeal.

Federal Administrative Agencies

Prominent among the federal administrative agencies is the Federal Trade Commission, which enforces the Sherman Act forbidding combinations in restraint of trade, the Clayton Act, which makes it unlawful to create monopolies and to do certain acts in restraint of trade, and the Robinson-Patman Act, which is intended to prevent direct and indirect price favoritism. The Federal Trade Commission may issue orders to offenders to cease and desist, and may refer matters to the Department of Justice for prosecution.

The National Labor Relations Board holds elections among workers, by secret ballot, to determine the collective bargaining agents and to prevent unfair labor practices.

Other examples of important federal agencies are the Social

Security Board, the Securities and Exchange Commission, the Federal Power Commission, the Federal Communications Commission, and the Interstate Commerce Commission.

State Judicial System

The state, a sovereign body, may not be sued except by its own consent. Its immunity from suit may be waived by a statute permitting the method of suit and providing for the payment of a judgment. Such a statute gives the plaintiff the same rights that he would have against an ordinary person as a defendant. It creates no liability, but removes a bar to suit which the state enjoys in its sovereign capacity.

The immunity enjoyed by the state against suit extends to all its boards, commissions, and agencies through which it acts, where the suit is one for money damages, or where the interference of the state in its sovereign capacity is threatened.

In general, the systems of state courts are organized along similar lines, although there are differences in such details as the number of courts, their jurisdiction, and titles.

Municipal, District or Justices Courts

The less important cases in cities and small towns are tried by municipal court justices, district court justices, or judges of the justices courts. The nature of the controversies as well as the amounts of money sought in these cases are defined by statute; the limits may vary from $200.00 to $3,000.00. These courts are an integral part of the state judicial system.

County and Circuit Courts

Most states have county courts which try both civil and criminal cases arising within the county. Generally, the amount of money damages sought in an action in this court is limited.

Some states have intermediate superior courts with original jurisdiction, but, in the main, such courts have only appellate jurisdiction. They may be known as circuit courts, supreme courts, district courts, or courts of common pleas. It is well to bear in mind that the title "Supreme Court" may in some jurisdictions apply to appellate courts only; in others, to trial courts. These courts may review cases appealed from the county and district courts.

Justice of the Peace Courts

Lowest in the order of importance in the state judicial system are the courts of the justice of the peace. Cases heard in such courts involve small sums and are tried without a jury. These courts function in small political subdivisions, as a village or town, or in rural areas. Their jurisdiction may extend to the preliminary examination of persons accused of felonies and the trial of misdemeanors, as well as civil cases involving small sums of money.

Surrogates Courts

The probating of wills, the administration of estates, the guardianship of minors and of incompetents come within the jurisdiction of the special court generally known as the surrogate's court. In some states it is termed the probate court; in a few, the orphan's court. These courts have equity powers in matters within their jurisdiction. Where such courts do not exist, matters are handled by county or district courts.

Supreme Courts or Courts of Appeal

Every state has a final court of appeals. It is known as the Supreme Court, in most states. In Connecticut it is called the Supreme Court of Errors; in Kentucky, Maryland, New York it is the Court of Appeals; in Maine and Massachusetts it is termed the Supreme Judicial Court; Virginia and West Virginia designate it as the Supreme Court of Appeals. Whatever its name, it is the final arbiter of the law involving appeals from the lower courts in the state.

The court consists of five to nine members, whose decision is final in all matters not involving rights and immunities under the Federal Constitution, federal laws, and treaties; such questions are reviewable by the United States Supreme Court.

State Administrative Agencies

The inability of the courts to deal effectively with the numerous and complex legal problems that arose with the growth of technology has made it necessary for legislatures to create administrative agencies, boards, or commissions to make rules and directives and to carry them out. Proceedings before such boards, commissions, or bureaus are informal, expeditious and less costly than court procedures; statutes creating such agencies often provide that the officers are not to be bound by technical rules of evidence.

On the state level, there are various administrative agencies. The better known are the Public Service Commission, which fixes utility rates, the Workmen's Compensation Board, and the professional practice boards which are empowered to license and revoke the licenses of professional people in the state. These administrative agencies are not bound by the technical rules of evidence found in the courtroom.

chapter 7

LEGAL PROCEEDINGS
BEFORE TRIAL

NOT every controversy or claim for damages for an injury to person or property results in a lawsuit. The person aggrieved may write a letter to the prospective defendant, stating the nature of his claim and urging a settlement. If an insurance company is involved, an investigator or an adjuster may call to interview the claimant for details of the occurrence and an itemization of the damages claimed. The demand for settlement may include compensation for pain and suffering, loss of wages, hospital and medical expenses, loss of future income, and a claim for possible permanent injuries. A physician representing the insurance company may examine the injured party. The patient's hospital record, if any, may be examined to determine his injuries.

In an effort to adjust the claim, the parties will take into consideration the delays inherent in a lawsuit, the expense, inconvenience and uncertainty of the result of a trial. If it appears that the liability of the assured is questionable, the insurance company may offer a nominal amount or a "nuisance settlement" rather than undertake the expense of a lawsuit.

Should settlement negotiations fail, an attorney may be employed. He generally communicates with the other party or his insurance company with a settlement in view. If the claim is settled, the claimant is required to sign a general release.

Should settlement fail, the claim may be dropped or an action commenced. Frequently the attorney is retained at the outset to conduct all negotiations or to commence legal proceedings.

Disposition of Claims and Suits

Every claim, case, or trial is terminated by a settlement, discontinuance, dismissal, or judgment. When there is no suit pending, a general release only is given by one party to the other in settlement of the claim. A pending action may be settled by signing a stipulation of discontinuance of the action and the giving of a general release.

A case may be dismissed when the action is reached for trial and the plaintiff fails to appear, or when the court holds that the evidence presented by the plaintiff does not establish a case. Failure of the defendant to answer the summons or to appear at the trial permits the plaintiff to enter a judgment by default, which has the same effect as a judgment after trial.

At a trial without a jury, after each side has presented its case, the court will grant a judgment on the merits; if it is in favor of the defendant, it is a judgment dismissing the complaint; if it is in favor of the plaintiff, it is called a judgment for the plaintiff.

The rendition of a verdict terminates a trial by jury. The entry of the verdict in the court records is the judgment. The successful party includes in the filed judgment certain disbursements he has had, as well as nominal costs which are permitted to be assessed against the losing side, by statute.

Breaches of Contract and Torts Distinguished

Basically, suits at law involve two broad classes of actions: (1) those arising out of breach of contract, and (2) those arising out of injury or wrong committed against the person or property of another, and designated by the term "tort." The wrongdoer is known as the tortfeasor.

Contractual disputes may deal with the sale of merchandise,

real estate controversies, the rendition of work, labor and services, or professional services, the ownership of property or property rights, and the payment of negotiable instruments, among others.

Torts may consist of a trespass upon another's land, committing an assault and battery upon the person of another, false imprisonment, the unlawful taking and using of another's property, fraud and deceit in connection with commercial transactions under certain conditions, committing a nuisance, damage through negligence to the person or property of another, defamation of character (libel and slander), malicious prosecution, inducing a breach of contract, interference with marital relations, and false imprisonment.

Any of these situations may give rise to a claim for damages which can be resolved by either settlement or a lawsuit.

Parties and Pleadings

The litigants or parties involved in a lawsuit are the plaintiff and the defendant. In a civil action, the plaintiff may also be known as the petitioner, complainant or declarant; the defendant may be termed the respondent.

The papers setting out the claims of the plaintiff and the defenses of the other party are the pleadings. Attorneys in some of their professional functions are considered officers of the court, as, for example, in issuing a summons or a subpoena.

The pleadings are the written allegations of each party, which are filed with the court; they compose the record of the case. This may include the bill of particulars, which details the claims. Some papers are not considered pleadings for the purpose of the record, as motions, mere statements, and certain affidavits.

The pleadings generally consist of the complaint, which is also known as the petition or declaration, and the answer; the defendant in his answer either admits or denies the various allegations in the complaint, and may set up defenses to the action or interpose a counterclaim.

After the service of the answer, the defendant may serve a demand that the plaintiff provide a bill of particulars, which gives in detail the particulars of his claim. Similarly, the plaintiff may require the defendant to give him a bill of particulars of the defenses. The demand for the particulars may be a separate document or as part of the paper constituting the answer.

Service of the Summons

Service of the summons may be made by the attorney for the plaintiff, by a sheriff or constable, or by any mature person not a party to the lawsuit. Personal service consists of delivering the paper to the defendant; if he refuses to accept it, he is told what the paper is, touched slightly with it, and the paper left with him. In some jurisdictions, service may be made upon an adult member of the defendant's family. Service must be made within the geographical jurisdiction of the court.

Should the defendant be evading service, a court order may be obtained for substituted service, by which a copy of the complaint is left at the home of the defendant and another sent to him by mail. Where the defendant has property within the jurisdiction of the court, but he himself is outside of its area, the law may authorize the court to acquire jurisdiction by attaching his property. Notice of the attachment and the nature of action must be given to the defendant by newspaper or otherwise. The jurisdiction is *in rem* (of the property) as distinguished from jurisdiction *in personam* (of the person).

The Complaint

The complaint is the statement in legal form of the allegations or charges against the defendant. Before a man may be brought to trial in civil, criminal, or quasi-criminal proceedings, a complaint must be served upon him which sets forth the cause of action or the offense charged. The complaint must clearly indicate the theory of law on which the plaintiff is proceeding. The plaintiff may allege on information and belief any matters which are not within his personal knowledge, if he has information leading him to believe that they are true.

The Answer

The answer is the plea interposed to the complaint by the defendant. The answer may deny any or all the allegations of the complaint.

Certain specific defenses may be set up in a civil action, as for example, that the claim is outlawed by the statute of limitations; that the plaintiff was guilty of contributory negligence; that the plaintiff gave a general release to the defendant; that the contract is illegal, or has been cancelled by mutual consent; or that the obligation has been paid.

Although the defendant admits every allegation in the complaint, he may file a "demurrer," which claims that the facts alleged do not constitute a cause of action, or that there is some other legal impediment to the cause of action. The original answer is filed in court and a copy is served on the attorney for the plaintiff.

The Counterclaim and Reply

In his answer, the defendant may not only set up his defenses to the complaint, but may also interpose a counterclaim for damages due him from the plaintiff. The counterclaim, if proved, will defeat the plaintiff's cause of action, in whole or in part. In most jurisdictions, the plaintiff is required to file a reply, in which he answers the allegations of the counterclaim.

The Bill of Particulars

The bill of particulars gives the defendant a more detailed statement of the claim than appears in the complaint. Similarly, the plaintiff may require the defendant to give a statement of the particulars of the defense or counterclaim.

In civil actions, the bill of particulars is an itemized or detailed account of matters which are set forth only generally in the pleading. In criminal cases, the bill of particulars is a statement by the prosecution fully informing the defendant of the matters of which he stands accused. Actually, the bill of particulars does not expand the claim; it limits the scope and generality of the pleading.

Hearing of Motions

In the course of a lawsuit, the attorney for either side may apply to the court for a ruling or for an order directing some act to be done in favor of the applicant. The application, or motion, is heard in open court, on a day appointed by the court for the hearing of motions; the litigants need not be, and generally are not, present. There is no testimony taken; the application is supported by affidavits and exhibits or copies of the pleadings. The other side may oppose the motion by answering affidavits; if no one appears in opposition, the motion is granted by default. After hearing the arguments and reading the motion papers, an order is made by the court granting or denying the motion.

Motions have a wide use before the trial. They may be used to compel an adversary to provide a bill of particulars; to submit to questioning on matters which one side or the other has to prove; to permit the inspection of documents in the possession of the other side; to take the depositions of witnesses for use at the trial; to request the court to grant summary judgment on the pleadings on the ground that the complaint fails to state a valid cause of action; or to strike out the defense as inadequate in law.

Examination Before Trial

Before the trial, either party may examine the other side or his witnesses, under certain circumstances, in support of the claim or the defense. The examination before trial is usually restricted to taking the deposition or sworn statement of one who is about to leave the jurisdiction of the court, or where the witness lives more than a certain distance from the court, or is seriously ill, or under other special circumstances. A demand or notice for such examination may be served on the adversary, and attendance of the party or witness be compelled by court order or by the service of a subpoena.

The testimony is taken under oath, in the form of a written deposition in which the party or witness answers certain questions; the attorney for the other side may cross-examine the party or witness. At the trial, the deposition is read and offered in evidence with the same force and effect as if the party or his witness were testifying in person.

The examination before trial is sometimes permitted before the commencement of an action for the purpose of identifying one or more proper defendants to frame a complaint.[1] The examination cannot be used to gain information as to who might be called as a witness; it is limited to instances of express statutory authorization.[2] A witness may be examined, although not a party to the action, where "special circumstances" are shown. A member of a religious order was permitted to have her deposition taken in lieu of her appearance in court.[3]

Interrogatories and Commissions

When it becomes necessary to have the testimony for the trial of some witness who is outside the jurisdiction of the court, he may be compelled to submit to an examination before trial in the county of his residence, but he cannot be compelled to attend the trial as a witness. The commission is the authorization of the court to take the testimony of the witness.

---

[1] *Cidilko* v. *Palestine Mid Island Hospital*, 207 N.Y.S. 2d 727 (1961).

[2] *Lipsey* v. *940 St. Nicholas Ave. Corp.*, 12 App. Div. 2d 414 (N.Y.) (1961).

[3] *Gillingham* v. *L.I.R.R.Co.*, Sup. Ct., Queens County, Hallinan, J., N.Y.L.J., March 10, 1944, p. 96.

In the federal courts, the witness can be compelled to attend, although living in a state other than the place of trial, if he resides within a certain distance of the court; otherwise his deposition is taken.

The order for the examination is granted by a court of the state wherein he resides. He is served with a subpoena or a copy of the order requiring his appearance at a fixed time and place. He is paid the ordinary witness fee, plus mileage, by the party calling him. Written interrogatories or questions are asked of him, which have been prepared beforehand with the consent of the opposite party and in a form approved by the court. The other party has the same right to propound questions to him that have also been prepared in advance. His answers are under oath, and are read at the trial with the same force and effect as if he were testifying personally.

Demanding Admission of Facts

Either party may serve a demand upon the other side to admit certain material facts in writing. The denial of such facts, if they are within the knowledge of the party, may cause the imposition of a penalty for the cost of proving such facts.

Notice of Trial

Some time after the pleadings have been served, either party may serve a notice of trial on the other. The original is filed with the clerk of the court, who places the case on a trial calendar to await its turn for trial. When the case appears on the ready calendar of the day on which it is reached for trial, both sides appear and announce that they are ready to proceed or ask for an adjournment. If they are ready, the case will go to trial that day or as soon thereafter as it can be reached after the ready cases ahead of it have been tried. An adjournment may be secured on consent of both attorneys or by presenting an affidavit which gives reasons for the request.

Memorandum of Law

In preparation for trial, the attorneys may write a memorandum of law or a trial brief for use by the court. The memorandum, similar in content to a brief on appeal, states the nature of the case and cites decisions to substantiate the arguments of the party. The memorandum helps the court in its rulings on points of law, and may serve to assist the court in formulating its charge to the jury.

chapter 8

SUBPOENA OF WITNESSES
AND RECORDS

M EDICAL record librarians should understand the legal
significance of subpoenas, for the duty of citizens to appear and testify to facts within their knowledge, as an aid to the administration of justice, is an obligation of citizenship. To secure the attendance of a witness, a subpoena is served upon him; it commands him to appear at a trial or other proceeding and to give testimony. The words "sub poena," now used as one word, mean "under penalty."

A person present in court or before a judicial officer may be required to testify as if he were there under subpoena. By statute, it is required that the witness, once subpoenaed, must attend until he is no longer needed. A person who acknowledges receipt of the subpoena, although not actually served, and attends court, is entitled to the usual witness fee.

The Power to Subpoena

By statute, the power to issue subpoenas to compel the attendance of witnesses is given to judges, clerks of the courts, referees, attorneys, arbitrators, municipal corporations and various boards and commissioners, as well as legislative committees. In criminal cases the subpoena on behalf of the state is issued by the office of the prosecuting attorney.

An attorney may issue a subpoena, unless it is otherwise provided by statute, signing it himself and attesting it in the name of a judge, the court, clerk, or other proper officer. A party to an action not represented by an attorney may apply to the court, justice, or referee, to have a subpoena issued.

Service of the Subpoena

The manner of serving a subpoena is determined by statute. Depending on the statute, service may be made by leaving a copy with the witness, after showing him the original and reading it to him. It is sufficient, however, that the contents are made known to the witness in a general way. The witness may not deny knowledge because he refused to accept it, or would not remain until it was read.

The service of a subpoena must be personal in all cases. An acknowledgment on the back of the paper by the party intended to be served, or the voluntary appearance of such a person, or the acceptance of the paper by someone authorized to accept it, is the equivalent of personal service.

The service of the subpoena must be made so as to allow the witness a reasonable time for preparation and travel to the place of attendance; the time is usually prescribed by statute.

A subpoena is valid only within that state and has no extraterritorial effect; a state court may not punish a non-resident who has not been personally served with a subpoena within the state. A subpoena to appear before a federal court may be served within 100 miles of the location where the witness is required to attend, although the place of service is outside of the federal district.

It may be an abuse of process to use a subpoena to compel a witness to be examined at the office of a party or his counsel, unless there is a court order to that effect or it is permitted by statute.

The word "forthwith" when incorporated in a subpoena with respect to the time for appearance means with all reasonable diligence and dispatch; within a reasonable time.

Compelling Attendance of Witness

Willful disregard of a subpoena is punishable as a contempt of the court. The willfulness may be inferred from the failure to obey the subpoena, without sufficient excuse. If the subpoena is erroneous in form, or if the witness has been excused by counsel, or illness of the witness or of his family can be shown, among other reasons acceptable to the court, the failure to attend is not punishable. One served with two subpoenas to appear in two places at the same time may choose the one to which he wishes to go first.

Payment of Fees and Mileage

In civil actions, it is necessary that at the time of the service of the subpoena, the fees to which the witness is entitled for travel to and from the place at which he is commanded to appear, and for one day's appearance, be tendered or paid to him. If the witness refuses to appear, he must refund the monies paid to him.

One who receives insufficient mileage fees without objecting to the amount paid must obey the subpoena notwithstanding; the question of the inadequate payment may be raised on the return day before the court; the objection is waived if he fails to raise it at that time.

In a criminal case, the witness must obey the subpoena served on behalf of the defendant as well as of the state; there need be no payment or tender of fees in advance. When there is an endorsement on the subpoena in a criminal case, it is a sufficient guarantee that the witness fee will be paid by the county.

An attorney is not personally liable for the fees of witnesses who appear on behalf of his client, unless he has specifically agreed to pay them. One who has attended as a witness is entitled to his fees, although he has not testified, or if he is found to be incompetent to testify, or if the case is postponed. Some decisions hold that one who has been called as a witness by both sides is entitled to a fee from each party; others, that he should be paid only one fee.

Subpoena of Records

Where the witness is required to produce certain records in his custody or possession, a subpoena *duces tecum* is served upon him. In form it is like the ordinary subpoena; it includes a command for the witness to bring with him the documents, papers or books noted in the subpoena. If both the witness and the documents in his possession are actually in court, he may be required to produce such documents, although no subpoena *duces tecum* has been served upon him.

The subpoena must specify with as much particularity as possible the record or papers sought; the witness or hospital is not required to search through a mass of documents or records to select and produce those which may bear on a particular matter. The description of the papers or documents need not be full and precise; it is sufficient that the records are designated with reasonable certainty. The command to produce the record is not satisfied merely by bringing the record before the court, but refusing to permit its inspection during trial; it must be handed to the court or at least read by the witness.

Power to Subpoena Hospital Records

If the records are those of a public hospital, the subpoena *duces tecum* may be required to be signed by a judge; otherwise, it is sufficient if it is signed by an attorney. A statute authorizing a clerk of the court to compel testimony by subpoenaing witnesses also permits him to issue a subpoena *duces tecum*. The subpoena may be issued not only in a matter pending before a court of the state, but also in aid of a commission from a court of another state for the taking of testimony in the state in which the record is located.

Ten points should be borne in mind when the medical record

is summoned to court by a subpoena *duces tecum:*

1. Verify with the court that the case is actually on the calendar;
2. Read the record, be assured that it is complete and that signatures and initials are identifiable;
3. Remove the record to a safe place, preferably under lock and key, so that it cannot be taken away before the appointed date for the trial;
4. Make photostatic copies of the record if in doubt as to its safety. This may be expensive but may save a total loss of the record;

RECEIPT FOR HOSPITAL RECORD PRODUCED IN COURT

I, the undersigned, attorney for plaintiff/defendant agree to act as trustee of the records produced in court of

____

and promise to rerurn same to the ______________________________ Hospital

upon completion of the trial.

______________________ (ATTORNEY)

______________________ (DATE) ______________________ (ADDRESS)

______________________ (PHONE NUMBER)

FIG. 29 — RECEIPT FOR HOSPITAL RECORD PRODUCED IN COURT

5. Do not give up possession of the record unless instructed to do so by the judge;
6. Do not permit examination of the record by anyone prior to its identification;
7. Do not leave the chart in the court unless it is in the possession of the judge or jury, and a receipt (Fig. 29, above) for it has been obtained;

8. Comply with all instructions given by the court;

9. Direct testimony to the identification of the record only, and refrain from giving opinions as to quality of care recorded in the documents;

10. When in doubt call the hospital attorney.

There are good reasons for all these rules. The hospital, as custodian of the information contained in the medical record, must preserve the integrity of the documents as legal evidence. Any suggestion that they have been altered, tampered with or partially destroyed while they were outside the custody of the hospital reduces their importance as evidence, and may prejudice the patient in his efforts to establish his just claims.[1]

Who May Be Subpoenaed

The person who is in control of, and has the ability to produce, the desired record, is the person to be subpoenaed. In the case of a hospital corporation, which can act only through its officers or servants, a subpoena *duces tecum* served on the employee having actual custody of the record is sufficient service. Unless the subpoena is served personally on the administrator, he need not appear; he may delegate the record librarian or some other representative to appear for him.

Disobedience of the Subpoena

The custodian or other person who fails to honor a subpoena served upon him may be punished for contempt, unless it can be shown that the service was defective, or some other reasonable excuse is shown.

The time to serve the subpoena is generally fixed by statute as at least 24 hours before the attendance of the witness is required; in an emergency the court may order the record to be produced forthwith, which means as soon as possible. The

---

[1] "When the Medical Record is Summoned to Court," LeTourneau, C. V., *Hosp. Mgt.* 80:42, Aug. 1955.

failure to produce the record may be excused upon showing that the subpoena was served so late that it could not be complied with.

The witness may be punished for contempt if he leaves the court, knowing that his presence is still needed; however, if the party calling him tells him he may depart, and he does so although still needed, he is not guilty of contempt.

While strictly speaking, it has been held that a subpoena *duces tecum* gives counsel no right to inspect the records which have been ordered to be produced, the court may, and usually does, instruct the witness to allow the record to be examined by counsel.

Erroneous advice by counsel that the subpoena need not be honored will not protect the custodian who fails to appear; it may mitigate the penalty. The penalty for failure to honor the subpoena is fixed generally by statute; it may be a fine, imprisonment or both. In addition, there may be a civil suit, if damages can be shown by the party who issued the subpoena.

The custodian of the record should make known to the person subpoenaing the record that the fee and mileage must be paid in advance, and that he will refuse to appear without payment. Where the fee is neither tendered nor paid, there is no contempt for failure to obey the subpoena. In the case of a subpoena issued out of a federal court, it is only where the witness has no means of paying for his traveling expenses that his compensation must be paid in advance.

Subpoena for Medical Witness

While it is recognized that the conduct of the business of the courts cannot depend upon the convenience of litigants, lawyers or witnesses, arrangements can and should be made for the attendance of the physician as a witness which take into consideration the professional demands upon his time. Such arrangements contemplate reasonable notice to the physician of the intention to call him as a witness and to advise him by telephone, after the trial has commenced, of the approximate time of his required attendance. The attorney should make every effort to conserve the time of the physician.

The physician is entitled to reasonable compensation for time spent in conferences, preparation of medical reports, and for court or other appearances. These are proper and necessary items of expense in litigation involving medical questions.

In a particular case or jurisdiction, or because of the necessity for protecting himself or his client, the attorney is sometimes required to subpoena the physician as a witness. Although the physician should not take offense at being subpoenaed, the attorney should not cause the subpoena to be issued without prior notification to the physician. The duty of the physician is the same as that of any other person to respond to judicial process.[2]

The patient sued a physician for damages because he was the "treating physician" who failed to testify at the trial in his action for personal injuries, with the resultant expense of $250.00 for "other medical testimony." The cause of action was not for failure to appear and testify pursuant to subpoena, but is predicated on alleged duty to testify. The complaint was held to be insufficient unless the patient can show a duty to testify by virtue of a special agreement.[3]

Records of Mental Patients

A psychiatric patient's chart enjoys no greater legal privilege against subpoena than any other record relating to the care and treatment of the patient. If the medical record librarian is served with a subpoena for the production of the medical record of a patient who has received psychiatric treatment, such a mandate must be complied with. The argument is

---

[2] *National Inter-Professional Code.*

[3] *Wallach* v. *Hand,* Sup. Ct., N.Y.Co., N.Y.L.J., June 27, 1963, p. 9, Col. 5.

often presented that some of the information in such a record is hypothetical, and this argument has some merit, because of the unique nature of some psychiatric medical records. Since the court aims at the administration of substantial justice, such extraordinary or peculiar features of the psychiatric medical record should be brought to the attention of the court. The contents of the psychiatric medical record can be evaluated by the court with reference to its introduction into evidence.

chapter 9

THE LAW OF EVIDENCE

THE rules under which the facts in a case are proved constitute the law of evidence; the facts proved are called evidence. Facts are not limited to tangible or visible things; mere thoughts, intentions, or fancies of the mind, may be proved as existing facts.

Evidence includes any alleged fact which is proved or disproved; the term evidence embraces testimony, documents such as medical records, written instruments, objects, and admissions of the parties.

Direct Evidence

Direct evidence is proof through the testimony of persons or witnesses who have actual knowledge of the facts acquired by means of their senses. A nurse who is present in the operating room can testify as to what she witnessed during the course of an operation. The patient himself may tell what he saw the physician do.

Indirect or Circumstantial Evidence

Not all facts can be proved by direct evidence. Indirect or circumstantial evidence consists of proof of related facts and circumstances from which by human experience the court or the jury may infer other connected facts usually and reasonably following from proven facts and circumstances, without direct proof thereof. The inferences may not be based upon speculation or mere possibilities nor be deduced only from inferences based upon other inferences.

If a patient falls out of bed and is found on the floor suffering from a fractured skull, it may be impossible to prove by any witness that the patient actually fell out of bed. Other modes of evidence may have to establish such a conclusion as the occurrence of the accident. Thus, if it could be shown by the testimony of nurses that the patient was disoriented and sideboards had been placed on his bed, the inference could follow that he had climbed over the siderails and had fallen to the floor. An Incident Report, (Fig. 22, p. 81) such as used by most hospitals, although not filed with the medical record, but in the administrator's office, can be used to refresh the recollection of the nurse.

Real or Demonstrative Evidence

In place of the testimony of witnesses from which the court or jury may draw inferences of the fact, directly or indirectly, the fact to be proved may be of such a nature that the court or jury may apply its own senses upon the person or objects in its presence. Such evidence is sometimes called autoptic proference: the thing is offered for sight, rather than for feeling, hearing, taste or smell.

For example, a patient in the hospital claimed that he was injured as the result of the hospital furnishing him with a defective footstool. The footstool could be offered in evidence for the inspection of the jury. Likewise, if a patient suffered a deformity as a result of negligent treatment by a surgeon, the jury would be allowed to examine the limb to see the nature and extent of the deformity.

Where it is not possible to bring the object into court, the jury may be permitted, in the court's discretion, to go to the scene to view the object, such as an x-ray machine, or to visit the location of an accident or crime.

The Judicial Notice Rule

Certain well-known facts need not be proved. Facts which well-informed persons generally know are presumed to be known by the court. The "judicial notice" rule allows the court to take cognizance of such facts without proof.

Counsel for parties to a lawsuit may prove certain facts of which the court can be asked to take judicial notice, without submitting any evidence. Among these are the mortality tables embodied in statutes; when men lift heavy objects they are subject to strain and resulting injury; the period of gestation of a fully developed baby; that fractures should receive prompt attention; that two x-ray plates of the person taken at the same time or at different times will not always show the same thing.

If the fact is one which can be disputed by evidence the rule does not apply. Where a case concerns the highly specialized art of treating disease with respect to which a layman can have no knowledge at all, the court and jury must be dependent upon expert evidence; the judicial notice rule will not be available to prove the proper method of treatment. On the other hand, where the question of the propriety of treatment by a physician is a matter of common knowledge to laymen, expert testimony is not necessary to establish malpractice.

Presumptions of Law

A legal presumption is a rule of law which requires that a certain fact must be inferred by the court from the existence of certain other facts. Thus, where a marriage ceremony is shown to have been performed, it is presumed to have been properly and legally performed. The law presumes that every child is legitimate; that one in possession of property has lawful possession of it.

In the absence of evidence to the contrary, there is a legal presumption in favor of the physician that he exercised proper

skill and care in the treatment he rendered. Unless the patient
submits sufficient evidence to overcome this presumption, he
will be non-suited; i.e., his case will not be permitted to go to
the jury. If the plaintiff succeeds in getting to the jury, he still
has the burden of convincing the jury of the merits of his
claim. The inference which is created by law may be overcome
or nullified by contradictory evidence.

Doctrine of Res Ipsa Loquitur

The maxim *res ipsa loquitur* means "the thing speaks for
itself." A jury may infer negligence from the fact that an injury has occurred where that which caused the injury was
within the exclusive control of the defendant and ordinarily
could not have occurred but for the negligence of the defendant. However, if the injury can be accounted for on any reasonable theory other than that of the defendant's negligence,
or if the responsibility for the injury may be that of one of
two or more parties, so that it is not clear whose negligence
caused it, the inference will not stand.

Where the doctrine of *res ipsa loquitur* is applied, as in the
case of a foreign object left in the patient's body, an inference
of negligence is created having the effect of establishing a
prima facie case which the physician must rebut. The plaintiff
need not show negligence by expert testimony, and the issue of
negligence is left for the jury, regardless of the evidence offered by the physician that due care has been used.

The doctrine of *res ipsa loquitur*, which is based on common
law principles, has no application in the courts of Alabama,
Arkansas, Kentucky, North Dakota, Utah, and Wisconsin.
There the patient must prove the negligence of the defendant,
and cannot submit the issue of negligence to the jury merely
upon proof of the injury.

Admissibility of Evidence

In actions to recover for negligence, which include malpractice, the rules governing the admissibility of evidence are similar to those in other civil actions. Any relevant evidence is admissible which is competent and tends to support the plaintiff's complaint or the defense or defenses of the defendant.

Although relevancy, strictly speaking, is a matter of logic rather than law, the courts are called upon frequently to decide whether some particular evidence is relevant or should be excluded as remote. For instance, in an action for personal injuries due to an excessively waxed floor in the hospital, it would be proper to show that other persons had slipped that day. Proof that visitors had slipped a month before would not be relevant to prove that there was excessive wax on the later occasion.

Evidence that the surgeon being sued for malpractice was a habitually careful practitioner who had never been charged with negligence before the incident in question would be inadmissible as irrelevant.

The Burden of Proof

The burden of proof is the obligation which rests on one of the parties to an action to persuade the court or jury of the truth of his case. In a malpractice claim it is the obligation of the injured patient to prove by a fair preponderance of the evidence that the defendant was under a legal duty to exercise the proper degree of skill and care; that there was a breach of that duty; that as a result he suffered injury. If the plaintiff fails to offer evidence to support his allegations, he has failed to make out a prima facie case; the court will rule as a matter of law that there is nothing for the jury to consider and the case will be dismissed.

A prima facie case is established when the party upon whom the burden of proof rests has introduced enough evidence to prove the facts he has alleged. When the facts are in dispute and evidence is put in to the contrary, there is no longer a prima facie case.

Nature of Hearsay Evidence

Hearsay evidence is evidence of the existence of a fact based not on the observation or own personal knowledge of the witness but on what someone else said. It may be oral testimony or a written document. It is not admissible in evidence, with certain exceptions, since the original declarant is not under oath nor subject to cross-examination nor available for judge and jury to note his demeanor and determine his credibility.

In general, the rule prevents a witness from giving testimony as to information which he obtained from a third party. A witness is supposed to testify as to what he himself saw or heard, not what another reported that he had heard or seen. The reason for excluding such testimony as "second hand" is that the information is considered unreliable.

However, necessity and experience have created exceptions to the hearsay rule. These exceptions are recognized where the evidence is reasonably reliable and such proof is the only way in which the event can possibly be established. One exception is the "pedigree" rule which permits an individual to prove the date of his birth or his parentage, or his family relationships, by writings or oral statements made by members of his family, entries in a family diary or Bible, or other family record.

Another exception is the "business records" rule, which allows ordinary business records made and kept in the regular course of business or a professional activity to be admitted in evidence. While there are certain variations in the rule in different states, the records of the physician are admissible in evidence at least in a case in which he is a party to the suit or a witness and nothing suggests that the records are untrustworthy or made with the intent to falsify the facts.

Hospital records are another exception. In some states they are not admissible for any purpose, while in many other states they may be admitted for limited purposes, such as to prove matters of hospital routine, the length of stay in the hospital,

medications and treatments administered, pulse and temperatures, visits of physicians and other factual data. A few courts
permit the record to be introduced in evidence to show the
history and diagnosis without the presence or testimony of the
treating physician. The extent to which the exception to the
hearsay rule applies is a matter of court decision or statute in
the particular state.

Another exception is in the case of official public records
which are kept by governmental agencies, such as birth and
death reports, disease reports, and similar matters. A medical
examiner's report of the cause of death in a criminal case may
be admitted in evidence.

Competency, Relevancy and Materiality of Evidence

Where evidence has no bearing on the facts in issue, but
only on some collateral fact, it may be objected to by counsel
during the trial as "incompetent, irrelevant and immaterial;"
it is evidence which is not fit for which it is offered. The three
terms indicating the objectionable character of the evidence
are generally used together. It is for the trial court to determine whether the objection to the evidence has merit.

The Res Gestae Rule

Statements or acts incidental to the main act and explanatory of it, so closely connected with it as to constitute a part
of the main transaction, and serving to explain the main transaction, are admissible in evidence from the lips of others than
the participants. What they did or said is part of the *res gestae*
(the thing done) ; it is a part of the transaction itself. Whether
a statement or declaration is part of the *res gestae* should be
left to the trial court's discretion and, where no abuse of discretion appears, the trial court's ruling must stand.

A spontaneous exclamation by a nurse that she forgot to
turn off the current, the patient at that moment complaining

of an electrical burn while receiving diathermy treatment is admissible evidence. Declarations by an injured person to the first persons who came on the scene shortly after the accident, apparently called forth by nervous excitement and at the very place where the accident happened, are admissible as part of the *res gestae*. The statement of an injured workman made a month after the accident to his physician as to a fact connected with the accident is not part of the *res gestae*.

Dying Declarations

A dying declaration is a statement of fact, relating to the circumstances leading up to the death of the declarant, made under the solemn belief that death is inevitable, and that the end is near at hand. Death must have ensued from the injury in issue to make the statement admissible. Testimony as to what the decedent said as to the cause of his death is admissible to acquit as well as to convict the accused, in some states. The witness testifying to the statements stands in the same position as the decedent, were the decedent available as a witness.

Dying declarations have been held admissible in civil death cases in Arkansas, Kansas, Nebraska, North Carolina, Oregon, and Pennsylvania. The fact that the declarant dies is not enough; there must be evidence of a sense of imminent death.

Self-Serving Declarations

A self-serving declaration is an oral or written statement made by a party to an action which tends to support his claim at the time of the trial. In effect, a party would be creating evidence for himself if such statements were admissible. Oral or written statements of a self-serving character are inadmissible, unless they are clearly a part of the *res gestae*.

A statement made by a patient at the hospital to which he is brought after the accident, and which statement is included in the medical record as part of the history, would not be admissible in evidence if the information furnished would tend to show another was at fault for the accident. The patient would be creating evidence for himself, which could be done deliberately by him during the lapse of time between the accident and his arrival at the hospital. His utterances would not be spontaneous, so as to constitute part of the *res gestae*. People have the motive while they are in a deliberative frame of mind to favor themselves. On the other hand, statements made either as part of the *res gestae* or at any time thereafter which are prejudicial to the declarant are admissible as admissions against interest.

chapter 10

DOCUMENTARY EVIDENCE

HOSPITAL records, although designed primarily for patient care, are also legal documents. A document is "any matter expressed or described upon substance by means of letters, figures or marks, or by more than one of these means, intended to be used, or which may be used, for the purpose of recording that matter." Documentary evidence is "any tangible object capable of making a truthful statement." These include deeds, agreements, title-papers, letters, receipts, and other writings to prove a fact. Documents are a form of real or demonstrative evidence.[1]

All writings may be classified either as (1) public or official documents, or (2) private documents. Public or official documents include all writings or records made by public officers in any governmental department in the performance of their duties. All other writings are private documents.

The Best Evidence Rule

The "best evidence" rule requires that where it becomes necessary to prove the contents of a paper, the original must be produced or its absence accounted for. The rule was adopted to prevent fraud or mistake as to the contents of a written paper.

Where the writing is collateral to a fact, the best evidence rule has no application. If a receipt for payment cannot be

---

[1] *Ticknor* v. *Ticknor*, 200 N.Y.S. 2d 661 (1960).

produced, the fact of payment can be established independent of the writing.

In the case of judicial records and entries in public books or registers, the original document need not be produced; certified copies of the record are admitted.

Voluminous entries and records may be proved by an expert or other competent person, in the discretion of the court.

Proof by Secondary Evidence

Upon satisfactory proof to the court that the original writing has been lost or destroyed, or that it is not available because outside of the jurisdiction of the court, secondary evidence of its contents becomes admissible. If a paper is in the possession of an adverse party who, after due notice, refuses to produce the original, secondary evidence may be used to prove its contents.

The party seeking to prove the contents of an alleged lost or destroyed paper must account in good faith for its loss or destruction. If the last custodian of the paper or record is alive, he should be produced; if he is deceased, his personal representative must testify. It will be for the trial judge to determine whether there has been sufficient proof of the loss.

The Parol (Oral) Evidence Rule

When a written contract has been completed, all the prior discussions between the parties generally are considered to be merged in the written agreement. Any oral conversations between the parties either before or at the time of the signing of the contract are inadmissible as evidence to vary, add to, or subtract from its terms. The writing itself is a protection against fraud and perjury, the infirmity of memory, or the death of the parties.

There are two exceptions to the general rule that parol (oral) evidence is inadmissible to vary the terms of a written instrument: (1) to prove that the contract or document is invalid or that it never had legal inception, as where there was fraud or duress or mistake and therefore no true consent to its terms; (2) where the writing covers only a part of an oral and entire contract, the unwritten part may be produced by parol evidence.

Public Documents as Evidence

Records kept by persons in public office which they are required to keep either by statute or by the nature of their office are admissible in evidence, and are evidence of those matters which are properly required to be recorded therein. The testimony of the officer who made the record is not required. This is an exception intended to avoid the inconvenience to public officials which might be caused by the need for their personal appearance. Such records or entries have the sanction of the oath of office by the public official.

Before a public document can be admitted in evidence, proof of its authenticity must be submitted. The proper official seal or signature by a governmental officer must be affixed to the documents. The certification attached to the copy indicates that he compared the copy with the original and that the same is a correct transcript. Judicial notice will be taken by the court of the authority of the officer and of his official seal and his signature.

The fact that a public document has been certified as correct does not prevent any of the parties from introducing other evidence to contest the validity of any part thereof or to correct it in any detail.

Authentication of Private Documents

In order for a private writing to be admitted in evidence, the party offering it must satisfy the court that it was duly executed by the person who is claimed to have executed it. No proof is necessary if the adverse party admits its genuineness, or if it is properly identified and authenticated.

A witness to the signature may testify as to its execution. When subscribing witnesses are necessary to prove the validity of a writing, such as the witnesses to a will, they must be produced or their absence accounted for. It may be shown that the witness is dead, insane, ill, or absent from the jurisdiction.

Unattested private documents are those which are not required by law to be signed. Written statements made in books of accounts or books kept regularly for business purposes may be admitted in evidence. Hospital records produced by one in charge of them, which meet the requirements of the Shop Book Rule or the rule as to Entries Made in the Regular Course of Business are admissible with limitations.

Use of Photographs

Properly identified photographs are admissible as aids in arriving at an understanding of the evidence. The testimony of one or more witnesses familiar with the subject portrayed who state that the photograph is a correct representation or a fair likeness of the person, place, condition or object sought to be described is necessary. Likewise, the testimony of the photographer is sufficient authentication.

Medical Books as Evidence

Medical books may not be read to the jury as evidence, nor may the treatise be offered in evidence to prove a medical fact. The author of the text is not open to cross-examination and what is contained in the book therefore is hearsay.[2]

The medical expert may testify, however, as to the medical opinions he has formed from scientific books which he has read. In that case the opinion is his own.

A medical treatise may be used to contradict or impeach a medical expert, but it may not be used to demonstrate the

---

[2] *Eckleberry* v. *Kaiser Foundation Northern Hospitals*, 359 P. 2d 1090 (Cal.) (1960).

truth of the facts contained therein. A medical witness who
testifies on a particular subject may on cross-examination be
presented with contradictory statements from medical books.
He may be asked for his comment thereon, even though he
does not recognize the authority of some of them. If he relies
on a book as authority for his opinion, he may be confronted
with contrary passages of the book on cross-examination. The
book may not be used unless he has conceded its authority or
has relied on it for his opinion.

Where a psychiatrist acknowledged the authenticity and
applicability of a published medical standard called "Standards
for Electroshock Therapy," prepared by the American Psychiatric Association, it was held that this information should
have gone to the jury to enable it to determine whether or not
the defendant was guilty of negligence in failing to take x-rays
to ascertain the cause of the patient's low back pain.[3]

---

[3] *Stone* v. *Proctor*, 131 S.E. 2d 297 (N.C.) (1963).

chapter 11

TISSUE COMMITTEE REPORTS
AS EVIDENCE

HOSPITAL administrators and physicians have become apprehensive as to the possible abuse of tissue reports for medicolegal purposes. Fear is expressed that such reports can and may be used as a basis for malpractice claims against members of the medical staff or to make committee members available as expert witnesses against their colleagues who are made defendants in malpractice suits. The hospital, too, has a stake as a possible defendant for the alleged negligent acts of its resident staff or other professional persons.

In addition to tissue committee reports there are reports of certain other medical staff committees such as medical audit, mortality, morbidity, utilization and others, as well as the nursing audit committee that cause concern for fear they will be used against the hospital or doctor in court.

These are all committees working to raise the standards of medical care and so they must use the medical records in their studies. However, none of the records of these committees except the Medical Audit Work Sheet (Fig. 30, p. 144), (which is not preserved after the work of the committee is finished) is a record of the condition of any one patient but rather a collection of data regarding several patients and are usually unidentifiable as to the care of any one patient, or the work of any one doctor. Physician's Index Cards (Figs. 31-32, p. 145) also cause concern in hospitals.

Functions of the Tissue Committee

Hospitals applying for accreditation by the Joint Commission on Accreditation of Hospitals are required to meet, among

MEDICAL AUDIT WORK SHEET

Patient's Family Name	First Name	Attending Physician	Room No.	Hosp. No.

THIS RECORD LACKS THE PARTS CHECKED

IDENTIFICATION DATA ☐

DIAGNOSIS
- Provisional ☐
- Final ☐

HISTORY
- Present Complaint ☐
- Present Illness or ☐
  - Analysis of Complaints and Inventory by Systems ☐
- Family History ☐
- Past History ☐

PHYSICAL EXAMINATION ☐

PHYSICIAN'S
- Orders ☐
- Discharge Order ☐
- Progress Notes ☐
- Condition on Discharge ☐
- Signatures ☐
- .... ☐

SPECIAL REPORTS
- Anesthesia ☐
- Autopsy ☐
- Consultation ☐
- Electrocardiogram ☐
- Laboratory ☐
- Obstetrical
  - Labor ☐
  - Pelvic Measurement ☐
  - Physical Examination ☐
  - Prenatal ☐
- Treatment: Medical or Surgical (Operation) ☐
- Tissue: Gross ☐
  - Microscopic ☐
- X-ray ☐
- Other ....

AUTHORIZATIONS FOR
- Medical and/or Surgical Treatment ☐
- Release of Information ☐
- Discharge without Physician's Orders ☐
- Responsibility for Abortion ☐
- Autopsy ☐
- Other ☐

NURSES' BEDSIDE RECORD
- Date Admission ☐ Time ☐ Manner ☐
- Date Discharge ☐ Time ☐ Manner ☐
- Nurses' Signature
  - On admission ☐
  - On discharge ☐

DATE ....

.... Medical Record Librarian

MEDICAL AUDIT FINDINGS

INCOMPLETE as indicated above
- By blue pencil on 1st review ☐
- By red pencil on 2nd review ☐

★INFECTIONS
1. Institutional ☐
2. Noninstitutional ☐
3. Postoperative ☐
4. Puerperal ☐

★COMPLICATIONS
1. Inevitable ☐
2. Preventable ☐

★CONSULTATION
1. Was it requested ☐
2. Was it given ☐
3. Was it recorded ☐
4. Recommendations followed ☐

PROVISIONAL and FINAL DIAGNOSES
1. Agree ☐
2. Disagree ☐

FINAL and PATHOLOGICAL DIAGNOSES
1. Agree ☐
2. Disagree ☐

★NORMAL TISSUE REMOVAL
1. Justifiable ☐
2. Not justifiable ☐

FINAL DIAGNOSIS Incomplete according to
1. History ☐
2. Progress Notes ☐
3. Report of Pathologist ☐
4. Report of Operation ☐

DEATH
1. Postoperative ☐
2. Anesthesia ☐
3. Institutional ☐
4. Autopsy performed ☐

RESULT OF TREATMENT
1. Expected ☐
2. Inevitable ☐
3. Justifiable ☐
4. Not justifiable ☐

REFER TO
1. Physician for additional information ☐
2. Chairman of department for opinion ☐

REMARKS ....

★MEDICAL FINDINGS
1. Diagnosis not justified ☐
2. Judgment faulty ☐
3. Treatment not warranted ☐
4. Technic erroneous ☐

★Numbers under these heads are intended for use as code numbers on Physicians' Index for hospitals conducting a Medical Audit.

The data established must be held in STRICT CONFIDENCE and MUST NOT BE FILED WITH MEDICAL RECORD.

PATIENT'S MEDICAL RECORD
- Ready for indexing ☐
- Not ready ☐

DATE ....

Call to attention of Program Committee ☐

.... M.D. Medical Audit Committee Representative

FORM C-501 PHYSICIANS' RECORD CO., BERWYN, ILLINOIS - PRINTED IN U.S.A. MEDICAL AUDIT WORK SHEET

FIG. 30 — MEDICAL AUDIT WORK SHEET

other criteria, the appointment and maintenance of a tissue committee or some other committee incorporating these functions with its own, which studies and reports to the medical staff the agreement or disagreement between preoperative diagnoses and subsequent reports by the pathologist on the tissue removed at operation.

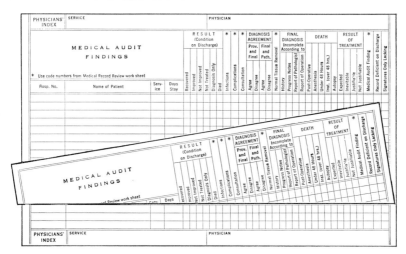

FIG. 31 — MEDICAL AUDIT FINDINGS

FIG. 32 — PHYSICIANS' INDEX

Some hospitals refer to the committee as the audit committee, surgical review committee, tumor and tissue committee, or some other title. By whatever name it is called, such a group fulfills a legal obligation of both the hospital and the medical staff to provide standards of medical care which are the result of conscientious and vigilant effort. There is also an ethical obligation imposed by section 4 of the Principles of Medical Ethics as adopted by the American Medical Association for the medical profession to "safeguard the public and itself against physicians deficient in moral character or professional competence."

Doctors thus associate themselves to impose discipline on their own colleagues, the tissue committee being a jury of their peers. Those who sit in judgment, so to speak, are experts in the very field in which they serve, thus assuring to the physician sympathetic understanding of professional problems. This is a jury whose primary function is not to impose punishment in the form of damages or to determine guilt or wrongdoing, but to benefit the public through improved standards of patient care in hospitals.

The tissue committee's main function in reviewing medical records is that of improving surgical care of patients. However, in carrying out its functions, the committee should not be content solely to eliminate outmoded methods of treatment: it should strive for the adoption of better procedures, which can be attained only by continuing analysis and education.

The Utilization Committee

A Utilization Committee is established within the medical staff of a hospital to assure that all of the in-patient service given is necessary and could not be provided as effectively in the home, office, hospital out-patient department or some other more appropriate, available facility. The Utilization Committee analyzes and identifies factors that may contribute to unnecessary or ineffective use of in-patient services and facilities, and make recommendations designed to minimize ineffective utilization.

The work of the Utilization Committee is largely dependent

upon the availability in the hospital of up-to-date charts which contain sufficient information to justify the decisions made by the attending physician in charge of the case and to permit objective review. The analyses of the Utilization Committee may point up inadequacies in the charts not revealed by review from the standpoint of accrediting bodies, legal requirements or quality control. Recommendations for improvement of medical records, including possible revision of forms, should be referred to the Medical Record Committee for appropriate action. In conjunction with its work, the Utilization Committee may wish to recommend various changes in forms and record procedures to the Medical Record Committee.

The Utilization Committee will need to maintain closest liaison with the Tissue Committee which is responsible for establishing the justification for surgery done in the hospital.

The Work Sheet

The Joint Commission on Accreditation of Hospitals does not recommend any specific type of work sheet. The tissue committee of each hospital may formulate one which best meets its purposes (Fig. 33, p. 148).

A sample format, suggested by the Commission, which has been successfully employed in a number of hospitals, includes the following items: 1. Tissue number; 2. Age; 3. Hospital number; 4. Pre-operative diagnosis; 5. Post-operative diagnosis; 6. Operative procedure; 7. Tissue removed; 8. Pathological diagnosis; 9. Normal tissue; 10. Acceptable—Yes or No.

The work sheets should include every operation performed during the preceding month and should indicate whether or not the work was acceptable; only the cases deemed unsatisfactory in diagnosis and treatment should be referred to the executive committee or medical board for action.

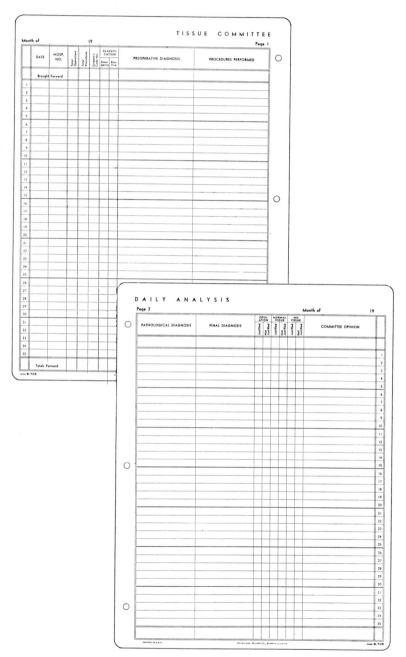

FIG. 33 — TISSUE COMMITTEE (DAILY ANALYSIS)

Retention of Tissue Committee Reports

The Joint Commission on Accreditation of Hospitals in 1959 stated that although it has carefully investigated all rumors it has yet to find that the records or minutes of a tissue committee of a hospital have ever been subpoenaed. The Commission is aware that any information is subject to subpoena if it is pertinent to a legal proceeding, but it is of the opinion that the problems in this regard have been greatly exaggerated. The situation, however, has changed: it is becoming more common to subpoena tissue committee records as lawyers become aware of the existence of such data.

The minutes of the tissue committee, according to the Commission, should show that the work of the physician has been reviewed. Such minutes should be kept in a permanent file. It is asserted that if disciplinary action ever has to be taken against a staff member, the hospital must have also the necessary information recorded with case numbers, dates, etc., to authenticate the material presented to the executive committee, staff or board as the case may be; sufficient material therefore must be kept on file to assure that this information may be easily located.

The work sheets have served their purpose through recording in the minutes of the tissue committee, and may be destroyed, unless it is necessary to use the information for disciplinary purposes against any physician. It would be a rare case in which an extended period would elapse before a final determination is made, and it is even less likely that the same report would be needed in connection with a malpractice action against the doctor or a suit against the hospital.

Hence, the report of the findings of the tissue committee should be used only as a working document for the purposes of the medical staff and should not be retained as a permanent record in the hospital. It should, of course, never be attached to or otherwise incorporated in the patient's medical record.

To prevent identification of the proceedings of the committee in any given case, the record of its activities should not be preserved except in tabular form (Fig. 34, below). In many

REPORT OF TISSUE COMMITTEE

Month__________ 19___	THIS MONTH	THIS MONTH LAST YEAR	THIS YEAR TO DATE	LAST YEAR TO DATE
Total Operations (Patients Operated Upon)				
Total Operations Not Justified				
Total Surgical Procedures Performed				
Total Emergency Operations				
Operations Not Justified as Emergency				
Total Exploratory Operations				
Exploratory Operations Not Justified				
Normal Tissue Removed				
Normal Tissue Unjustifiably Removed				
No Tissue Removed				
No Tissue Removed, Operation Not Justified				
Disagreement Between Preoperative and Postoperative Diagnoses				
Disagreement Not Justified				
Disagreement Between Final and Pathological Diagnoses				
Disagreement Not Justified				
Disagreement Between Provisional and Final Diagnoses				
Disagreement Not Justified				
Cases Referred to Surgeon for Additional Data				
Cases Referred to Chief of Department				
Cases Referred to Executive Committee				

Signed____________________
CHAIRMAN TISSUE COMMITTEE

FORM B-706 PHYSICIANS' RECORD CO., BERWYN, ILLINOIS PRINTED IN U.S.A.

FIG. 34 — REPORT OF TISSUE COMMITTEE

hospitals the findings of the committee are reported in code to the medical staff and only the code numbers are entered in the medical staff minutes for permanent filing.

Use for Medicolegal Purposes

The questions most frequently asked by hospital administrators and by members of the medical staff are: Are the tissue committee reports available to attorneys who seek evidence for a malpractice action or who look for potential expert witnesses to testify in a contemplated or pending suit? May the reports which have been subpoenaed for inspection be used as evidence? Can the information in the reports be obtained through pretrial discovery proceedings? May the reports serve as material for the cross-examination of a committee member who is testifying as an expert?

These reports do not constitute a recognized part of the patient's clinical record, which is divided into three sections: (1) nurses' records, (2) records and reports from adjunct and special departments and (3) the medical record proper, which is the direct responsibility of the physician. As such, the tissue committee report has no bearing on what was wrong with the patient or what treatment should have been provided. It is rather a review of what was done for the patient, made after he has left the hospital, to evaluate the care which he received.

Despite the fact that the records of the tissue committee are not an integral part of the patient's clinical record, such status does not *ipso facto* exclude the records as evidence in the trial of a negligence or malpractice case. Certain rules of evidence govern its admissibility or exclusion. These rules are encompassed within certain general rules of evidence, such as (1) the hearsay rule, (2) the "business entries" rule, and (3) the doctrine of privileged communications.

At common law, it is the usual practice to require the testimony of the writer of a record or identification of his handwriting and of each piece of writing or notation offered in evidence. The record or writing would be excluded as evidence under the "hearsay rule," if the person who testified had no personal knowledge of the facts, but relied on what someone else had written. Furthermore, the person who wrote the record cannot be cross-examined as to its accuracy, nor can the person testifying, other than its maker, prove the correctness of the entries.

Many states have modified the rule against hearsay to provide an exception in the case of certain records made in the regular course of business. The purpose of the statutes is to secure a more workable rule of evidence in the proof of business transactions under existing business conditions. The term "business" in the statute may include "business, profession, occupation and calling of every kind." The statute gives competency as evidence to regular records in business, without the preliminary proof being required.

These statutes, in substance, usually provide that "any writing or record, whether in the form of an entry in a book or otherwise, made as a memorandum or record of any act, transaction, occurrence or event, shall be admissible in evidence in proof of such act, transaction, occurrence or event, if the trial judge shall find that it was made in the regular course of any business, and that it was the regular course of such business to make such memorandum or record at the time of such act, transaction, occurrence or event, or within a reasonable time thereafter."

The fact that the maker of the record lacks personal knowledge of the transaction does not affect its admissibility if it was made in the regular course of business at the time of the recording of the event, since the statute in part may read that: "All other circumstances of the making of such writing or record, including lack of personal knowledge by the entrant or maker, may be shown to affect its weight, but they shall not affect its admissibility."

In order for the records to be admitted in evidence under the business entries rule, it must not only be identified as that of the patient, but must be authenticated also as to the method of making it; it must be shown that the entries were made in the regular course of business, at or near the time of the act or event. The court then rules on their admissibility.

Hospital records which relate to diagnosis, prognosis or treatment or which are otherwise understanding of the medical aspects of the hospitalization are admissible in evidence, under the provisions of some of the statutes.

In New York State, section 412 of the Civil Practice Acts permits a photostatic copy of the record to be delivered to the court under a subpoena *duces tecum* if it is "duly certified by the superintendent, or head of such hospital," as being a true copy of a record made in the regular course of business of the hospital. Delivery of such copies of the record generally eliminates the necessity of personal testimony authenticating the record.

A hospital record of a patient, as stated above, is not admissible in evidence unless the entries were made at the time of such act, transaction, occurrence or event, or within a reasonable time thereafter. Thus such report of a tissue committee does not meet the requirement of the statute as a record made in the regular course of business, and objection to its admissibility in evidence should be sustained by the court.

Records as Privileged Communications

The doctrine of privileged communications in New York State was adopted in 1828, as the first state to provide that "a person duly authorized to practice physic or surgery, or dentistry, or a registered professional or licensed practical nurse, shall not be allowed to disclose any information which he acquired in attending a patient in a professional capacity, and which was necessary to enable him to act in that capacity."

The privileged status accorded to the information imparted to the physician extends to the patient's clinical records, both at the hospital and in the physician's private office. However, the privilege is only to that testimony or information acquired by him in his capacity as attending physician; he is not disqualified to testify to information learned by him in his unprivileged capacity.

In a decision in a malpractice action in New York State, the attorney for the patient sought to subpoena all tissue committee reports of the hospital concerning the patients of a certain physician. The court held that "production of the records showing treatment of persons other than plaintiff is privileged and may not be required. That privilege applies not only to trials proper but also to examinations before trial, and extends both to the oral evidence requested as well as to any documentary proof sought to be used in connection therewith. Even if the defendants, as doctor and hospital respectively, sought to waive the privilege, they would be unable to do so, as the privilege belongs to the patient, and may be waived only by him or his committee or guardian, or at the trial by his attorney. An examination before trial dealing with such issues, or the production of records relating thereto, thus may not be ordered."[1]

A subpoena was served upon a hospital in connection with a notice of examination before trial in a malpractice action against the hospital and certain members of its medical staff, whereby the patient required that certain records be produced. These records consisted of the "Surgical Log Book," operation and disease index cards or records relating to surgical treatment performed by the defendant doctors in the hospital prior to the time of plaintiff's treatment, records of "any and all medical staff discussions and meetings of committees relative to the surgery performed upon the plaintiff."

The plaintiff's attorneys also sought to inspect and make copies of the bylaws, rules and regulations governing the hospital and its internship and residency training program and,

[1] *Strattard* v. *Health Ins. Plan of Greater New York*, Sup. Ct., Queens Co., Sp. 1, Shapiro, J., N.Y.L.J., June 10, 1960, p. 15, col. 6.

if approved by the Joint Commission on Accreditation of Hospitals, copies of the bylaws and regulations of said Joint Commission adopted by the hospital.

The court held that the "Surgical Log Book" could not be examined in its entirety because it contained entries referring to patients other than the plaintiff, but that the hospital should furnish the plaintiff with a copy of the portion or portions referring to the plaintiff's treatment.

The information sought concerning the operation and disease index cards or records obviously contemplated disclosure of privileged information relating to treatment of other patients and plaintiff was not entitled thereto.

The demands for records of medical staff discussions and committee meetings, relative to surgery performed upon the plaintiff obviously called for the disclosure of hearsay and statements not shown to be binding upon the defendants or any of them. "Such records, if there be any, are to be distinguished from entries in the patient's record made contemporaneously with the treatment and received in evidence pursuant to section 374-a Civil Practice Act."

The defendant hospital also opposed disclosure of the rules and regulations on the basis of the general rule in negligence actions that private rules and regulations of a defendant are not admissible in evidence. The rationale of this general rule is that since, in the ordinary negligence case, the defendant is held to the standard of care of the average reasonably prudent and careful person, he should not be penalized by the adoption of rules requiring his employees to adhere to a higher standard of care. A somewhat different situation obtains with respect to the standard of care required of hospitals and physicians in treatment and care of the ill. In general, the hospital's duty to the patient is measured by the degree of care, skill and diligence customarily exercised by hospitals generally in the community. "It thus appears that within reasonable limits the hospitals in a given community may themselves establish the standard of care applicable to them. While in a community such as this, having several hospitals, the rules and regulations of the defendant hospital alone are probably not admissible, I am unable to say that, were it shown that the hospitals of this community have established reasonably uniform rules and regulations with respect to the care of their patients, such rules and regulations might not be admissible. Without in any way undertaking to pass upon the eventual admissibility of such evidence, I feel that the plaintiff should be permitted the examination sought. While the defendant argues that the by-laws and regulations of the Joint Commission on Accreditation of Hospitals should be sought from the Joint Commission itself, the fact that such evidence might be procured from other sources is no bar to examining the defendant hospital in that respect provided the hospital in fact has in its possession such bylaws and regulations."

The subpoena was quashed and the plaintiff granted the limited rights indicated.[2]

Statutes on Tissue Committee Records

A number of states have adopted statutes which remove the fear of legal inquiry into the conduct of physicians who judge their colleagues on the basis of scientific standards of medical care through tissue committees. These committees are enabled through this form of legal immunity to maintain adequate records and to perform their functions in seeking better standards of medical care.

The states which have enacted these statutes are: California, Connecticut, Michigan, Minnesota, Nebraska and South Dakota. In substance, these laws provide that (1) all information used in the course of medical study shall be strictly confidential; (2) such information shall not be admissible in evi-

---

[2] *Judd v. Park Avenue Hospital*, 235 N.Y.S. 2d 843, affirmed, 235 N.Y.S. 2d 1023 (1963).

dence; (3) the furnishing of such information shall not subject any person or hospital to any damages.

Legislation was recently adopted by the State of Illinois by the passage of S.B. No. 320, approved by the Governor on August 21, 1961. The provisions of the bill state that:

"Section 1. All information, interviews, reports, memoranda or other data of the Illinois Department of Public Health, Illinois State Medical Society, allied medical societies, or in-hospital staff committees of accredited hospitals, but not the original records pertaining to the patient, used in the course of medical study for the purpose of reducing morbidity or mortality shall be strictly confidential and shall be used only for medical research.

Section 2. Such information, records, reports, statements, notes, memoranda, or other data shall not be admissible as evidence in any action of any kind in any court or before any tribunal, board, agency or person.

Section 3. The furnishing of such information in the course of a research project to the Illinois Department of Public Health, Illinois State Medical Society, allied medical societies or to in-hospital staff committee or their authorized representatives, shall not subject any person, hospital, sanitarium, nursing or rest home or any such agency to any action for damages or other relief.

Section 4. No patient, patient's relatives or patient's friends named in any medical study, shall be interviewed for the purpose of such study unless consent of the attending physician and surgeon is first obtained.

Section 5. The disclosure of any information, records, reports, statements, notes, memoranda, or other data obtained in any such medical study except that necessary for the purpose of the specific study is unlawful, and any person convicted of violating any of the provisions of this Act is guilty of a misdemeanor."

Hawaii, Maryland, Montana and Utah adopted statutes in 1963 authorizing physicians, hospitals, etc., to provide information, reports, data, records, etc., to the state medical society, in-hospital staff committees, and/or the state health commissioner for use in mortality and morbidity studies. The data used in such studies, and the findings, conclusions or summaries resulting therefrom, are privileged and may not be used in legal proceedings.

California has passed a new law authorizing in-hospital medical staff committees to engage in research and medical study for the purpose of reducing morbidity and mortality. The California statute makes the records, reports, memoranda, etc., of such hospital committees subject to legal discovery proceedings, but provides that they may not be admitted in evidence in any action of any kind in any court or before any administrative body, agency or person.

chapter 12

X-RAYS, MICROFILMS, AND
PHOTOGRAPHS AS EVIDENCE

LIKE other photographs, x-ray plates cannot be received as evidence until proper proof of their correctness and accuracy is produced.[1] The witness must be able to say that he is skilled in the use of the x-ray machine and in the taking and developing of x-ray films. He must have taken the picture offered in evidence with the body in a certain position, which he described, with a machine which he knew to be in good working order and accurate, and that from his experience he was able to say that the picture produced by the machine was an accurate picture of the area.[2] The methods of establishing the accuracy of the picture are not exclusive, but whatever method is used its accuracy must be established before the x-ray plate is admitted.[3]

Medical experts may prove the existence of a fracture by clinical signs or inspection without the aid of x-rays. In most instances, however, it is necessary that x-ray films be produced as proof. It is not always essential that the roentgenologist who made them testify in court; the films can be introduced in evidence if the patient's physician directed the taking of the x-rays and was present when they were taken and developed. He must be able to testify that they are correct repre-

---

[1] *Bartleville Zinc Co.* v. *Fisher*, 60 Okl. 139, 159 P. 476 (1916).

[2] 20 Am. Jur. Evidence, sec. 737 (1939).

[3] *Hardesty* v. *Sparrow*, 275 S.W. 2d 587 (Ky.) (1953).

sentations of the patient's condition as of the time when such films were made. If the physician was not present, the technician who took them may identify the films.[4]

However, it is improper to permit an x-ray specialist to testify from his notes concerning a film which he has examined, where he has not taken the picture nor seen the film made. The testimony of the physician that the film which he examined bore the name of the patient is insufficient.[5]

In practice, however, the opposing attorney frequently concedes at the trial or in advance of trial that the films are those of the patient. Often the x-ray readings are admitted in evidence as part of the patient's medical record. It is when the opposing attorney wishes to be technical or he doubts the x-rays are correct or those of the patient that he insists on proper identification and interpretation by an expert.

Marking Films for Identification

X-ray films in most instances are valueless as legal evidence unless there is competent proof of their identity. It is for the trial court in its discretion to decide whether the person is qualified.

Where x-ray reports were part of a hospital's records, the qualifications of the technician who took the x-rays did not have to be proved before his report was admissible under the Uniform Business Records as Evidence Act.[6]

When Identification is Unnecessary

There are cases where the x-ray films are used merely to confirm clinical observations and diagnoses; in such instances they are not indispensable. Should the x-ray pictures be used by the physician who examined the patient only to refresh his recollection but not as evidence, there can be no objection.

---

[4] *Lazarus* v. *Friel*, 73 N.E. 2d 647 (Ill.) (1947).

[5] *Simon* v. *Hendricks*, 330 P. 2d 186 (Okl.) (1958).

[6] *Webber* v. *McCormick*, 164 A 2d 813 (N.J.) (1960).

Where it appears that the films which have been improperly used in evidence would not have affected the oral proof of the fractures by the physician, the court will ignore the improperly proven films or reports.[7]

Where a state statute permits the introduction of the medical record in evidence upon proof that the entries were made in the regular course of business of the hospital, the x-ray readings which are part of the written record are admissible without the need of producing and identifying the x-ray films.[8]

Admissibility of Copies of X-rays

The need may arise for using copies of x-rays in court or for including them in the record of a case on appeal. Any method for reproducing x-rays must assure a faithful copy, preserving all the details and clarity of the original film.

The print made from the negative of the x-ray is no less authentic than a print made from the negative of any other film. It is an exact reproduction of the picture on paper, or some other material, and often, if not always, is clearer than the negative to the eye of a layman. A print from a negative, properly identified, is admissible in evidence to the same degree as would be the negative itself.

Admission of Photostatic Copies of Records

The "best evidence rule" requires that in proving a writing the writing itself must be produced, unless it is not feasible to do so. There is a twofold purpose to the rule: the original will prevent fraud and error. This rule has been applied also to photostatic copies of records.

The federal and New York business entry statutes permitting the use of photostats refer only to situations where photo-

---

[7] *Williamson Candy Co.* v. *Lewis*, 144 So. 2d 522 (Fla.) (1962).

[8] *Rouse* v. *Fussell*, 126 S.E. 2d 830 (Ga.) (1962).

stats, microfilms, or the like have been made in the ordinary course of business and not in preparation for the trial.[9]

In a suit by the beneficiary of an insurance policy against the company, a photostatic copy of a purported record of a veterans' hospital consisting of a narrative summary of a certain date, with respect to the insured, which purported record was not proved or authenticated in any way as being an official hospital record of such hospital, was properly excluded.[10] To admit a photostatic copy of a record, a proper foundation must be laid as to its authenticity.[11]

Reproductions from Microfilm

Under the best evidence rule the record may be proved by a photographic reproduction upon showing that the original was destroyed without improper motives even if done intentionally.

On the other hand, there are situations where the original record has not been destroyed, intentionally or otherwise, but has been lost or mislaid. In such a case it is more difficult to predict precisely what proof would be necessary as a prerequisite to admitting a photographic reproduction. The one offering it in evidence must show that he has in good faith exhausted, to a reasonable degree, all sources of information and means of discovery which the nature of the case would naturally suggest, and which were accessible to him. The person known to have been in possession of the record must be examined as a witness, to prove its loss.

The business entries doctrine is, of course, entirely distinct from the best evidence rule. In *United States* v. *Manton*,[12] the United States Circuit Court of Appeals for the Second Circuit placed reliance on a federal statute in holding that it was not

---

[9] *Toho Bussan Kaisha, Ltd.,* v. *American President Lines, Ltd.,* 265 F. 2d 418 (C.A.N. Y.) (1958).

[10] *Dixie Life Ins. Co.* v. *Landrith,* 339 S.W. 2d 376 (Tex.) (1960).

[11] *Kneeland* v. *Shroyer,* 328 P. 2d 753 (Or.) (1958).

[12] 107 F. 2d 834 (1938), cert. denied 309 U.S. 664 (1940).

error to receive in evidence photographic reproductions of the face of checks which had been paid. There evidently had been no attempt at the trial to show loss, destruction or other un-availability of the checks themselves. In an opinion by Justice Sutherland, the court spoke of photographic reproductions in language which has been taken as laying down the rule, for the federal courts at least, that photographic reproductions, made under circumstances consistent with the statutory requirements, are not to be excluded from evidence on the basis of the best evidence rule.

Public Law 129, approved August 28, 1951, added a new subdivision to Section 1732 of the federal judicial code on the subject of photographic reproductions of business records. The statute is based on the proposed Uniform Photographic Copies of Business and Public Records Act approved by the National Conference of Commissioners on Uniform State Laws and the American Law Institute in 1949. The statute applies to "any memorandum, writing, entry, print, representation or combination thereof, or any act, transaction, occurrence, or event" which is both made and photographed in the regular course of business.[13]

The view now generally accepted is that a destruction in the ordinary course of business, and, of course, a destruction by mistake, is sufficient to allow the contents to be shown as in other cases of loss, and a destruction otherwise made will equally suffice, provided the proponent first removes, to the satisfaction of the judge, any suspicion of fraud.

The courts are liberal in admitting carbon copies, loose-leaf ledger sheets, etc., made in the regular course of business. Film records, therefore, should be admissible upon establishing the following requirements: (1) the accuracy of the photographic process; (2) the existence at one time of the original and its competency as primary evidence; (3) the reasons for destroy-

[13] 28 U.S.C., Sec. 1732 (b).

ing the original; (4) the local statute or case law in verifying
the film picture records.

Photographs as Evidence

Photographs to be admissible in evidence need not necessarily be identified by the photographer who took them. One
who has personal knowledge of what is depicted thereon would
be qualified to prove that it is a correct representation of the
person, place or condition as of the time in question. The basic
requirement for the admission of a photograph is that it be
shown to be a fair and accurate representation of the object
sought to be proved. Thus, a photograph taken after autopsy
is admissible upon the pathologist's testimony. A patient may
introduce a photograph of his physical condition before his injury as well as a photograph of the injury complained of, or a
print of a fractured arm shortly after the removal of splints,
or to show a scarred face, or to prove the nature and location
of wounds.

In a suit against a hospital for burns resulting from a hot-
water bottle, the patient introduced pictures taken after a skin
graft. The photograph was admitted in evidence after a showing that it was a correct representation of the wound at the
time.

A photograph intended to prove that a certain condition was
caused by trauma is not admissible unless causal connection is
first established medically. A patient, claiming that she sustained hot-water bottle burns while in shock, offered pictures
of the healing wounds in her legs to allow the jury to determine whether the injury was caused by hot-water bottle burns.
The pictures were properly excluded; no doctor testified that
the lesions were due to burns; the jurors were not qualified to
make a diagnosis as to the cause of the lesions.[14]

---

[14] *Wallstedt* v. *Swedish Hospital,* 19 N.W. 426 (Minn.) (1945).

chapter 13

HOSPITAL RECORDS IN COURT

CALLING all persons as witnesses who have made entries in a medical record is a serious interference with the management of a hospital. Hospital records are reliable; they are made by trained personnel, according to modern methods of record keeping, for use in matters of life and death. When a record is made by one person and he takes the stand to authenticate it, the record is admissible. However, no such one-man records are made in hospitals.

The Business Entries Rule

The legislatures of many states have met the problem of using hospital records as evidence by enacting statutes which enable business entries and records of all kinds, made in the regular course of business, to be used in evidence. Hospital records which relate to diagnosis, prognosis or treatment or which are otherwise helpful to an understanding of the medical aspects of the hospitalization are admissible in evidence.

The Uniform Business Records as Evidence Act adopted by many states has the purpose of avoiding the technical rules of the common law regarding the admissibility of business records as evidence. The Act does not make all business records competent evidence regardless of by whom, in what manner and for what purpose they are compiled or offered. When the entry is not of such character as to give it the status of a business entry, it is inadmissible.[1]

---

[1] *Maggi* v. *Mendillo*, 165A. 2d 603 (Conn.) (1960).

The admissibility of hospital records depends generally upon whether such records relate to acts, transactions, occurrences or events incident to the treatment.[2] The facts or events incident to treatment are not invariably limited to observable, in the sense of being visual, facts or events. However, the entry must be relevant and useful in the diagnosis and treatment of the patient's injury, and not based upon speculation and conjecture.

Entries in the hospital record are of two classes: (1) notes made by a person having personal knowledge of the recorded transaction or event which occurred within the regular course of hospital business, such as a nurse recording a temperature reading, and (2) entries in which a hospital employee, with no personal knowledge, records information provided by the patient or information given by a third person not employed by the hospital.

The purpose underlying the enactment of such statutes is to avoid the necessity and thereby the expense, inconvenience and sometimes impossibility of calling as witnesses attendant nurses and physicians who collaborated in the making of the record.[3] The record, when admissible in evidence under a statute, may properly include the history, diagnosis by one qualified to make it, the condition and treatment of the patient covering such items as temperature, pulse, respiration, symptoms, food and medicines, analysis of tissues or fluids of the body, and behavior and complaints of the patient. Such portions of the hospital record made in the regular course of business and pertaining to the business of hospitalization, and the recording of observable facts, transactions, or occurrences or events incident to the treatment of a patient, are useful to the understanding of medical or surgical aspects of a case.[4]

Under the Federal Shop Book Rule (28 U.S.C.A. sec. 1732),

---

[2] *Chilton* v. *Dockstader*, 126 So. 2d 281 (Fla.) (1960).

[3] *Di Re* v. *Central Livestock Order Buying Co.*, 91 N.W. 2d 453 (Minn.) (1958).

[4] *Lewis* v. *Woodland*, 144 N.E. 2d 322 (Ohio) (1957).

which applies to trials in the federal courts, medical records kept by a group of physicians, in which one of the physicians recorded his observations of physical facts upon which competent physicians would not be likely to disagree, were admissible in evidence. The physician who made the examination and the entries was not called as a witness.[5]

Preliminary Proof Required for Admissibility

In order for the record to be admitted in evidence under one of the business entries acts, the record must not only be identified as that of the patient while in the hospital, but must be authenticated also as to the method of making it; it must be shown that the entries were made in the regular course of business, at or near the time of the act or event. The court then rules on its admissibility.

The business records acts eliminate calling each witness, and substitute the record of the transaction or event. It is not necessary that the person testifying to the making of the entries have personal knowledge of the transactions.[6]

Whether the entire record or only certain parts of it are admissible in evidence is for the trial court to determine, based on rules of evidence and statutes or legal decisions in the particular state. There is no uniformity in the decisions as to admissibility, because the basic philosophy of the law is not uniform in all the states. There is a uniform basis, however, in that hearsay statements, with certain exceptions, are inadmissible.

Many courts hold that such records are regular business entries and are therefore admissible provided the declarant appears to have the necessary qualifications to render an expert opinion. Other courts oppose the admission of medical diagnoses on the ground that opposing counsel is deprived

---

[5] *Washington Coca-Cola Bottling Works, Inc.* v. *Tawney*, 6 CCH Neg. Cases 2d 218 (USCA-DC) (1956).

[6] *Hermann* v. *St. Louis Public Service Co.*, 345 S.W. 2d 399 (Mo.) (1961).

thereby of the opportunity for cross-examination. Doctors frequently disagree when it comes to a diagnosis and therefore medical opinions and diagnoses do not have the inherent guarantee of accuracy of routine business entries.

Factual statements made by physicians and contained in the hospital records are admissible in the same manner as factual statements made by nurses and other employees of the hospital in connection with the routine business of the hospital. For example, medical statements, made as routine entries in the course of hospital business, consisting of reports of the patient's temperature, blood pressure, pulse, medicines and treatment prescribed, external bruises, skin rash, alcoholic breath, lacerations or injuries observable to persons generally, routine laboratory tests, expressions of pain, noticeable external physical marks or defects, and similar facts not involving medical opinions, should be admitted. Where, however, the statement of the physician consists of an opinion, conclusion or diagnosis based on his medical examination or findings of conditions not obvious or patently observable to persons generally, it may be excluded. In such a case the doctor should be brought into court where he may be cross-examined by opposing counsel. The decision as to whether the record falls within one category or the other should be left largely to the sound discretion of the trial court.[7]

Some states limit the admissibility of the record to facts which are non-medical, such as the age of the patient, dates of treatment, but not opinions of physicians or facts concerned with medical care. The age of a patient as stated in a hospital record is a medical fact which is admissible as a "memorandum of an act, transaction, occurrence or event."

The Medical Record Librarian as a Witness

The medical record librarian usually is competent under the business entry statutes to identify the record for the purpose

---

[7] *Martinez* v. *Williams*, 312 S.W. 2d 742 (Tex.) (1958).

of admitting it in evidence. The medical record librarian, in one case, testified that she had custody of the hospital medical records, but was not present at the time of the patient's admission, or when the x-rays were taken, or when his history was taken or when entries were made. She was permitted to state, nevertheless, routine matters appearing in the record, such as the patient's name, date of admission and discharge, and the injury for which he was treated.[8]

Where the hospital's medical record librarian testified that the doctor who prepared a certain patient's hospital record was then a resident physician of the hospital, such evidence justified the presumption of the doctor's qualifications to make the report concerning the patient. She also testified that she was custodian of the records, identified the record of the patient, and explained the procedure relating to the manner of keeping such records.[9]

It has been held that the testimony of a medical record librarian in a personal injury action that she had begun work at the hospital approximately 14 months after the accident, and had been working in the record room continuously since then, and had charge of the records and was familiar with them, was sufficient to admit the records in evidence, even though the witness was not the record custodian at the time the records were made.[10]

The Hearsay Rule and Admissibility

Hearsay evidence is evidence intended to provide proof of the existence of facts based not on personal knowledge and observation but upon what someone else said. Hearsay declarations to be admissible must be made under such circumstances as will raise the reasonable presumption that they are spontaneous utterances springing out of the transaction itself or

---

[8] *In re Bush*, 116 A. 2d 410 (D.C. Mun. App.) (1955).

[9] *Allen* v. *St. Louis Public Service Co.*, 285 S.W. 663 (Mo.) (1929).

[10] *Webber* v. *McCormick*, 164 A. 2d 813 (N.J.) (1960).

so soon thereafter as to preclude a presumption that they are the result of premeditation and design.

Hospital records when offered as primary evidence are hearsay, but they come within the exception to the hearsay rule as entries made in the regular course of business, contemporaneously with the occurrences, acts, and events recorded by one authorized to make them and before litigation has arisen.[11] On this basis, while hospital records are hearsay, nevertheless they are admissible as being an exception to the hearsay rule, and therefore an objection on the ground of hearsay is not valid.[12]

Statements made by a nurse of what she heard others say or what others said to her generally are not admissible if the third party is not available for cross-examination. The contents of a letter or writing are hearsay if the writer is not available as a witness. When the medical record is banned as evidence in some states by the hearsay rule, it is on the ground that those who wrote the record cannot be cross-examined.

It may be necessary as precedent to the admission in evidence of an offered record for a qualified witness not only to identify the record, but also to testify to the mode of its preparation. It must appear that the record in question was made in the regular course of business, at or near the time of the act, condition or event purportedly recorded. A "Narrative Summary" signed by the chief surgeon in the clinical record, which was a compilation and summary of various record entries in other portions of the hospital record, was held to be hearsay.[13]

Records which contain the version of third persons as to the manner in which an accident occurred are not admissible in

---

[11] *Sims* v. *Charlotte Liberty Mut. Ins. Co.,* 125 S.E. 2d 326 (N.C.) (1960).

[12] *Frampton* v. *Hartzell,* 4 Cal. Rptr. 427 (Cal.) (1960).

[13] *Gray* v. *St. Louis-San Francisco Ry. Co.,* 1 CCH Neg. Cases 2d 881 (Mo.) (1952).

evidence, because such extrajudicial statements are not subject to cross-examination and are barred by the hearsay rule.[14]

Records and Notes Must Be Relevant

While the statute may permit the introduction of hospital records as an exception to the hearsay rule, the records will be admissible only if they are relevant.[15] For that reason not every "act, condition, event or occurrence" stated in the record by the physician becomes admissible; it must be germane to the treatment.[16]

A hospital record for a 15 year period, long before the accident in point, was admitted to show the patient's physical condition before the occurrence; the notation that she stated she could not support herself on old age pension which was her sole income was properly excluded.[17]

Defendant was tried for the murder of a man; both were colored. The hospital record contained a notation that the decedent told the doctor he had been shot by a white man whom he did not know. The accused objected to having this part of the record excluded. The court, however, excluded it, holding that the entry as to the color of the man who shot the patient was gratuitous reporting, not made in the regular course of the physician's business. Hospital business and police business are two different matters.[18]

A statement in a clinic record that on the morning after the accident the patient had visited his lawyer who had referred him to the doctor was properly excluded as not pathologically germane to the physical condition which caused the patient to go to the clinic in the first place.[19]

[14] *Cox* v. *State of New York*, 171 N.Y.S. 2d 818, 3 N.Y. 2d 693, 148 N.E. 879 (1958).

[15] *Ocean Shore R. Co.* v. *Doelger*, 3 Cal. Rptr. 706 (Cal.) (1960).

[16] *Old* v. *Cooney Detective Agency*, 138 A. 2d 889 (Md.) (1958).

[17] *Gallagher* v. *Portland Traction Co.*, 182 P. 2d 354 (Ore.) (1947).

[18] *Commonwealth* v. *Harris*, 41 A. 2d 688 (Pa.) (1944).

[19] *Yellow Cab Co.* v. *Hicks*, 168 A. 2d 501 (Md.) (1961).

Narrative Statements Must Be Those of Patient

A hospital record was admissible where the custodian of the records testified that the record which contained a statement how the patient was injured was made in the regular course of business of the hospital by one of its employees at or near the time of entry of the patient into the hospital and that it was customary for a record to be kept of the personal history of the patient.[20]

However, to be admissible, the statement in the record made to a physician or a nurse as to how the accident occurred must come from the lips of the patient and not from some third party or unidentified source.[21] A notation that the patient had taken ten bichloride of mercury tablets was declined as hearsay, since there was no proof that the information came from the patient.[22]

It was proper to admit in evidence that portion of a hospital record which said, "Patient states that she fell down as she was getting off a street car. She doesn't recall how she fell but she thinks her heels slipped on the street." The history had been given by the patient herself to the testifying witness.[23]

The statement by a patient as to how the accident occurred was held to have been recorded for the apparent purpose of furthering the hospital's business and was admissible.[24] The entry that the patient stated he hurt his ankle while walking on the street was deemed admissible, although the intern who wrote it could not remember who told it to him; the statement was held to have been made as an entry in the regular course of business and "pathologically germane" in aiding prompt diagnosis.[25]

---

[20] *Skillern & Sons, Inc.* v. *Rosen*, 359 S.W. 2d 298 (Tex.) (1962).

[21] *Cox* v. *State of New York*, 3 N.Y. 2d 643, 171 N.Y.S. 2d 818 (1958).

[22] *Cottrell* v. *Prudential Ins. Co.*, 28 N.Y.S. 2d 335, 260 App. Div. 986 (1940).

[23] *Cerniglia* v. *City of New York*, 182 Misc. 441, 49 N.Y.S. 2d 447 (1944).

[24] *Melton* v. *St. Louis Public Service Co.*, 251 S.W. 2d 663 (Mo.) (1952).

[25] *Watts* v. *Del. Coach Co.*, 58 A. 2d 689 (Del.) (1948).

It has been held that "a memorandum made in a hospital record of acts or occurrences leading to the patient's hospitalization—such as a narration of the accident causing the injury—not germane to diagnosis or treatment, is not admissible. . . . . " under the Act. The erroneous admission of such evidence required a new trial.[26]

Effect of Privileged Doctrine on Admissibility

Another rule which may prevent the use of the chart or bar the testimony of the physician or nurse is the doctrine of privileged communications, under which such professional persons in some states are enjoined from disclosing information received or observed in the course of treatment. That which does not concern diagnosis or treatment is not privileged and may be admissible.

An insurance company sought to cancel a policy on the ground that the patient had made false statements concerning treatment and hospitalization at the time the policy was issued. Two witnesses, both of whom were interns at the hospital where he had been treated, testified that each had taken a history for the purpose of the record in accordance with a rule of the hospital, and not for treatment. Neither witness was under the supervision of the doctor who treated the patient. Their testimony was held not privileged; at no time did they do anything for the patient except to take his history.[27]

Where death occurs, it is necessary that the privilege be waived by the personal representative of the estate. The waiver need not be in writing and it is not necessary that there be an express intention to waive; it may be inferred from the conduct of the representative.[28]

[26] *Williams* v. *Alexander,* 129 N.E. 2d 417, 309 N.Y. 283 (1955).

[27] *Frederick* v. *Federal Life Ins. Co.,* 57 P. 2d 235 (Cal.) (1936).

[28] *Eder* v. *Cashin,* 281 App. Div. 456, 120 N.Y.S. 2d 165 (1953).

Self-Serving Declarations Not Admissible

A self-serving declaration is an oral or written statement made by a party to an action which tends to support his claim. In effect, a party would be creating evidence for himself if such statements were admissible. Oral or written statements of a self-serving character are inadmissible, unless they are clearly a part of the *res gestae.* "Res gestae" refers to acts and words which are so closely connected to the main fact as to constitute a part of the transaction.

A statement made by a patient at the hospital to which he is brought after the accident, which statement is included in the medical record as part of the history, would not be admissible in evidence if the information furnished would tend to show another at fault for the accident. The patient would be creating evidence for himself during the lapse of time between the accident and his arrival at the hospital. His utterances would not be spontaneous so as to constitute part of the *res gestae.*

The patient claimed that the nurse bumped into her, knocking her to the floor and causing her to fracture her left hip. The court held that no error was committed in excluding the testimony of witnesses who were offered by plaintiff for the purpose of showing statements made by plaintiff after the accident, which statements were to the effect that a nurse had bumped into her. Such statements were self-serving and therefore inadmissible.[29] In fact, any hearsay or self-serving statements contained in a hospital record are not ordinarily admissible.[30]

A declaration made by the patient to the physician as to his symptoms, if given for the purpose of treatment, is admissible.[31] But if it is made for the purpose of leading the physician

---

[29] *Lagrone* v. *Helman,* 103 S.W. 2d 365 (Miss.) (1958).

[30] *Roeder* v. *North Am. Life Ins. Co.,* 106 N.W. 2d 624 (Minn.) (1960).

[31] *Petersen* v. *Dept. of Labor and Industries,* 217 P. 2d 607 (Wash.) (1950).

to form an opinion for the purpose of testifying, the statement as to symptoms is inadmissible.[32] A "case history" given to a physician for the purpose of securing his testimony at the trial is not admissible as a record made in the regular course of business.

Admissions Against Interest

An admission against interest is a statement made by one person to another against or in conflict with the interests of the person making the declaration, or inconsistent with the facts asserted by him in a judicial proceeding; it may be admissible as an exception to the hearsay rule.

Thus, when it comes to an admission against interest, there is a clearcut distinction between what a defendant says caused the accident and what was said to him by others as to the cause. In the one situation, he testifies from his personal knowledge concerning the disputed facts, while in the other he merely attests what someone said.[33]

It was held in a malpractice action against a physician that his statements at the trial that certain entries made in the record by another which he had examined and approved were binding upon him.[34]

In the case of a patient who was found lying in the street about midnight, it was held to be improper to exclude part of a hospital record disclosing that he admitted to heavy drinking of "over a pint of whisky a day."[35]

Admissibility of Diagnoses and Medical Observations

Some diagnoses are a matter of observation, some of judgment, while others may be pure conjecture. The admissibility of the diagnosis depends on its character. Regularly recorded

[32] *Parker v. State*, 55 A. 2d 784 (Md.) (1948).

[33] *Cox* v. *State of New York*, 3 N.Y. 2d 693, 171 N.Y.S. 2d 818 (1958).

[34] *State to Use and Benefit of Miles* v. *Brainin*, 167 A. 2d 117 (Md.) (1961).

[35] *Shaughnessy* v. *City of New York*, 180 N.Y.S. 2d 621 (1959).

facts as to the patient's condition or treatment on which the observations of competent physicians would not differ are admissible in the same manner as records of sales or payrolls. Findings based on a routine examination of a patient on admission showing, for example, that there was a deviation of the septum, or that there were no visible external injuries, or that he had a compound fracture of a limb, are admissible. Events or narrations which have no bearing on diagnosis are excluded.[36]

In New York State, the record, including the medical opinions noted by the physician, is admissible. An action was brought against a hospital for the premature discharge of the patient. The record was offered in evidence. Even though the physician who made certain entries was in court to testify, the records including medical opinions should have been received in evidence.[37]

An official record of a hospital kept in the regular course of its business of treating sick and injured persons and identified by the official records custodian was admitted together with the doctor's diagnosis, under the statute.[38] Admission of a record showing a diagnosis of leukemia was held proper.[39]

If any part of the record is deemed objectionable by the patient, it is the obligation of his attorney to raise the objection, otherwise the statements cannot be excluded as evidence. It was held that although evidence of previous intoxication was not competent proof of intoxication at the time of the accident, the evidence, having been properly admitted for another purpose, was before the jury.[40]

Under both the Maryland and federal so-called shop book rules, hospital records may be admitted in evidence in personal

---

[36] *Borucki* v. *MacKenzie Bros.*, 3 A. 2d 224 (Md.) (1939).

[37] *Meiselman* v. *Crown Heights Hospital*, 285 N.Y. 396, 34 N.E. 2d 367 (1941).

[38] *State Auto. and Cas. Underwriters* v. *Reagan*, 337 S.W. 2d 522 (Tex.) (1960).

[39] *Travis Life Insurance Co.* v. *Rodriguez*, 326 S.W. 2d 256 (Tex.) (1959).

[40] *Miller* v. *City of New York*, 286 App. Div. 1033, 145 N.Y.S. 2d 295 (1955).

injury cases, at least in so far as they relate to medical and pathological conditions regarding patients. Similarly, reports from doctors' offices are admissible when shown to have been in accordance with customary routine office practice relating to the patient.[41]

Georgia, on the other hand, does not admit the diagnoses or opinions under the so-called "shop book" rule. That the patient was intoxicated was not admissible.[42]

Admissibility of Psychiatric Opinions

Generally, records of psychiatric cases do not meet the test of admissibility, since not infrequently trained psychiatrists come to opposite conclusions in certain cases. The diagnosis of psychiatric conditions is not within the same class as routine observations of conditions or ailments easily identified. Although the record itself is admissible, a diagnosis of a psychoneurotic state may involve conjecture and opinion; it must be subject to cross-examination of the physician who made it.

In one case, the court held that the science of psychiatry has not yet reached the plateau of infallibility where courts must cede their powers of adjudication even when a pronouncement has been made by a psychiatrist in answering the ultimate question that his patient was incompetent.

The rule is otherwise in New York State. A diagnosis involving observations on a mental condition is admissible as a record of an act, transaction or event made in the regular course of business. In a reported case, a record was admitted, the court holding that "a physician who has examined a patient first states the objective facts of the examination and then his scientific appraisal. Without his opinion, his testimony often has little value. We see no difference in a recorded diagnosis of a physical condition and of a mental condition."[43]

[41] *Wojciechowski* v. *States Marine Corp. of Del.*, 155 F. Supp. 874 (D.C., Md.) (1958).

[42] *Meeks* v. *Lunford*, 126 S.E. 2d 531 (Ga.) (1962).

[43] *People* v. *Kohlmeyer*, 284 N.Y. 366, 31 N.E. 2d 490 (1940).

Hospital records made in the regular course of the hospital's business were competent evidence in a proceeding involving the mental capacity of the patient to change the beneficiary of a life insurance policy.[44]

That the patient was suffering from a psychiatric disorder and delirium tremens to such an extent that he was not in fit condition to drive an automobile at the time of his injuries was excluded from admissibility, because these conclusions were irrelevant to his treatment.[45]

Reports of Laboratory Tests

Results of tests made in the course of routine laboratory examinations will be admitted in evidence if a proper foundation is laid. In a prosecution for rape, a medical technician testified that she found spermatozoa on the glass slides of smears taken by a physician from the vagina of the victim soon after the alleged rape. Even though the slides were not in evidence, the testimony was admitted on a showing that the tests were routinely made by persons of superior technical training.[46]

A hospital record showing the result of a Bogen's test for intoxication was admissible as a business record under the federal shop-book rule (28 U.S.C.A. sec. 1732). "We read the statute," the court declared, "as supplying a presumption that diagnoses and scientific tests are properly made by qualified personnel, if the recorded information reflects usual routine of the hospital and if it is the practice to record such data contemporaneously or within a reasonable time. * * * There is good reason to treat a hospital record entry as trustworthy. Human life will often depend on the accuracy of the entry, and it is reasonable to presume that a hospital is staffed with personnel who competently perform their day to day tasks. To

---

[44] *Travelers Ins. Co.* v. *Childs*, 272 F. 2d 855 (C.A.N.Y.) (1960).

[45] *Peagler* v. *Atlantic Coast Line R. Co.*, 107 S.E. 2d 15 (S.C.) (1959).

[46] *State* v. *Romo*, 185 P. 2d 757 (Ariz.) (1947).

this extent at least, hospital records are deserving of a presumption of accuracy even more than other types of business entries."[47]

In a case involving a transfusion of incompatible blood, the pathologist who made tests of the patient after difficulties had developed was evasive and refused to concede the patient had died as a result of a transfusion reaction. The court said: "The fact that he repeatedly refused to admit that there was any evidence from which a conclusion could be drawn that the patient had had an incompatible blood transfusion or that her death resulted from one, shows plainly that the entries in the record did not represent merely a recapitulation of other testimony brought out at the trial, but could reasonably be interpreted as opposed to his testimony. It was therefore evidence of extreme importance to the plaintiff's theory as to the cause of death."[48]

Nurses' Notes as Evidence

A nurse may testify to an entry in the chart if she has personal knowledge of the truth of the notes.[49] A record of what transpired during the day, the temperature, pulse of patient, his condition and treatment may be accepted in evidence, together with surgical notes as dictated by the operating surgeon. When a record is made by a number of nurses, each nurse may testify as to the entries which she herself has made; each may refresh her recollection from her own notes as to her observations.[50] To prove the pain and suffering of a patient while in the hospital, the nurses themselves must be called.[51]

Notations in a nurse's handwriting were admissible where the nurse testified that she worked in the doctor's office, came

---

[47] *Thomas* v. *Hogan*, 309 F. 2d 355 (C.A.4th) (1962).

[48] *Joseph* v. *W. H. Groves Latter Day Saints Hospital*, 318 P. 2d (Utah) (1957).

[49] *Lund* v. *Olson*, 234 N.W. 310 (Minn.) (1931).

[50] *Wright* v. *Upson*, 303 Ill. 120, 135 N.E. 209 (1922).

[51] *McMahon* v. *Bangs*, 5 Penn. 179, 62 A. 1098 (Del.) (1904).

to know the individual as a patient, that the entries were made by her and were truthful and accurate when made, that she relied upon the entries, and that no changes had been made from the time the entries were made.[52]

Records of Public Hospitals

The laws of the various states require that records be kept of patients in public hospitals. Public hospital records properly identified and shown to have been kept pursuant to statutory requirements are admissible in evidence as an exception to the hearsay rule, unless they are privileged or otherwise restricted. Records of patients in voluntary and private hospitals are not public records. For a public record to be admitted in evidence, it must be shown that it was made by an official or other person pursuant to governmental duty.[53]

Records of a state hospital for the insane are acceptable in evidence, since the law requires that they be kept and be available in proper proceedings where the mental condition of the patient is involved.[54] A statutory requirement that the admitting physician of a municipal hospital report the diagnosis of every case received rendered such report admissible as a public or official document.[55] In a negligence case, the record of a county hospital as to the patient was admissible as a public record required to be kept by statute.[56] However, only those parts of the record which are pertinent to diagnosis and treatment are admissible. Portions of a public hospital record containing a declaration by the patient that he had suffered from epilepsy long prior to the accident were relevant and admitted;[57] in contrast, narrative statements by an unidentified

---

[52] *Stanton* v. *Pennsylvania R. Co.*, 178 N.E. 2d 121 (Ill.) (1961).

[53] *Roberts* v. *Permanente Corp.*, 10 Cal. Rptr. 519 (Cal.) (1961).

[54] *Motely* v. *State*, 174 Miss. 568, 165 So. 296. (1936).

[55] *Spraug* v. *Doench*, 24 Ohio L. Rep. 188.

[56] *Dallas Coffee and Tea Co.* v. *Williams*, 45 S.W. 2d 724 (Tex.) (1932).

[57] *Schaefer* v. *Lowell-Krekeler*, 49 S.W. 2d 209 (Mo.) (1933).

relative of the patient appearing in the hospital record were excluded.[58]

By statute in many states a certified copy of the record of a public hospital may be made admissible in evidence in lieu of the original.

Admission of Financial Records

Index cards of business transactions are competent evidence under The Uniform Business Records as Evidence Act if, in the court's opinion, they are authenticated and the source of information, method and time of preparation are such as to justify their admission. The Act is not limited to books of account.

An account card to establish the value of hospital services may not be admitted to show entries that do not belong there. Damages for injuries were sought by a person injured in an automobile accident. The hospital account card had the following notation in the right-hand corner: "Man promised to pay hospital bill," with the name and address of the owner of the automobile written above the notation. There was no verification as to who made the notation, nor under what circumstances. Such an entry was one not made in the regular course of business, nor was it binding on the owner of the car.[59]

In an action for personal injuries, hospital records to show the cost of medical services were properly admitted to prove the extent of the patient's damages.[60]

A hospital account, including charges for two x-rays, proved in accordance with the shop-book rule (business entries), was sufficient to show that the patient who was trying to collect under a sickness and indemnity policy had been x-rayed.[61]

---

[58] *Lamkins* v. *Copper-Clad Malleable Range Corp.*, 42 S.W. 2d 941 (Mo.) (1932).

[59] *Petterson* v. *Lake*, 26 N.E. 2d 763, 136 Ohio St. 481 (1939).

[60] *Missouri Pac. R. Co.* v. *Soileau*, 265 F. 2d 90 (C.A. La.) (1959).

[61] *Texas Reserve Life Ins. Co.* v. *Texas Rehabilitation Center*, 332 S.W. 2d 403 (Tex.) (1960).

Correspondence and Social Service Records

Social case records are as important as medical or financial records. The information may be useful for the clinical services in the care of the patient. It has been suggested that the record be divided into four major sections: the first to deal with the patient's physical condition, past and present; the second to include a statement of the social problem as seen by the patient himself, by the physician, and by the medical social worker following study; the third to record the activities of the social worker in handling the patient's problem; and the fourth the details as to the patient's home environment, his finances and similar matters relating to his social diagnosis.

The kind and amount of social information contained in the record is influenced by the medical and social problems of the patient. Some of the information comes from the attending physicians, other information may be derived from the family or friends; frequently it is necessary to secure reports through correspondence with social agencies and other organizations.

Letters received by the hospital from other agencies or sources are not regarded as an integral part of the medical record, because they are not made in the course of treatment and are not a part of the "act, transaction, occurrence or event." The reports of social workers, which may be attached to the record, would be inadmissible even though made in connection with the patient's welfare. It is conceivable that, in an exceptional case, the social service entries or reports may be related to the patient's medical care or as admissions against interest if containing prejudicial statements by the patient.

Private Medical Records of Physician

Medical records of a physician made in the course of his professional office practice are in the same category as hospital records: they must be shown to have been made contemporaneously with the visits and examinations of the patient, under circumstances which suggest no motive for falsification. However, the courts are reluctant to extend this rule to claims for professional services, because of the ever-present possibility of fraudulent self-serving entries.

When the physician himself is called as a witness, his office records, when identified and verified by him, are admissible in evidence to the extent that they are relevant, in the discretion of the trial judge.[62]

Records of certain doctors were held admissible in conjunction with their testimony, in an insurance policy case, to establish the prior illness of the insured. The company proffered evidence that the insured died of coronary occlusion and had been treated for various complaints within the five-year period previous to the issuance of the policy. The evidence, which was held acceptable, consisted of record cards made by two doctors of the visits of the insured, history and treatment, the cardiogram prepared by another doctor, and copies of prescriptions filled by the pharmacist.[63]

Medical records of a doctor, deceased at the time of trial, kept in the regular course of business, were admissible where the deceased's son identified the handwriting and signature of his father, and recognized the records as those kept by his father.[64] However, records of a deceased physician will be excluded if no custodian identifies and verifies them when some of the entries are in dispute and illegible.[65]

The patient was awarded a jury verdict of $5,500.00 for personal injuries, and special damages incurred and anticipated, caused by fragments of a "coca-cola" bottle introduced into her system while she was drinking a beverage bottled and sold by the defendant. The trial court admitted in evidence, under the

---

[62] *Ettelson* v. *Metropolitan Life Ins. Co.*, 164 F. 2d 660 (1947).

[63] *Freedman* v. *Mutual Life Ins. Co. of New York*, 21 A. 2d 81 (Pa.) (1941).

[64] *Duffy* v. *Edison*, 240 App. Div. 1002 (N.Y.) (1934).

[65] *Rupp* v. *Travelers Indem. Co.*, 115 N.W. 2d 612 (Wis.) (1962).

so-called Federal Shop Book Rule, entries in the medical records kept by a group of physicians, which concerned the patient's condition as observed by one of the physicians subsequent to the time when she drank the beverage. These entries included statements as to the presence of fragmented glass and fissures discovered during rectal examinations of the patient. The court held that: "Regularly recorded facts as to the patient's condition or treatment on which the observations of competent physicians would not differ are of the same character as records of sales or payrolls." The judgment was affirmed.[66]

The office memoranda of a psychiatrist who was sued by a patient, which records were made, according to his testimony, in the regular course of office and hospital interviews in the treatment of the patient, was admissible.[67]

Evidence of doctor's written report containing his interpretation of an electroencephalogram examination which was unauthenticated and unproven either as applied to findings upon the examination or as applied to his opinion based thereupon was inadmissible as hearsay evidence.[68]

---

[66] *Washington Coca-Cola Bottling Works, Inc.* v. *Tawney,* 6 CCH Neg. Cases 2d 218 (USCA—DC) (1956).

[67] *Benjamin* v. *Havens, Inc.,* 373 P. 2d 109 (Wash.) (1962).

[68] *Atkins* v. *Graves,* 367 S.W. 2d 372 (Tex.) (1963).

chapter 14

TRIAL PROCEDURE

THE purpose of a trial is to ascertain the truth concerning matters in evidence before the court, and to apply the law to such matters. For this purpose it is one of the functions of the court to see that a trial is conducted properly. The trial judge must strive for an atmosphere of impartiality and his conduct in trying the case must be fair to both sides. He must refrain from any act, word, sign, gesture, or inflection of the voice, the effects of which would be to emphasize a predisposition toward one side or the other. Nor may the trial judge act as counsel for a party by raising objections which the party should make; he should not assume a partisan position.

The trial court has wide discretionary powers in the trial of a case and is not prohibited from questioning witnesses, but may make no comment upon the facts or the testimony which would tend to influence the jury. Questioning of witnesses by the court may help to clear up matters for the jury, provided the court's attitude is unbiased.

Right to Trial by Jury

The right of trial by jury is a constitutional right which has been guaranteed by the Bill of Rights in the Seventh Amendment of the Constitution. It applies to those cases in which the right existed at common law or was provided by statute at the time the Constitution was adopted. It is inapplicable to certain legal remedies which have been included by statute after the adoption of the Constitution.

The constitutional right of trial by jury in civil cases may be waived, expressly or impliedly, by failing to follow the method prescribed by statute for indicating that the parties desire it, or by appearance and participation in the case without demanding a jury.

Both parties may agree to waive trial by jury, in which event the judge acts as the jury and becomes the trier of both the facts and the issues of law.

In criminal cases there is a guaranty of trial by jury in both federal and state constitutions. Some states permit trial by jury to be waived in all cases; in others, only in cases of misdemeanor; and not at all in still others.

Qualifications of Jurors

The persons eligible for jury duty are selected from a jury list; they are summoned to court by a paper called a jury process. The qualifications of a juror are a matter of legislative control; the legislature may restrict, abridge, deny or enlarge the right and duty of jury service.

Fairness and impartiality are prerequisite qualifications in all jurors. The "impartial jury" guaranteed by the Constitution is one of an impartial frame of mind at the beginning of the trial, which will be influenced only by legal and competent evidence.

Questions of Fact Are for Jury

It is the exclusive province of the jury to determine from the evidence the existence or non-existence of a thing, condition, or circumstance, i.e., a fact. The jury may draw inferences from the evidence, provided such inferences are not unreasonable. The jury has no right to decide questions of law; such function belongs to the court.

The weight and value to be given to the evidence likewise is for the jury. It would be error for the court to tell the jury what facts have been proved, what inferences may be drawn, or to inform the jury as to what weight to give to any of the evidence.

Where there is an irreconcilable conflict in the evidence as to the method of treatment used by a physician, the evidence creates a fact question for the jury.

Whether the defendant in a negligence or malpractice case used due care is a question of fact; what legally constitutes the exercise of due care is a question of law. The law does not undertake to define with precision what a person should do under all possible circumstances that may arise, but contents itself with flexible and sufficiently indefinite rules to apply to all cases. The question of negligence consequently is said to be a mixed question of law and fact.

Credibility of Witnesses Is for the Jury

Where the testimony of the witnesses is contradictory, it is for the jury to determine whom to believe. The jury may believe or disbelieve the testimony of any one or all of the witnesses, but it may not wholly disregard testimony which is unsuspicious and uncontradicted.

The credibility of a witness may be impeached by showing that he is of generally bad reputation as to truth; by questioning him as to any immoral or criminal acts affecting his character; by indicating that he made prior inconsistent statements; by demonstrating his bias in favor of the party calling him, or his prejudice against the adverse party; or showing that he was under the influence of drugs or liquor at the time of the occurrence to which he has testified.

In judging the credibility of witnesses, and the value to be given to their testimony, the jury may consider their interest in the result of the case, their motives, the manner in which they testify, and the contradictions noted in their testimony.

Questions of Law Are for the Court

Questions of law are for the trial judge. Whether there is sufficient evidence to warrant that the case go to the jury is for him to decide. If insufficient evidence is adduced, in the opinion of the court, to satisfy the jury that the facts to be proved are established, the court may dismiss the case before it goes to the jury. Where the evidence offered by one party so far outweighs the evidence offered by the other, the court may direct the jury to bring in a verdict for the first party. The court has the power and duty to set aside a verdict brought in by the jury if it is against the weight of the evidence, and order a new trial.

Some Questions of Fact Are for Determination of Court

There are some questions of fact, however, which are for the determination of the court, as those which refer to the admissibility of evidence, to the competency of witnesses to testify, and to matters of which the court will take judicial notice.

Amount of Verdict Is Fixed by Jury

In a jury trial, the amount of the damages and the verdict is fixed by the jury. In estimating personal injury damages, the jury may consider among other things loss of profits or earnings; expenses incurred, to include the cost of medicine and medical attendance; mental and physical suffering caused by the injuries; future damages for loss of health, time, and permanent physical disability or impairment. These are compensatory damages.

In an action for a personal injury, the jury may assess what are called exemplary, punitive, or vindictive damages upon a defendant, not as compensation to the plaintiff, but as a deterrent to others inclined to commit a similar offense.

Findings of Fact by Court

If the case is tried without a jury, where there has been a waiver of trial by jury, the judge becomes the trier of both the law and of the facts. The court can be required, unless the right is waived, to render written findings of fact on all the material issues raised in the case. These findings state the court's conclusions of fact which form the basis of the judgment rendered. The party adversely affected then can decide whether to take an appeal, based on specific findings to which exception has been taken.

Selection of the Jury

A few classes of persons are excused by law from sitting as jurors; usually among those so exempted are doctors, druggists, lawyers, and government employees. The classes of persons who are excused are named in the statute; others may be relieved from serving, in the discretion of the court.

After the clerk of the court calls the names of twelve prospective jurors, counsel for the parties may question each member of the jury to ascertain his qualifications. Each side has the right to interrogate the prospective jurors to mak certain that they are impartial; that they do not know the parties to the case and are not connected with or interested in any way in the witnesses or parties. A juror who is considered prejudiced or interested may be "challenged for cause" by either party and may be excused by the judge from sitting in the case. When both sides are satisfied with the impartiality of all the jurors the court is so informed, and the case is ready to proceed to trial. The jurors are sworn in by the clerk.

Opening Address to the Jury

Following the swearing in and the seating of the jury in the jury box, counsel for the plaintiff makes his opening address to the jury, stating briefly what he claims to be the facts in the case that he intends to prove. The attorney for the defendant follows with an outline of his defense. Arguments and detailed statements of the facts are not allowed in the opening of the case.

Preliminary Motions

Before putting any witnesses on the stand to testify, either side may make motions dealing with the case. The plaintiff's attorney may move for a judgment based on the pleadings in the case or to dismiss the counterclaim, if any, of the defendant. The defendant may ask for a dismissal of the complaint on the ground that it does not state a cause of action, or that the court has no jurisdiction of the subject matter of the suit. If the court denies these motions the case proceeds to trial.

Direct Examination of Witnesses

The initial examination of a witness by the party calling him is the direct examination. It must cover all the facts which are expected to be proved by that witness. Leading questions which suggest the desired answer are not permitted, except in the case of a hostile witness. Every witness whose direct examination is taken is subject to cross-examination.

In order to aid the witness to make his testimony clear or to contradict him, diagrams, models, photographs, and records may be used. A writing made by the witness or by any person at or about the time of the event may be offered to him to refresh his recollection of a past event.

The witness is not permitted to read a prepared statement to the jury; he may be allowed to give his testimony in narrative form. The question and answer method of oral testimony is followed for at least the major part of the testimony.

Questions to the witness must be so phrased as not to be objectionable under the rules of evidence. Defendant's counsel may object to any questions he considers improper, stating the grounds for the objections. If the objection is overruled by the court, the witness is permitted to answer. If it is sustained, the witness may not answer.

The party whose objections are overruled may "take an exception," i.e., indicate that he may use the court's ruling as a ground for appeal.

Cross-Examination of Plaintiff's Witness

At the end of the direct examination of the witness for the plaintiff, counsel for the defendant may cross-examine him in an effort to weaken or break down the testimony of the witness or to discredit his veracity. The cross-examination may deal only with the matters brought out on direct examination. After the cross-examination, the plaintiff's counsel may conduct "re-direct examination" as to any new matters brought out on cross-examination. This procedure is followed with each witness; the defendant's witnesses are first called by his own counsel who begins with direct examination of his own witnesses.

Motion to Dismiss at End of Plaintiff's Case

After the plaintiff has completed the presentation of his evidence, the counsel for the defendant may move for nonsuit or dismissal of the case, specifying why the plaintiff has failed to make out a case. In ruling upon the motion, the evidence must be viewed in the light most favorable to the plaintiff; it is also assumed that all the evidence in favor of the plaintiff is true.

If the motion to dismiss is granted, it is the court's determination that there is not sufficient evidence to support a verdict in favor of the plaintiff. To fail to make such motion is to concede that the plaintiff has proved a prima facie case. Granting the motion means the end of the case. If the motion is denied, counsel for the defendant must take an exception and proceed with his defense and counterclaim, if any.

Testimony of Defendant's Witnesses

Following the testimony of the defendant's witnesses and their cross-examination, the defendant's counsel announces that he "rests." At this time the plaintiff's counsel may produce any additional evidence to rebut or to contradict new matters brought out by the defendant; the defendant may then offer evidence in "surrebuttal" to contradict or rebut the plaintiff's evidence.

Use of Exhibits in Evidence

During the trial, either side may produce and have marked in evidence any records, documents, papers, objects, or other exhibits, which serve to prove or disprove any of the claims, provided the evidence is relevant and a proper foundation for the exhibit is laid.

Motion at Close of Entire Case

At the close of the entire case, the defendant may again move for a dismissal, and if the motion is denied, he may take an exception. If the defendant has introduced evidence of a counterclaim, plaintiff's counsel may make a motion to dismiss the counterclaim. If the motion is granted to dismiss the plaintiff's case, that terminates the action. By granting the motion to dismiss the counterclaim, only the counterclaim is terminated. Either side may make a motion for a "directed verdict" where there appears to be only a question of law to be decided by the court. The motion will be granted if the court believes there is no question of fact to be decided by the jury.

"Summing Up" to the Jury

If the motion to dismiss is denied, both counsel will "sum up" to the jury, each attorney in turn summarizing the facts as indicated by the evidence, pointing out relationships, inconsistencies, improbabilities and impossibilities. The demeanor of the witnesses and their credibility or interest or bias may be discussed by the attorneys. Each attorney gives the reasons which he believes entitle his client to a verdict.

Considerable latitude is permitted counsel in summation to the jury. Counsel may comment on the testimony of the witnesses and may argue such conclusions as he pleases, if he does not misquote the witnesses; he may state and suggest what he believes that the evidence shows. The witnesses who are required to appear at the trial are entitled to protection from unjustified derogation of their character; counsel in summing up may assail their credibility when it has been impeached by direct evidence or inconsistency in their testimony.

Instructions to the Jury

After both attorneys have summed up to the jury, the court charges the jury, giving it instructions based on the evidence as to what are the issues in the case and the law which is applicable to the facts.

After the court has given its instructions to the jury, counsel for either side may request the court to give specific charges or instructions to the jury in addition to those given. The trial court may refuse the proposed instructions or charges if they have been adequately covered already, or if they contain an incorrect statement of law or law which is not applicable to the facts. An exception may be taken to the court's charge or refusal to charge as requested, for the purpose of an appeal.

Where there are no material issues of fact, the trial judge may direct the jury to bring in a verdict for the party entitled thereto, upon the evidence submitted. The motion for a directed verdict is denied where there is competent evidence to support the opposing party's case. If there is more than one inference which can reasonably be drawn from the evidence, it is the duty of the trial judge to submit the case to the jury.

The Verdict of the Jury

The jury leaves the courtroom to deliberate, and returns when it is ready to announce the verdict or its inability to reach an agreement. The verdict makes no legal precedent, and settles nothing but the immediate controversy to which it relates.

In an action for money damages, the verdict for the plaintiff carries with it a specified amount of money which the defendant must pay. If the verdict is for the defendant, the plaintiff gets nothing and has to pay to the defendant the costs of the litigation as fixed by statute. The statutory costs are considerably less, as a rule, than the actual expenses.

A mistrial is declared by the court if the jury fails to agree on a verdict, or some misconduct on the part of one of the attorneys or the jurors is called to the attention of the court, which the judge deems to have affected the jury's verdict.

The attorney for the defeated side, after the verdict is announced by the jury foreman, may move to set it aside as contrary to law or against the weight of the evidence, or that the damages are excessive. He may take an exception at this time for the purpose of an appeal if the verdict is not set aside. At the request of either counsel, the clerk of the court may be asked to poll the jury by asking each one if the verdict represents his decision.

If the jury has failed or neglected to follow the directions of the judge upon matters of law, it is said to be a "verdict contrary to law." The court may set the verdict aside, discharge the jury, and either order a new trial or dismiss the case.

chapter 15

THE PATIENT'S PRIVACY

I N THE hospital, the patient must make adjustments to the numerous persons who are required to intrude upon his privacy. All that is done for him and his reactions become a matter of record, open to those concerned with his care.

The presence of the patient in the hospital may become a matter of public interest, as when he is a prominent figure or has been the victim of an unusual occurrence. The hospital authorities may then be beset with inquiries concerning his condition. The right of the patient to remain in the hospital without subjecting him to undesired publicity is supported by legal decisions, but the courts may limit this right where the public interests are involved.

Right of Privacy

The right of privacy is the right to be let alone; to be free from unwarranted publicity; to live without having one's name, picture or private affairs made public or published against one's will. "The modern doctrine of the right of privacy is a development of the common law to fill a need for the protection of the interest which a person has in living without unwarranted publicity."[1]

A man has the right, in the states where this doctrine of privacy is accepted, to pass through this world if he so wills, without having his picture published, his business enterprises

---

[1] *Bremmer* v. *Journal-Tribune Publishing Co.*, 76 N.W. 2d 762 (Iowa) (1956).

discussed, his successful experiments written up for the benefit of others or his eccentricities commented upon, either in hand-bills, circulars, catalogues, periodicals, newspapers or other media of communication.[2]

States in Which the Right Exists

Where the right of privacy is recognized, it exists either by statute or common law. Actions have been permitted in Arizona, California, the District of Columbia, Florida, Georgia, Indiana, Iowa, Kansas, Kentucky, Louisiana, Massachusetts, Michigan, Missouri, New Jersey, New York, North Carolina, Ohio, Oregon, Pennsylvania, South Carolina, Utah and Virginia, for an unwarranted exploitation of one's personality, the publicizing of one's private affairs or activities in such a manner as to cause mental suffering, shame or humiliation to one of ordinary sensibilities.

Rhode Island and Washington do not recognize the right of privacy. Wisconsin denies the right and holds that such a right would be created better by the legislature than the judiciary.[3]

Public Personages in Hospitals

Prominent persons who become patients may be of news interest. The hospital should not release information of a personal nature to the press nor permit photographs of such patients without the written consent of both patient and attending physician. A hospital official familiar with press relations may be the best individual to handle such situations.

Many hospitals to which public personages are admitted frequently have found it useful to make specific plans at the time of the patient's admission for releasing news bulletins at regular intervals to the press, either from the hospital or from a representative of the patient outside the hospital.

[2] *Roberson* v. *Rochester Folding Box Co.*, 171 N.Y. 538, 59 L.R.A. 478 (1902).

[3] *Yoeckel* v. *Samonig*, 75 N.W. 2d 925 (Wis.) (1956).

Death Ends Right of Privacy

It has been held that there is no right of privacy in respect of a dead man. The executor of the estate, in one case, entered into a contract with a motion picture company which planned the production of a film based on the life of the decedent, who had been a successful writer of lyrics. The objection of a brother of the decedent to the production of the film was overruled by the court, as death had terminated the right.[4] The right is essentially personal and does not survive after death, in the absence of a contract.[5]

The right of privacy is not to be confused, however, with the duty of a physician or nurse to refrain from disclosing confidential information obtained in the course of treating a patient. Death does not terminate the privileged status of confidential communications.

Newspaper Publicity of Patients

If the hospital has no definite plan of operation for handling press relations, the arrival of a newsworthy person at the hospital can give rise to confusion, ill will, and blundering on the part of the hospital staff with patient or press. On the other hand, a written procedure can prevent many an embarrassing or tense situation.

The entire public relations effort in connection with a newsworthy patient at the hospital should be geared with the following objectives in mind to promote: (1) the well-being of the patient, (2) the protection of the privacy of the patient, and (3) the assistance of the press in covering the news.

Hospital personnel generally have followed the traditional view that sickness is a personal matter. Newspaper people, however, have been taught that what happens to people is news, especially if it is out of the ordinary. The needs of news-

---

[4] *In re Hart's Estate*, 83 N.Y.S. 2d 635 (1948).

[5] *Lunceford* v. *Wilcox*, 80 Misc. 194, 88 N.Y.S. 2d 225 (1949).

papers for information about the admission and condition of police cases must be recognized. Police cases involve accidents which are reported to the police department or cases involving suspicion of the commission of a crime.

Hospitals should designate spokesmen competent to give authentic information to the press at any time, equally to all newspapers, and who will also aid in obtaining interviews and consent for pictures, provided that the welfare, privacy or legal rights of the patient are preserved. In cases of accident or other emergency, the spokesman should identify the patient, give the general nature of the injuries when ascertained and the degree of seriousness. The hospital should refrain from giving information on hospital procedures, equipment, facilities for treatment or other features of hospital services, by implying that such facilities or features exist only in the hospital named, unless it is the ascertained fact. For the publication of stories on medical research, unusual operations or new procedures, only authentic information from hospital authorities should be released.

Detailed questions about the condition of any patient should be answered only by the attending physician and in any event this information may be released only with the consent of the patient or a responsible family member. General questions, such as verification that a patient has been admitted to the hospital and an evaluation of his condition as "critical," "satisfactory," "not serious," may be answered by the administrator or his representative, who may also add information, with the consent of the patient or a member of the family, about the nature of the illness or injuries.

In keeping press relations satisfactory, it is important for the hospital or hospitals to have an understanding with the newspaper or newspapers in the community about the kinds of information that can be released under various circumstances, and it is important for some one named person to be

available at all times to release the kind of information that
has been agreed upon.

The most common complaint newspapers have about hospitals is that their inquiries, particularly at times when the administrator's office is not covered, get transferred from one
person to another, and nobody is authorized to release any information at all. With a little planning, it is not difficult to
provide the information newspapers want without violating
any patient's right to privacy.

Press, Radio and Television Relations

In recent years, many hospitals, hospital associations, newspapers and other media of communication have developed hospital press codes. These codes grew out of a need for setting
forth in writing, over the signatures of hospitals and the press,
the responsibilities, obligations and limitations of each in dis-
seminating news of the hospital and its patients.

In the adoption of such codes, agreement may be reached as
to what information should be made available by the hospitals;
the hospitals may be contacted 24 hours daily; some one person
is to be available from whom reporters may seek information.
The code provides a rules book to guide both the hospital official and reporter on press-hospital contacts.

The main points to be covered are:

1) Sources and persons officially authorized to give information that may be released to news agencies on police cases.

2) A listing of the type and amount of information that may
be released to news agencies on police cases.

3) A listing of the type and amount of information that may
be released to the press in other than police cases.

4) Procedure to be followed in taking photographs of patients.

5) Listing of information to be withheld from the press.

One essential step in formulating a guide is to examine

whatever state laws exist for governing the release of patient information. State laws will give a good indication of the sentiment in each state regarding medical information, and it would be wise to adapt a press code accordingly.[6]

Patient's Privacy in Medical Teaching

The teaching hospital has been called the conscience of the medical profession; it provides a place in which questions may be asked by anyone concerned with patient care and answered if possible. The patient on the ward of a teaching hospital may be visited, questioned and examined by interns, residents, attending physician on teaching rounds, and medical students.

The making of physical examinations without diagnosing, treating or prescribing, the taking of medical histories, the viewing of operations and deliveries by medical students are phases in their clinical education. Ward patients who come to teaching hospitals are presumed to know that their cases may be of teaching value; their consent to be used for educational purposes is implied.

A patient ordinarily would have no cause of action against a physician, nurse, hospital or medical student for an invasion of the right of privacy during demonstrations and conferences. However, as a matter of good public relations, consent, oral or written, should be obtained from the patient for demonstrations, conferences and the witnessing of operations.

Private Patients for Clinical Instruction

Two problems in medical education today are the extent to which private patients may be utilized in the education of nurses, medical students, interns and residents, and the best methods of developing teaching programs centered entirely or largely around private patients. A related problem of importance to hospitals with few or no service beds is how such hos-

---

[6] "A Press Code Helps Strike a Public Relations Balance," Bender, W., *Hosp.*, 35: 40-41, Jan. 1, 1961.

pitals can develop teaching programs enabling them to compete successfully for competent interns and residents with hospitals maintaining large public wards.

With the decline in the number of ward patients and the increase in semi-private and private patients, due largely to hospitalization insurance, some hospitals make it a condition of admission, except in emergency cases, that the semi-private or private patient agree to permit his case to be used for teaching purposes. It has been the experience of those interested in clinical instruction that a private patient will rarely object to the presence of a small number of medical students if approached for consent by the attending physician.

The usual teaching exercises, such as bedside rounds, detailed case presentations, checking of physical findings and amphitheater demonstrations have been successfully carried out with private patients. These courtesies should be carried out by: (1) Always asking both the patient's and the attending physician's permission; (2) Always telling the patient what to expect; (3) Never discussing details of diagnosis, therapy or prognosis before the patient unless properly authorized. These rules are as applicable on a ward as on a private pavilion.

Intrusion on Patients by Laymen

Patients in hospitals are subjected to handling by both medical and paramedical personnel. The patient may be partly exposed for the taking of an x-ray by a technician or may be bathed by a practical nurse. Other lay persons may participate in his care, for not all services require the attention of professional personnel.

An implied element of every contract wherein one person is placed in the control or protection of another is that he will receive decent and respectful treatment. The surgeon does not have jurisdiction, as a rule, as to who shall be permitted to attend the operation. He himself practices in the operating room as a privilege granted to him by the hospital's board of trustees. He may be assisted by other physicians and by nurses; it is not expected that laymen will be permitted to be present at an operation.

Only two cases have been reported in the legal literature of actions based on the unauthorized presence of laymen during surgical procedures. In one case, a young man accompanied the physician to a confinement case. Believing him to be a medical assistant, the patient and her husband permitted his presence; the physician had taken him along to help carry the equipment. An action based on deceit was brought against the physician and layman. The court charged the jury that the husband and patient had a right to assume that a physician would not on such an occasion bring into the house a young man in no way connected with the medical profession by education or otherwise; that his presence could be justified only if the husband and wife consented with a full understanding of the facts. The jury held both defendants liable for damages for the invasion of the right of privacy.[7]

The second case involved a layman who was introduced to the patient as "Dr. Smith" by her own physician. "Dr. Smith," a salesman for a surgical supply house, treated the patient for a small uterine growth. Actually, he did this to demonstrate to the physician the operation of a new cauterizing apparatus. Suit was brought against the physician for negligence in permitting an untrained layman to treat her. No recovery was allowed because the patient failed to show any injury from the treatment. Damages for mental anguish were denied by the court, since in the District of Columbia, as in certain of the states, mental suffering must be accompanied by a physical injury.[8]

Visitors to the Patient in Hospital

The patient has the right to be protected against intrusion

[7] *DeMay* v. *Roberts*, 46 Mich. 146, 9 N.W. 146 (1881).

[8] *Carr* v. *Shifflette*, 82 F. 2d 874 (USCA-DC) (1936).

upon his privacy in the hospital by laymen who have no connection with his treatment, such as insurance company investigators, salesmen and other persons whom he has not authorized to visit him.

It is the practice of some insurance company investigators to visit patients in hospitals to obtain statements from them as to the cause of accidents or the injuries sustained. It may be unlawful, as in New York State, for such persons to enter a hospital for the purpose of negotiating a settlement or obtaining a general release or a statement, oral or written, within a specified number of days after the accident. However, the patient may request, in writing, that the investigator see him at any time.[9]

The right of privacy may be waived by express or implied consent or it may be limited by the patient. A patient recovering from injuries allegedly caused by drinking a bottled beverage informed the insurance company investigator that he could investigate the truth of her claim. He installed a listening device in her room; from a room above, he listened to conversations between the patient, her husband, her friends and the nurses. Her right to privacy was held invaded; she had given consent for a limited purpose only. This eavesdropping was an extreme interference with her private life; the company had to compensate her in damages.[10]

Rules for Visits by Attorneys

The United States Public Health Service Hospital at Staten Island, New York, has adopted rules and procedures to govern visits to patients in the hospital and conferences between hospital patients and their attorneys. These regulations should be of interest to hospitals, and provide that a person shall be permitted to enter the hospital for the purpose of conferring with a patient as an attorney or as the representative of an attorney

---

[9] Sec. 270-c and 270-d Penal Law (N.Y.).

[10] *McDaniel* v. *Atlantic Coca-Cola Bottling Co.*, 60 Ga. App. 92, 2 S.E. 2d 810 (1939).

or of visiting or otherwise conferring with a patient only in accordance with the following rules:

Patients may be visited by their attorneys or representatives of their attorneys only in accordance with scheduled appointments, between the hours of 8 a.m. and 4:30 p.m. during any day of the week other than Saturday, Sunday and holidays. The officer of the day may, in cases of undue hardship or emergency, authorize visits or appointments at other times.

After a medical officer has indicated on Form GS-1, his approval of the medical propriety of the requested conference,

U. S. PUBLIC HEALTH SERVICE HOSPITAL
STATEN ISLAND, NEW YORK

Request No.________ Date________

PATIENT'S REQUEST TO BE VISITED BY AN ATTORNEY

I,________a patient at this hospital on the____floor, Ward____

Bed No.____hereby request permission for my attorney Mr.________

a member of the law firm of________

Address________to visit me at about____a.m., p.m.,

on or about (date)________for approximately 15 30 45 60 minutes (please place check after time needed).

Signature of Staff Witness________ Signature of Patient________

Patient may go to conference room.
Medical Officer's Approval.

FIG. 35 — PATIENT'S REQUEST TO BE VISITED BY AN ATTORNEY

the completed GS-1 (Fig. 35, above) shall be forwarded to the general services section of the hospital, which shall issue Form GS-2 (Fig. 36, p. 205), "Authorization for Visits by an Attorney," on which the general services section shall designate the time and place of the requested conference.

All persons wishing to visit or otherwise confer with a patient in the hospital shall enter the hospital only at the main entrance. No such person shall be permitted to be in any area of the hospital building other than the lobby at the main entrance of the hospital, without a visitor's pass, an escort or a duly scheduled appointment in the attorney's conference room, as hereinafter provided.

Each attorney or representative of an attorney who presents himself for an appointment with a patient shall sign the attorneys' register maintained by the information clerk at the information desk in the hospital lobby, setting forth therein, in legible form, the following information: (1) the name of the patient by whom his visit was requested, (2) his own name and address, and if any, the firm he represents or of which he

---

U. S. PUBLIC HEALTH SERVICE HOSPITAL
STATEN ISLAND, NEW YORK

Authorization No._____   Date_____

AUTHORIZATION FOR VISIT BY AN ATTORNEY

As requested on Form GS-I, "Patient's request to be visited by an attorney," date_____

Mr._____from the firm of_____.

Address_____

has permission to visit (name of patient)_____Ward_____at_____a.m., p.m., on_____

(1) in the designated conference room on the first floor of the main hospital building or, (2) in patient's room, No._____

Chief, General Services Section

NOTE: Attorneys or attorneys' representatives must present this slip to the information clerk who will make arrangements to: (1) have the patient report to a conference room or (2) have an escort take the attorney or attorney's representative to the patient's room.

FIG. 36 — AUTHORIZATION FOR VISIT BY AN ATTORNEY

is a member, and, if he is not an attorney-at-law, his own name and address and address of the attorney and/or firm of attorneys by whom he is employed. An attorney's representative shall file with the information clerk of the hospital, for filing in connection with the attorneys' register, the original copy of his authorization to represent the designated attorney-at-law in the matter which is the subject of his visit. An authorization so filed shall remain effective for the duration of the patient's hospitalization, with respect to subsequent visits between the same patient and attorney's representative. The information clerk, after verifying that the registration and personal identification hereinafter described are in order, shall record the time of the registration and the ward number of the patient, and instruct the visitor to wait in a designated conference area of the hospital, pending arrival of the patient or an escort to take the attorney or attorney's representative to the patient's room.

A patient desiring a conference with an attorney or representative of an attorney shall complete and sign Form GS-1, "Patient's Request To Be Visited by an Attorney." If the patient is unable to sign such a request, the form (Form GS-1) may be completed by someone acting on his behalf. If Form GS-1 is completed by someone acting on the patient's behalf, the person so acting shall sign the patient's name on the patient's signature line and his own name and address below the patient's signature line in the presence of a duly authorized member of the hospital staff, who shall verify on Form GS-1, that the form was so executed at the patient's request.

The general services section of the hospital will schedule, on the basis of the properly completed Forms GS-1 submitted to it, appointments between patients and attorneys (or attorney's representatives, as the case may be) for one-half hour periods or longer, as needed and consistent with the patient's health. After recording such appointments on Form GS-2, "Authorization for Visit by an Attorney," the general services section shall issue copies of the complete form to the patient, to the designated attorney and to the information clerk of the hospital.

Any person entering the hospital for the purpose of conferring with a patient as an attorney or representative of an attorney shall furnish to the information clerk at the information desk in the hospital, (a) his "Authorization for Visit by an Attorney," signed by the chief of the general services section or his representative (Form GS-2), and (*b*) personal identification which establishes that he is the attorney named in the "Authorization for Visit by an Attorney" (Form GS-2), or if he is a representative of such attorney, evidence of his personal identification and of his authority to represent the attorney or law firm designated on such "Authorization for Visit by an Attorney."

All meetings within the hospital between a patient and his attorney or the representative of his attorney shall be arranged to promote maximum privacy. Such meetings shall be held in a designated conference room on the first floor at the hospital, except that if the patient's health so requires, such meetings may be held in the patient's room. In the latter case, the attorney or representative of an attorney shall be escorted to the office of the charge nurse for the patient's ward by a staff member of the general services section of the hospital.

After reporting to the charge nurse, such escort of the general services section shall accompany the attorney or attorney's representative to the patient's room. No patient's attorney or representative of such attorney shall be admitted to the patient's room without such an escort. Any attorney or representative of an attorney admitted to a patient's room is authorized and shall be permitted to visit only the patient designated on his "Authorization for Visit by an Attorney" (Form GS-2) and all such visits shall be subject to such supervision as may be deemed necessary to assure compliance with this section.

Upon completion of his meeting with the patient in the hospital, an attorney or representative of an attorney shall notify the information clerk. If such meeting occurred in the patient's room, he shall also first notify the charge nurse that the conference has been completed. The charge nurse shall notify the general services section, who will arrange for an escort to take the attorney or representative of an attorney to the information clerk. The information clerk shall record on the attorneys' register the time of each departure.

No patient in the hospital shall be permitted to have visitors during such time as the physician assigned to his case determines that such restriction is necessary for the proper treatment and care of the patient. No attorney or representative of an attorney shall be permitted to visit or confer with a patient as his attorney or representative of his attorney prior to the day following date of the patient's admission to the hospital.

Rules on Seeking Legal Business

No person in the employ of or in any capacity attached to or for any reason visiting the hospital should communicate, directly or indirectly, with any attorney or person acting on behalf of an attorney, for the purpose of aiding, assisting or abetting such attorney in the solicitation of legal business or the procurement through solicitation of a retainer, written or oral, or of any agreement authorizing the attorney to perform or render legal services.

No person who solicits or attempts to solicit, or employs any person for the purpose of soliciting or aiding, assisting or abetting in the solicitation, within the hospital, of legal business or the procurement through such solicitation, either directly or indirectly, of a retainer, written or oral, or of any agreement authorizing the attorney to perform or render legal services, should be permitted to visit the hospital without the written approval of the administrator of the hospital.

Any person who, in the opinion of the medical officer-in-charge of the hospital, has abused or abuses any of the privileges granted in connection with visits to patients in the hospital may, in the discretion of the administrator, be permanently barred from visiting patients in the hospital.

chapter 16

PHOTOGRAPHS OF PATIENTS

THE patient's right of privacy also extends to the publication of his photograph, whether for publicity or commercial purposes. Permission to photograph a patient who is of news interest, while he is in the hospital, should be given only if, in the opinion of the attending physician, the patient's condition will not be jeopardized and if the patient or his parent or guardian, in the case of a minor, consents.

The courts have ruled that damages may be recovered for the use of a photograph without authorization if the photograph is published for advertising purposes or if it is used with an article of fiction in a newspaper. No recovery will be allowed if the photograph is used without consent in connection with an article of current news of immediate public interest or for non-commercial purposes.

Pictures of Public Figures

A person who by his accomplishments, fame or mode of living, or by adopting a profession or calling which gives the public a legitimate interest in his affairs and character, becomes a public personage and to an extent relinquishes his right to privacy. There may be a limited scrutiny of the private life of such a public figure, so as to justify the use of his photograph without his consent.

While a patient who is a public figure or is presently newsworthy may be the proper subject of news or informative presentation, the privilege does not extend to commercialization of his personality through a form of treatment distinct from the dissemination of news or information. It is not so much the publication of the picture which violates the right of privacy as its improper use.

Photographs of News Interest

The fact that the patient is of news interest does not always justify the use of the photograph without the patient's consent. It was held that an action for an invasion of the right of privacy could be maintained for the unauthorized publication of the plaintiff's pelvic region which showed that a pair of hemostats was left therein.

If the publication of the photograph is not of immediate news interest, but is to be used in an article about the patient, it is necessary that his consent be obtained.

A news magazine published a close-up of a patient in a hospital bed, with the heading "Insatiable Eater—She Eats for Ten." The accompanying article, which described the patient's enormous capacity for food, appeared as a feature in a column devoted to medical news. The patient sued the magazine for the unauthorized publication; a jury rendered a verdict in her favor. It was not necessary, declared the court, to give the patient's name nor to show her photograph in order to give information to the public as to the symptoms, causes and nature of this unusual ailment. The right of privacy includes the right to obtain treatment at a hospital without publicity.[1]

What was once of immediate news interest does not entitle one to use a photograph at a later date for an article on a subject of general interest. The right to use the picture on the future occasion in some cases may be lost with the lapse of time; authorization should be secured for the subsequent use.

---

[1] *Barber* v. *Time, Inc.*, 159 S.W. 2d 291, 348 Mo. 1199 (1942).

Legal Consent to Photograph

The question may arise as to what types of photographs may be taken at will and those which require consent of the patient. Large hospitals with organized photography departments train their photographers to obtain legal permission (Fig. 37, below and Fig. 38, item 4, p. 212). In small hospitals and clinics, physicians who are amateur photographers, intent upon an interesting "shot," may fail to secure consent.

Photography should be permitted only under the following conditions:

CONSENT TO PHOTOGRAPH

The undersigned do hereby authorize_____Hospital, and the

attending physician, to photograph or permit other persons to photograph_____
                                                                    NAME OF PATIENT
while under the care of the above institution, and agree that they may use or permit other persons to use the

negatives or prints prepared therefrom for such purposes and in such manner as may be deemed necessary.

Signed_____

Signed_____

Date_____ Hour_____.M.   Witness_____

FORM C-415   PHYSICIANS' RECORD CO., BERWYN, ILLINOIS - PRINTED IN U.S.A.   CONSENT TO PHOTOGRAPH
                    (APPROVED BY CALIFORNIA HOSPITAL ASSOCIATION FORM CHA-10)

FIG. 37 — CONSENT TO PHOTOGRAPH

1. Consent to photograph should be obtained whenever a patient's face is exposed. No consent is needed if the body alone is to be photographed.

2. A copy of the photograph should be included in the patient's record, preferably in an envelope bound into the record.

3. The identity of the patient should not be divulged outside of the hospital.

4. The patient's consent should be obtained for the publica-

tion of the picture in scientific articles, provided his name is not used.

5. The face should be rendered unrecognizable by retouching, giving the patient dark glasses or otherwise concealing his identity.

6. If pictures are made of lesions so located that glasses cannot be worn, the picture should be limited to only a portion of the face.

7. A photograph involving unclothing the patient should

AUTHORIZATION FOR SURGEON TO OPERATE

Date __________ 19____ Time ________ a.m. / p.m.

1. I, the undersigned, a patient in ____________________ Hospital, hereby authorize Dr. ____________________ (and whomever he may designate as his assistants) to administer such treatment as is necessary, and to perform the following operation ____________________ (NAME OF OPERATION AND/OR PROCEDURES) ____________________ and such additional operations or procedures as are considered therapeutically necessary on the basis of findings during the course of said operation. I also consent to the administration of such anesthetics as are necessary, with the exception of ____________________ (NONE, SPINAL ANESTHESIA, OR OTHER)
2. Any tissues or parts surgically removed may be disposed of by the hospital in accordance with accustomed practice.
3. I am aware that sterility may result from this operation although such a result has not been guaranteed. I also know that a sterile person is incapable of parenthood.
4. I also consent to the taking and publication of any photographs in the course of this operation for the purpose of advancing medical education providing my identity is disguised.

I hereby certify that I have read and fully understand the above Authorization for Surgeon to Operate, the reasons why the above-named surgery is considered necessary, its advantages and possible complications, if any, as well as possible alternative modes of treatment, which were explained to me by Dr. ____________________. I also certify that no guarantee or assurance has been made as to the results that may be obtained.

Witness ____________________ Signed ____________________ (PATIENT OR NEAREST RELATIVE)

Witness ____________________ ____________________ (RELATIONSHIP)

Authorization must be signed by the patient, or by the nearest relative in the case of a minor or when patient is physically or mentally incompetent.

FORM C-408 PHYSICIANS' RECORD CO., BERWYN, ILLINOIS PRINTED IN U.S.A.

FIG. 38 — AUTHORIZATION FOR SURGEON TO OPERATE

have the specific consent of the patient in writing and be witnessed.

8. If the subject is an unclothed female, it should be an inviolable rule that a female nurse be present. However, a female nurse need not be present if the patient does not have to undress or if the photographer is a woman.

Clinical Photography

The value of photography as a teaching aid has been recognized for many years, for the photograph may eliminate lengthy description.

Medical photographs may be used under six major classifications: (1) the case history, (2) teaching, (3) research, (4) publications, (5) medical papers and exhibits and (6) lay education. An adequate collection of slides or photographs will permit the study of rare conditions. A series of photographs or slides will help to determine whether therapy is yielding successful results. In particular, color slides or photographs appeal because of their greater accuracy.

Permission is not required for photographing surgical or postmortem specimens, although here, too, the identity of the patient must be kept in the strictest confidence. A state department of health was not permitted to use photographs of patients afflicted with cancer, for public display and intended for educational purposes, without the written consent of the patients and without altering the pictures so as to make them unidentifiable and beyond possible recognition.[2]

Use of Postmortem Photographs

Photographs of monstrosities or of dead bodies may not be taken or used for scientific or commercial purposes without the consent of the next of kin, unless the identity of the body is beyond recognition.

A child born with its heart outside of the body died at the hospital; a newspaper photographer was permitted by the parents to photograph the nude body, but certain extrinsic facts were given to the newspaper without the consent of the parents. They brought an action against the hospital, the photographer and the newspaper, alleging a violation of the trust and confidence reposed in the hospital and a trespass upon their right of privacy. An injunction was granted prohibiting the further publicizing of the picture or details of the

[2] Op. Atty.-Gen. of New York (1934), p. 374.

case; the court added that the complaint stated a good cause of action for damages against the hospital, the photographer and the newspaper.[3]

A commercial photographer who is employed to take a picture may not use additional copies for his own purposes without proper authorization; by implication there is an agreement that the prints are for the use of the customer only.

Twin boy children were born joined together from their shoulders down to their hips; they had one chest and abdomen but were otherwise twins. Shortly after they died, a photographer was employed to make a dozen pictures of the nude bodies. He delivered the pictures but, contrary to his agreement, made additional prints and had a copyright issued to himself for the exclusive commercial rights to the pictures. The court held that he had invaded the parents' right of privacy in that the bodies were in the custody of the parents and he had secured no permission from them to use the photographs for his own ends. The parents were allowed damages.[4]

Publication of Photographs in Medical Journals

That a photograph of a patient is to be used in a professional journal devoted to the advancement of science does not authorize its publication without the patient's permission.

Where a physician, without the consent of the patient, took photographs of her in the course of treatment, the court, on the husband's application, issued an order forbidding the physician to publish the pictures. The husband, who had contracted with the physician for the wife's medical care, was entitled to sue for breach of an implied contract of trust.[5]

[3] *Bazemore* v. *Savannah Hospital*, 155 S.E. 194, 171 Ga. 257 (1930).

[4] *Douglas* v. *Stokes*, 149 Ky. 506, 149 S.W. 849 (1912).

[5] *Clayman* v. *Bernstein*, 38 Pa. D. & C. 543 (1940).

It may become a question of fact requiring a trial to determine whether photographs in a medical journal were used solely for scientific purposes or for advertising or trade purposes.

An action was brought by a patient against a medical society as publisher of a professional journal and against several physicians who had attended the patient. The complaint alleged that the physicians photographed the patient at the commencement and completion of treatment; that four "before and after" pictures were published as part of an article bearing the by-line of the doctors and the title "The Saddle Nose," without the patient's consent, for advertising purposes or purposes of trade. An article, said the court, even in a scientific publication, may be nothing more than someone's advertisement in disguise. "That the article in hand, with its accompanying photographs of plaintiff, was published by the defendants to advertise the defendant physicians and their handiwork is a fair inference to be drawn."[6]

Patient's Authorization for Demonstration

As in the case of photographs of patients whose faces have been made unrecognizable, there probably would be no violation of the patient's right of privacy if the face were not shown or if so covered that the features were not recognizable. However, it is advisable to obtain the patient's written consent on an appropriate form in advance of the telecast.

No consent would be necessary from the patient for a television demonstration of x-ray films or photographs, because of the impossibility of identifying the patient, provided the name of the patient on the film is covered. It may be expected that "telegnosis" (the teleoroentgen diagnosis obtained from facsimiles of original roentgenographs transmitted by radio or telephone wires over short or long distances) will be increasingly used by rural hospitals and rural practitioners.

---

[6] *Griffin* v. *Medical Society of the State of New York*, 11 N.Y.S. 2d 109 (1939).

Television Demonstrations

Television is recognized as a teaching aid not only in surgery but also in postgraduate clinics. A closed circuit telecast of a patient at a teaching hospital may be made from clinic to clinic or shown outside of the hospital limits to more than one group of doctors simultaneously.

Like other media of communication, television may have either a trade aspect or an informative or news aspect. In the latter two situations, it is entitled to the same privilege accorded other such media where the right to privacy is in issue.

Exhibition of Patient in Motion Pictures

The consent of the patient to be photographed for motion picture purposes should be secured, irrespective of the fact that the pictures are to be used for educational or scientific purposes. A distinction has been made between the use of a motion picture of a patient for strictly educational purposes and one which, in addition, was shown for commercial motives.

The exhibition of a motion picture called "Birth" in public theaters showing the performance of a Cesarean section upon a patient was adjudged to be clearly for the purpose of trade and in violation of the privacy statute. Oral consent had been given by the patient that the picture be exhibited in the interest of medical science. Showing the picture on the public theatre screen constituted a violation of the law which prohibits the use of a name, portrait or picture of a living person without consent for trade or advertising purposes, but excepts use which is educational or of legitimate public interest.[7]

Ownership of Medical Photographs and Negatives

In medical photography the negative is comparable to the x-ray plate, both of which are used for clinical purposes. There

---

[7] *Feeney* v. *Young,* 191 App. Div. 501, 181 N.Y.S. 481 (1920).

is no relationship of employer and employee between the patient and the photographer, whether or not the patient pays for the photograph. In the hospital both photograph and negative are part of the medical record. Unless there is an express agreement to deliver the photograph or the negative to him, the patient has no basis for claiming possession of either.

In the event that the photograph is taken by the photographer at his instance and for his benefit, the subject loses control of the disposition of the pictures; all proprietary interest in that photograph, including the right to copyright the same, lies solely with the photographer.[8]

---

[8] *Young* v. *Hickerson,* 159 N.Y.S. 2d 612 (1960).

chapter 17

PATIENTS' PROPERTY RECORDS

THE law imposes liability on the hospital for the negligent loss of property left with the institution, though the hospital may have acted in good faith. Evidence that routine care was used does not constitute a satisfactory explanation for the loss of the article so as to relieve the hospital from liability. It must be proved by the hospital that ordinary and reasonable care was exercised; the defense as to the cause and manner of the loss may not be left to conjecture.

Delivery is Contract of Bailment

A bailment is the delivery of personal property by one party (bailor) to another (bailee) to be held by the latter according to the purpose of the delivery and to be redelivered to the bailor when that purpose has been accomplished or otherwise dealt with in accordance with the directions of the bailor. The term bailment is derived from the French word "bailler," meaning "to deliver."

Upon delivery of a patient's valuables for safekeeping, a contract of bailment arises requiring the hospital to return the articles on demand or on discharge. Bailor is the term applied to the patient, bailee to the hospital. As bailee, the hospital agrees to exercise due care in keeping the property and to deliver it, upon reasonable notice, to the patient or on his order, and to no one else. The hospital impliedly contracts against negligence in that it will exercise prudence such as would be used by a reasonably careful person under the same or similar circumstances.

Hospital is Not Insurer

When property left in the custody of the hospital is demanded by a third person under legal process, as by the service of what appears to be a legal document, the institution must assure itself that the proceedings are valid; however, the hospital is not bound to litigate the matter for the patient. It would probably be evidence of due care if it is shown that the hospital's attorney took steps to assure himself of the propriety of the proceeding. The term legal process means a document not merely fair on its face but in fact valid.

A hospital holding property for safekeeping is not an insurer; it is not liable for the loss of the property caused by an act of God, such as a storm, earthquake or tornado; nor is it liable for acts committed by the public enemy, as in time of war. The hospital, however, remains liable for its own negligence or that of its agents if it is not immune by state law. The basic obligation is to keep the valuables in a safe and secure place in the hospital.

There are few statutes specifically defining the hospital's liability as to the valuables of a patient. Analogy must be sought in the common law as it affects innkeepers, as well as the special exemptions of hospitals from claims for negligence. California has a statutory limitation of liability which applies to voluntary hospitals up to $250.00.

Preparation of Clothes List

A clothes list (Fig. 24, p. 88) itemizing all clothing and articles in possession of the patient including their description should be used; the procedure should be explained to the patient upon admission. The form may include a statement of the patient's responsibility for his valuables and other possessions retained by him, and acceptance of the rules for the release of all items belonging to him. This sheet should be prepared in duplicate, the original filed with the patient's chart and the duplicate given to him.

Handling Cash and Valuables

The problem of handling cash and valuables varies somewhat, depending on whether the patient is private, semi-private or ward. However, in general, the primary effort should be directed toward the patient retaining the minimum amount of cash, jewelry or other valuable objects. If the patient cannot be persuaded to turn over such articles to relatives or friends for safekeeping (Fig. 39, p. 221), he should be requested to use the hospital facilities for safeguarding them. Where he still insists on retaining them against advice, he should sign a statement assuming responsibility for retaining the valuables. Dentures should be listed as valuables.

Whatever process of safeguarding patients' property is used, it should be a reasonable and safe procedure, and consistent with accepted practices among hospitals in the community.

Responsibility for Dentures

Few patients will surrender their dentures upon admission to a hospital. Should the patient wish to keep his dentures, the statement signed by him assuming responsibility for retaining his valuables should specifically include the dentures or they may be signed for on the Clothes List (Fig. 24, p. 88), or a statement should be used specifically and solely to cover the dentures (Fig. 40, p. 222).

One element of the bailment contract is the delivery of the valuables to an authorized employee. A private duty nurse is not an employee of the hospital; she is the special employee of the patient; her acts do not bind the hospital. A general duty nurse, on the other hand, is an agent, servant or employee of the hospital for the purpose of accepting property of the patient for safekeeping. The delivery of dentures or other prop-

VALUABLES ENVELOPE

N?_____

To be signed when valuables are deposited.

Signature of
Depositor_____

Received by_____

Date_____19____

Contents to be surrendered to owner only after
signature on depositor's receipt has been witnessed
and compared by custodian.

CONTENTS
(To be listed at option of depositor) √

FORM P-140 — PRINTED IN U.S.A.   PHYSICIANS RECORD CO., BERWYN, ILLINOIS

Fig. 39 — Valuables Envelope

erty to a private duty nurse does not bind the hospital unless actual delivery of the valuables is made to the appropriate representative of the hospital.

Deposits of Cash

The liability of the hospital for loss of money depends on whether the cash has been deposited with the hospital or entrusted for safekeeping in a container. Money left with the understanding that not the identical bills and coins but only a like amount is to be returned creates a deposit with the insti-

WAIVER OF RESPONSIBILITY

It has been explained to me that the hospital is NOT responsible for bridge work, false teeth, any items of personal property

or money which I have in my possession or which may be brought in to me while I am at the_____Hospital.

_____   _____   _____
WITNESS   SIGNATURE OF PATIENT/RELATIVE   DATE

Relationship to Patient_____

I have no money or valuables which I wish to deposit for safekeeping.

_____   _____   _____
WITNESS   SIGNATURE OF PATIENT/RELATIVE   DATE

Relationship to Patient_____

FIG. 40 — WAIVER OF RESPONSIBILITY

tution, not a bailment. The relationship of debtor and creditor thus is created as in the case of a bank, making the hospital absolutely responsible for the amount of money deposited. On the other hand, money left in an envelope or other container, to be kept separate from hospital funds and subject to call, creates a bailment wherein the hospital is not liable for loss unless negligence can be shown.

Money left for safekeeping may not be applied toward the payment of the charges incurred, unless there is an agreement to do so, or unless the patient consents at the time the money is to be applied. Applying the money toward payment of the hospital bill without the consent of the patient may subject the hospital to liability for a conversion. A conversion is the unauthorized act of another which deprives the owner of his property either permanently or for an indefinite period.

Property of Helpless Patients

The question of whether there has been a delivery of the property to the hospital may occur in the case of a helpless or incompetent patient.

An actual bailment exists where there is an actual delivery of the property through one of its agents. A constructive bailment occurs when the hospital receives possession of the property under such circumstances that the law imposes an obligation to protect it and return it to the patient.

In a constructive bailment there is no deliberate delivery of the property by the patient; it occurs in the case of an unconscious or helpless patient admitted to the hospital whose property is removed from his person for safekeeping. It may be negligence under such conditions for the nurse not to remove the property and provide for its safekeeping. The usual listing process should be followed, with the signature of at least one witness appearing on the record.

The hospital's duty is to protect the patient from damage to his person or property, whether by assault, theft or negligence.

Property of Deceased Patients

A greater degree of care is required in protecting the property of a deceased patient than is necessary in the case of a conscious patient.

In medical examiner and coroner cases, however, it may be

desirable to avoid listing the patient's property until the arrival of the police and the medical official.

It is the duty of the executor or administrator of the estate of a deceased patient to collect the assets of the estate. Property of the deceased may be released only to the one who produces a certified copy of his appointment as executor or administrator. One named in the hospital records as next of kin or closest friend of the patient is not necessarily the person legally authorized to receive his valuables. Where no executor or administrator appears within a reasonable time, the valuables should be turned over to the public administrator or similar official of the county in which the decedent last resided. That official will investigate for assets, seek relatives and pay the obligations of the estate in the order of their priority.

Money left by the decedent with the hospital for safekeeping belongs to the estate unless there is a signed agreement to pay the hospital charges out of such money.

Articles of little or no value left by the patient often are turned over to the family or closest friend in exchange for a signed receipt. The risk is said to be insignificant.

Liability for Misdelivery of Property

The delivery of valuables to one other than the true owner or his authorized agent, even though induced by trick or fraud, does not absolve the hospital of liability if it is at fault. It is negligence to deliver the items to one known not to be the true owner, in the absence of the express or implied consent of the patient. The safest policy is to require a specific written authorization from the patient.

Lost, Abandoned and Mislaid Property

Property is considered lost when the patient parts with its possession unwittingly and involuntarily, through neglect or inadvertence. The ownership remains in the patient who lost it. The finder of lost property receives a right of possession only, which right permits him to retain possession of the article against all except the true owner.

Abandoned property is left with an intention to terminate the ownership of it without giving it to another; there is no transfer of ownership as by sale or gift, nor any intention of reclaiming it.

Since there has been neither request to safekeep the items

Re: Patient's name:_____

Admitted:_____
                                    DATE

Discharged:_____
                                    DATE

Hospital Number:_____

Dear   :

During your hospitalization at the_____Hospital, as stated above, you delivered certain items of property to the Hospital for safekeeping. The following items are now being held by the Hospital and have not been claimed by you:

_____

_____

_____

_____

We request that you come to the Hospital immediately to pick up these items and that you bring with you your receipt that was issued at the time that the Hospital accepted your property.

If you fail to pick up your property within the next fifteen (15) days, the_____Hospital will have no alternative but to deem that you have abandoned this property. The Hospital will then take such legal action as is indicated to dispose of the property.

Kindly let us hear from you immediately.

FIG. 41 — NOTICE TO PATIENT TO PICK UP VALUABLES

nor an acceptance for such purpose by the hospital, no contract of bailment is created. Abandoned property (Fig. 41, above) may be destroyed after a reasonable time, or disposed of periodically by sale at public auction or otherwise. Notice of the sale should be sent to the patient or last owner at his last known address and the proceeds of the sale kept as an insurance fund, to pay any claims arising out of a demand for the return of the property.

Property intentionally laid down and then forgotten is mislaid, not lost nor abandoned; the ownership of the property remains in the patient; the finder acquires no ownership rights to it.

The right to possession of property determined to have been mislaid rather than lost is in the hospital where it has been found, and not in the person cleaning the room nor in a patient subsequently occupying the room.

Crime to Keep Found Articles

At common law, it was no crime for a finder of lost property to convert it to his own use; however, it was a larceny to retain the property if he knew the owner or could reasonably ascertain him. One may not refuse to return an article unless a reward is paid. The finder is a bailee who is under a duty to give up possession upon demand by the true owner.

It is a larceny, by statute, to keep the property, knowing of its true owner, in California, Idaho, Iowa, Minnesota, Montana, New York, North Dakota, and Utah. There may be local ordinances which require the finder of property lost in a public place to turn it over to the police department; after a specified time it becomes the property of the finder by operation of law.

chapter 18

CONSENTS FOR TREATMENT

THE Board of Commissioners of the Joint Commission on Accreditation of Hospitals have advised that many consent forms currently in use are inadequate and should be evaluated. They recommend that the hospital obtain the advice of local legal counsel in its preparation. In principle the form

AUTHORIZATION FOR MEDICAL AND/OR SURGICAL TREATMENT

Date________________19____ Time________ a.m. p.m.

I, the undersigned, a patient in____________________Hospital, hereby authorize Dr.________________(and whomever he may designate as his assistants) to administer such treatment as is necessary, and to perform the following operation________________ (NAME OF OPERATION AND/OR PROCEDURES) ________________and such additional operations or procedures as are considered therapeutically necessary on the basis of findings during the course of said operation. I also consent to the administration of such anesthetics as are necessary, with the exception of________________. (NONE, SPINAL ANESTHESIA, OR OTHER)

Any tissues or parts surgically removed may be disposed of by the hospital in accordance with accustomed practice.

I hereby certify that I have read and fully understand the above **Authorization for Medical and/or Surgical Treatment,** the reasons why the above-named surgery is considered necessary, its advantages and possible complications, if any, as well as possible alternative modes of treatment, which were explained to me by Dr.________________.
I also certify that no guarantee or assurance has been made as to the results that may be obtained.

Witness________________ Signed________________ (PATIENT OR NEAREST RELATIVE)

Witness________________ ________________ (RELATIONSHIP)

Authorization must be signed by the patient, or by the nearest relative in the case of a minor; or when patient is physically or mentally incompetent.

FORM C-410 PHYSICIANS' RECORD CO., BERWYN, ILLINOIS PRINTED IN U.S.A.

FIG. 42 — AUTHORIZATION FOR MEDICAL AND/OR SURGICAL TREATMENT

should be an informed consent (Fig. 42, above, Fig. 36, p. 205), which means that the signer knows what he is signing, knows what is to be done, and understands the risk involved. It should include such information as the following:

Name of the hospital in which the operation or procedure is to be performed, and date consent is signed.

Name of the patient on whom operation or procedure is to be performed.

Statement of the nature of the operation or procedure to be performed.

Authorization to perform such additional operations or procedures as are considered necessary or desirable in the judgment of the surgeon or physician.

Consent to dispose of tissues or parts removed at operation.

Statement that the signer is aware of the contents of the form he is signing.

Signature of patient or person legally authorized to give consent on patient's behalf.

Signature of witness.

Identification of Patient

In order to make certain that the patient to be operated upon is the one who has given consent, a proper system of patient identification must be adopted.

The wristband method of patient identification is the best means known in the field today. Reliance on any other method such as memory, asking or stating the patient's name, or the bed tag inevitably leads to errors.

All personnel and all departments servicing the patients must be taught and retaught to use the wrist band *at all times* for positive patient identification.

Each surgery should have a positive procedure for identification before the patient is placed on the operating table. Some one person of the operating staff must assume the final responsibility in conjunction with identification by the anesthesiologist, the operating surgeon and his assistant. Too often the anesthesiologist and the operating surgeon rely entirely on proper patient identification by the orderly and the operating room nurses. This is a combined responsibility of all parties concerned—each one must assume his proportionate share. Written medical staff and hospital orders should carefully delineate this responsibility. Such identification should include not only the patient, but also the procedure, and if bilateral, whether it is the right or left, and all pertinent information.[1]

Form and Necessity of Consent

Consent is defined as a free, rational act, which presupposes knowledge of the thing to which consent is given. This knowledge need not always be precise, but should be substantially correct. The patient need not know all the minutiae involved in his cure, but his consent is not free and rational when it is based on ignorance of the essential nature and consequences of the treatment or operation. "Blanket consents" do not offer the best protection against misunderstanding.

The fact that consent presupposes knowledge may pose delicate problems for the medical profession or hospital. In some cases it would be difficult to give a patient a correct understanding of the nature of a treatment. In other cases the patient might prefer not to know certain disagreeable things. In still other cases, an explanation might prove harmful to the patient by stimulating irrational fears.

Oral Consent is Valid if Proved

There is no legal requirement that a consent for surgical procedures must be in writing. Consent may be established by proof of a conversation between physician and patient. Or, it may be shown by evidence that the patient submitted without objection to the treatment which he was told would be performed. There are difficulties, however, inherent in relying upon an oral understanding.

---

[1] LUDLUM, J. E., "Problems of Patient Identification in Hospitals," *Hosp. Forum*, Sept. 1961.

Consent by Telephone

The use of the telephone to obtain consent for a surgical procedure, as in the case of a child who is hospitalized, would have certain disadvantages if it became necessary to prove the identity of the person with whom the conversation took place. Having another person listen in on a telephone conversation is of doubtful value if neither the hospital employee nor the so-called witness can identify the voice.

In case of emergency in which delay in treatment may be hazardous to the life of the patient, telephone consent would be a slight risk because the circumstances may have been such as to make consent superfluous. Wherever possible, written confirmation should be obtained and the circumstances of the telephone consent recorded in the patient's chart. Some hospitals use a recording device which is attached to the telephone for such conversations.

Consent by Telegram

Telegrams granting permission for treatment are more reliable than telephone calls, since there is some written record to support the authority to operate. If it becomes necessary to prove the identity of the sender, some problem may arise. Although there is some calculated risk in depending on the telegram's validity, this method for securing authorization may be a necessary expedient in some cases in which patients come from long distances and are unaccompanied by relatives or friends. The use of this standard media of communication may be regarded as the application of such "reasonable care" and good faith as to constitute a legal defense against the possibility of a lawsuit.

The telegram should become part of the patient's record as any other consent from the patient. Whenever possible, an effort should be made to confirm the consent subsequently in writing on the usual form.

Witnessing the Consent

There is no legal requirement that a consent signed by a patient must be witnessed. However, in the event of a dispute it is difficult for a written consent to be disproved when the signature is witnessed by another. There is at least one person able to controvert any claim that the patient did not consent or was not in condition to give valid authorization.

Procedures Requiring Consent

It may be taken for granted that a patient who presents himself for treatment implicitly consents to the ordinary diagnostic and therapeutic measures used by doctors and hospitals; that he knows in general that his diagnosis and cure may entail many procedures, and that his very request for a cure would include the willingness to submit to these ordinary procedures. Generally speaking, therefore, it is not necessary to explain each of these ordinary measures in order to obtain his consent.

It is neither necessary nor practical to obtain written consent in advance of every procedure. If the procedure is attended by some substantial risk, written consent is customarily obtained. Each doctor, based on his own training and experience, should decide whether or not a given procedure entails substantial risk for a specific patient. Although the responsibility for securing consent is that of the operator, for the sake of expediency the nursing staff often secures the permission of the patient.

Any list of operations or procedures can be only a general guide and cannot be all inclusive. The use of written consent is universal in cases in which general or spinal anesthesia is used.

Consent of the patient is necessary, except in an emergency, whether the surgical procedure is a minor or major operation. The phrase "minor surgical procedures," as used in the law, includes all surgical procedures except those involved in incision for the opening of a natural body cavity, the removal of benign or malignant tumors, bone fractures, amputation of an extremity or an appendage, the removal of any gland or organ or part thereof or plastic surgery of the human body.

Major surgery, more specifically, consists of operations within or upon the following cavities: the cranium, thorax and abdomen, including the pelvis; other operations which because of their locality, the condition of the patient, their difficulty or the length of time required to operate, constitute a distinct hazard to life.

The patient's written consent should be secured for minor procedures such as thoracocentesis, paracentesis, and lumbar punctures. No matter how minor the procedure may be in the mind of the physician or nurse, it should be explained in advance to the patient.

The use of a written consent is universal in cases in which general or spinal anesthesia is used. If the patient is capable of giving consent to an operation, authority should also be secured for the use of anesthetics, because the authorization does not include its use as a matter of course unless the form specifically provides for the use of "any anesthetics."

Informing the Patient

While the physician has a duty to explain the nature of a proposed procedure or operation in terms that the patient can understand, how far he need go in disclosing possible adverse results is a matter of medical judgment; expert medical testimony is necessary to show that failure to disclose harmful possibilities of treatment is inconsistent with accepted medical practice in the same locality in similar cases.

Where the patient claims there was no explanation of the risks inherent in an operation, and the physician testifies that he did explain the possible adverse consequences of the procedure, an issue of fact arises for determination by the jury.

No medical testimony is needed. The case concerned a woman who contended that she suffered a loss of hearing after electroshock treatments. Whether the injury resulted from the therapy would have to be established by medical testimony and for that reason the case was sent back to the local court for retrial. However, regarding consent, the opinion states: "An adult person, if he be of sound mind, is considered to have the right to determine for himself whether a recommended treatment or surgery shall be performed upon him, and to have the right even to expressly prohibit life-saving surgery or other medical treatment."

The court also declared that a physician has a duty to disclose the potential dangers of treatment unless his failure to do so comes within one of the exceptions to this rule, such as (1) an actual emergency when the patient is in no condition to make a decision, (2) where full explanation might so alarm an apprehensive patient that he may refuse needed surgery for fear of a minimal risk of harm, or (3) where the patient is not emotionally equipped to handle full information about the possible side effects.[2]

Adverse results of shock therapy resulted in litigation. Initially it was held to be negligence for a physician to fail to inform a competent patient of the harmful potential of the contemplated treatment. On retrial, the defendant doctors and hospital obtained a favorable verdict. The record of the second trial showed that the evidence, taken as a whole, supported a finding that the patient had been informed of the hazards of shock therapy, possible convulsions and fractures.[3]

It has been held that a physician who fails to inform the patient, generally, of the possible serious collateral hazards of a medical procedure may be held liable for malpractice even though he follows approved standards of medical care.

[2] *Woods* v. *Brumlop*, 14 CCH Neg. Cases 2d 1004 (N. Mex.) (1962).

[3] *Mitchell* v. *Robinson*, 14 C.C.H. Neg. Cases 2d 915 (Mo.) (1962).

The Supreme Court of Kansas held that if the defendant radiologist failed to fully advise his patient of the possible hazards of cobalt irradiation treatments, he would be guilty of malpractice. The court was careful to point out that such a holding would not be based on a charge of assault and battery, but rather on negligence for the failure to obtain an informed consent. At the same time, the court stated that where the patient is fully aware of the dangers involved, his consent to the proposed treatment would constitute an informed consent. The court acknowledged that there is a privilege based on therapeutic grounds to withhold a specific diagnosis where the disclosure would seriously jeopardize the recovery of an unstable person. The court added, in the ordinary case, there is no warrant for suppressing facts relating to treatment.[4]

A child suffering from a possible heart defect died in the course of a cardiac catheterization. The issue determining the outcome of the litigation was whether the physician had adequately disclosed the risks of the procedure to enable the parents to grant an informed consent. The parents knew there was some risk, but were told that the team of doctors who performed the procedure "had not had any trouble." One physician informed the father that there were absolutely no risks. Yet the court held that there had been a reasonable disclosure of the nature and consequence of the proposed treatment. It said that it is the duty of a doctor to make a reasonable disclosure to his patient of the nature and probable consequences of the suggested or recommended treatment, but this does not mean that a doctor is under an obligation to describe in detail all of the possible consequences of treatment. The duty of the physician to disclose, however, is limited to those disclosures which a reasonable medical practitioner would make under the same or similar circumstances. How the physician may best

---

[4] *Natanson v. Kline,* 350 P. 2d 1093 (Kan.) (1960).

discharge his obligation to the patient in this difficult situation involves primarily a question of medical judgment.[5]

The facts in this case are unlike the facts in the Natanson case.[6] There Dr. Kline made no disclosure whatsoever, and the treatment was new and very dangerous; while in the instant case[7] Dr. Menehan advised plaintiffs of the procedure sufficiently to constitute an informed consent. There was no evidence of this operation being extremely hazardous; no evidence of any death resulting from such an operation or any malpractice in performing the exploratory treatment. No evidence of fault or breach of proper medical standards was established against the defendant doctors. There is nothing in this action to detract from the rules of law laid down in the Natanson case.

The court noted in the Williams case that the doctors had explained the procedures to the parents and that the parents were aware that some risk was involved. Since there was no evidence presented that a reasonable doctor would have given a more detailed explanation, the court held that there was no basis on which a jury could find that the doctors had violated the standard of care prevailing in the community.

---

[5] *Williams* v. *Menehan*, 379 P. 2d 292 (Kan.) (1963).

[6] *Natanson* v. *Kline*, 350 P. 2d 1093, (Kan.) (1960).

[7] *Williams* v. *Menehan*, supra.

chapter 19

AUTHORIZATIONS FOR MINORS

A PERSON under 21 years of age is legally a minor or infant with reference to his capacity to enter into binding contracts, except in certain instances. In some states the minor becomes of age at the end of the eighteenth year. Although age is frequently looked upon as the sole criterion for ability to give legal consent for treatment, the effect of marriage, maturity and emancipation must also be considered. Where no statute or case fixes the age of majority, the common law rule applies that 21 is the age of majority.

Legal Principles in Cases of Minors

Court decisions have established a number of guiding principles in connection with operations and treatment of minors:

1. Operations on minor children, at least on those who have not attained years of discretion, may be lawfully authorized by the parent or, if there is no parent, by a guardian. Discretion means the ability to decide what is just and proper under the circumstances. The minor has a guardian appointed by the court to manage his affairs if he has no parents or the parents have been deprived of the child's custody or control by the court.

2. In the states where the parents have equal custody, the consent of one parent is sufficient. Where there has been a legal separation or divorce, consent should be secured from the parent who has custody of the child.

3. Except in an emergency, the authorization of the parent or guardian for an operation on an immature minor must be secured. An immature minor is one who does not have sufficient understanding by reason of intelligence and immaturity to know the significance of the act he is being requested to perform. Maturity for the purpose of giving consent for operation is not entirely dependent on age, but is related to the ability to exercise discretion. One may be a minor and mentally mature.

4. In an emergency, it is good practice to obtain the parent's consent in writing as soon as possible after the services have been rendered.

5. Although mature minors may be legally competent to permit operations on themselves, it is better procedure also to get the approval of the parent.

6. The permission of adult siblings of a minor may be valid under special circumstances, but it is safer to insist on the consent of the parent.

7. Married minors or mature minors earning their own livelihood and retaining their earnings are emancipated; their own consent to surgical procedures is sufficient. The term emancipated, as used with reference to the parent-child relationship, involves an entire surrender of the right to the care, custody and earnings of such child as well as a renunciation of parental duties. The emancipation may be express, as by voluntary agreement of parent and child, or implied from such acts and conduct as import independence.

8. If parents refuse to agree to an operation on a minor, even where death may ensue without medical attention, they are within their rights until a guardian has been appointed by the court to replace them and to give authorization, or a court of competent jurisdiction has ordered the treatment.

Consent is Implied in Emergencies

A surgeon confronted with an emergency which endangers the life of the child is under a duty to do that which the occasion demands, within the usual and customary practice among surgeons in the same or similar localities, without consent of the patient or his parent. The law implies consent from the circumstances.

Ratification of Unauthorized Operation

One who adopts the unauthorized act of his agent ratifies it as though it has been performed in the first instance by him or at his discretion. The ratification of an unauthorized act may be express, as by written or spoken words, or implied, the assent being spelled out of the individual's conduct. Thus, consent for an unauthorized operation may be spelled out by subsequent statements or by later conduct indicating approval of what the doctor has done.

Siblings Have No Authority to Consent

If a minor is involved, the parents should be consulted for authorization; siblings of the patient, where parents are available, have no authority to give consent.

If the physician operates in good faith, without proper consent, and the child benefits therefrom, the physician may be liable only for nominal damages.

Consents of Mature Minors

Where the patient is a minor of sufficient maturity and understanding, his consent may be adequate. The fact that a minor of mature mind can lawfully make a contract for medical services as one of the necessaries of life may be construed as authorizing him to consent to an operation or treatment, at least when the cost is to be paid from his own estate. There may be a conflict, however, between the authority of the parents and that of the minor if he is under treatment at the expense of his parents.

Although the consent of a mature minor probably would be valid, it is preferable to get the consent of the parent, where possible, to assure payment of the charges and in the interest of good public relations.

Emancipated Minors

An infant is described as a minor or not of age, or under the age of 21 years. He may petition the courts by statute to remove the disability of infancy from him in Alabama, Arkansas, Florida, Kansas, Louisiana, Mississippi, Oklahoma, Tennessee, Texas and Wyoming. This is called a statutory emancipation since it is specifically provided by law. The disability is the lack of legal capacity to perform certain acts which an adult may perform.

An unmarried minor may be emancipated from parental subjection when the father relinquishes the right to his services and earnings. If inferred from the circumstances, it is an implied emancipation; if done by consent or agreement, an express emancipation. However, such surrender of control over services and earnings may be only a partial emancipation if the father retains the right to the minor's care and custody.

Authorization of Emancipated Minors

An emancipated minor may sign his own consent for surgery if he is cognizant of the purpose of the operation. A mentally defective adult or an emancipated minor may not give a valid consent if he does not understand the nature of the authorization or the ensuing operation. Understanding is more important than age. The emancipated minor may consent to an operation upon himself and agree to the kind of anesthetic to be administered.

It is the practice of schools of nursing to have the students' parents sign a blanket permission form for any emergency operation should need arise and it is not possible to reach the parents. Such students are mature minors and can be regarded as emancipated. In an emergency no consent for operation would be needed, but the practice of securing a blanket consent in advance is good public relations.

Consent of Married Minors

At common law the age of consent for marriage was fourteen for males and twelve for females; by statute the required age has been raised. One general exception to the rule that the contracts of minors are voidable is the contract of marriage.

There is a difference between void and voidable contracts. Void in the strict sense means that a contract or transaction is invalid from its inception; voidable is the term used when an imperfection can be cured by the act of him who could take advantage of it. A marriage of two minors within the age permitted by statute binds both parties and differs in that sense from other contracts of minors which are voidable and can be repudiated at the pleasure of the minor before or on coming of age and within a certain time thereafter.

Parental control ceases upon the marriage of a minor, whether married with or without the consent of the parents. By statute, marriage specifically emancipates the female in Alaska, Florida, Iowa, Kansas, Louisiana, Nebraska and Utah. Since marriage emancipates the female minor, she has the same right to consent to an operation as her emancipated husband if he also is a minor. Her husband's or her parents' consent is not needed to an operation which she has authorized.

Court Orders May Grant Consent

In the matter of an operation upon a minor, the consent ordinarily is the decision of the natural guardian of the child. A physician has no right to proceed without consent, however necessary or beneficial the operation may be, except in an emergency. If parents or guardians fail to authorize necessary treatment, the courts may intervene in proper cases.

The court may, if the statute permits, order an operation not only in an instance where the life of the child is to be saved, but also in cases in which the health, limb or future of the child is at stake.

Unless there exist specific statutes, the courts may not order an operation upon a minor child. Where such state laws exist, the court makes a finding that the child is "neglected" or "dependent" and appoints a guardian to take the place of the parent.

Indigence of the father is no reason for depriving him of the custody of his children if he is otherwise a suitable person. Yet his inability to support them may be considered with other facts.

The vaccination of children may be enforced by the courts, inasmuch as legislation to protect the public health is within the police power of the state. Vaccination and quarantine regulations may be established by law and the enforcement delegated to local boards of health. Vaccination may be made compulsory in that a fine or other penalty is imposed for failure to be vaccinated. Vaccination as a condition to the entry or remaining in a public school also has been upheld.

chapter 20

OPERATIONS WITHOUT CONSENT

AN UNAUTHORIZED operation is considered an assault and battery. An assault is defined as an intentional attempt, by violence, to do an injury to the person of another. A battery consists of the unlawful touching of the person of another by the aggressor or by any substance put in motion by him.

Although a surgeon must be allowed some latitude in performing the operation within the scope of the patient's consent, no principle of law allows him to operate at will. In the absence of exceptional circumstances an operation without consent or in excess of consent express or reasonably implied constitutes a technical assault and battery for which he is liable in damages.

However, when the patient engages the services of a surgeon without any agreement as to what he is to do, the law authorizes him to do what he considers necessary. The proper exercise of professional judgment in such case protects him against liability for an assault and battery.

Damages for Operation Without Consent

As an element in every action for an unauthorized operation the burden of proof rests on the patient to show how he was damaged. The amount of damages may be nominal if the patient cannot establish real harm to himself; it may be considerable, depending on the actual damage, whether temporary or permanent, and the nature thereof. The surgeon may be liable for damages even though the operation was performed skillfully if there were no authorization for the procedure.

A surgeon examined a patient and found the existence of a left inguinal hernia and advised an operation. Upon the surgeon's arrival at the hospital on the date of the operation, a blackboard at or near the operating room indicated that he was to perform a *right* inguinal hernia operation. The incision was made on the lower right side and his assistant found a moderate-sized hernia. When the patient became conscious he noticed that his operation had been performed on the right side and not on the left side. The surgeon testified that he had not checked his records prior to going into the operating room. The court stated that a physician who neither conducts a pre-operation examination just prior to surgery, nor checks his records to refresh his recollection of the operation to be performed and consequently undertakes surgery on the opposite side of the body than has been intended, is negligent. The patient was awarded $4,500.00.[1]

Fraudulent Consent is Invalid

Fraud is an intentional perversion of the truth for the purpose of inducing another in reliance upon it to surrender a legal right whether by words or by conduct, or by concealment of that which should have been disclosed, which deceives and is intended to deceive another so that he shall act upon it to his detriment. As distinguished from negligence, fraud is always positive, intentional.

A consent to perform an operation is not valid if obtained by representations which are false or fraudulent to the knowledge of the surgeon; the performance of such an operation constitutes an assault and battery on the patient for which the surgeon is liable in damages. It is also a crime for a surgeon to represent fraudulently to a patient that he requires a surgical operation and to operate on him after obtaining his consent.

---

[1]*Kuchinsky* v. *McMahon*, Sup. Ct., Nassau Co., N.Y.L.J., Oct. 28, 1963, P. 17, Col. 6.

Progressive hospitals provide for a tissue committee composed of a pathologist and other members of the medical staff. Their duty is to scrutinize all tissue removed at operation. If tissues are normal, the committee has a duty to inquire into the reason for their removal.

Lack of Consent of Husband

If the patient consents, the husband's approval is unnecessary. However, where the operation involves danger to life, or where it may destroy or limit sex functions or may result in the death of an unborn infant, the spouse's consent is advisable for reasons of good public relations. There is no legal requirement that written authorization be procured from the spouse.

Auxiliary Operations Without Consent

In internal operations, the exact condition of the patient cannot always be definitely diagnosed until after the patient is anesthetized and the incision has been made. In such case, in the absence of proof to the contrary, the consent will be construed as general in nature and the surgeon may extend the operation to remedy any diseased condition in the area of the original incision whenever he, in the exercise of his sound professional judgment, determines that correct surgical procedure requires an extension.

The rule is that no additional unrelated operation may be performed while the patient is on the operating table unless further surgery is indispensable to his health or life. It is no defense that the additional unrelated surgery was performed with skill and care. On the other hand, the necessity for the additional operation creates an implied consent for the surgeon to proceed further without committing a trespass.

Emergencies as Implied Consent

The word implied is used in law as contrasted with express; i.e., where intention is not manifested by explicit and direct words, but is gathered by implication or deduction from the circumstances, the general language or the conduct of the parties.

Consent may be implied not only from the conduct of the parties but also by law. A consent implied by law is such as the law presumes the party normally would have given under the circumstances if he had a conscious, deliberate choice, but which he was prevented from exercising by reason of the special situation in which he found himself.

When an immediate operation is imperative, and the patient's state is such that he cannot rationally consent, or where delay in obtaining the consent of the parent or guardian involves serious risk to the patient, an operation may be performed on the theory of implied consent.

The law implies that the patient, if competent, would consent to whatever may be in his own interest. When a surgeon operates under such circumstances, he should be prepared to show (1) that an immediate operation was necessary, (2) that a lawful express consent could not be obtained from the patient or from any person authorized to act for him, without seriously endangering the health or life of the patient, and (3) that the operation performed was such as was necessary for the patient's life.

To constitute an emergency it is not sufficient that treatment be needed merely for the preservation of life, limb or health of the patient; the operation must be emergent in the sense that death would likely result upon failure to perform it.

Cesarean Sections as Emergencies

An elective cesarean section may be performed if there is medical necessity for the operation. Only the consent of the patient is necessary, but it would be desirable, in the interests of good public relations, to obtain the authorization of the husband. It should not be done merely because it is a matter of preference with the patient. In emergency cases, however, involving the life of the mother or infant, no consent is required.

The authority and duty of a physician in attendance at the death of a woman who has within her body at the time of death a viable child have not been defined by court decision. The husband ordinarily has the legal right to the custody of the body of his deceased wife in the condition in which it was when she died. Presumably he has certain legal authority and responsibility with respect to his unborn living child.

While his consent should be obtained if practicable, before delivering a viable child by postmortem cesarean section, a physician may probably with impunity perform the operation without that consent and even against the husband's wishes if there is reasonable belief that the life of the child will be saved.

In Oklahoma, by statute, a postmortem cesarean section is permitted upon the body of any female in an advanced stage of pregnancy, who is the victim of accidental death, where the physician has reason to believe that the child is viable in the mother.

chapter 21

CONSENT FOR BLOOD
TRANSFUSIONS

THERE is probably no biologic product in medical therapy
that carries with it more possible sources of dangerous
error than blood. This is true because of the large number of
persons who handle the blood from the time it is obtained from
the donor until it is administered to the patient, and because
of the uncontrollable complicating features which prevent
rigid standardization of such a procedure.

Blood transfusion has become a safer procedure for the patient as a result of two advances: first, the discovery of the Rh
factor, which led to new tests for the detection of intragroup
incompatibilities, and second, the discovery of the cause of
pyrogenic reactions and the development of methods of preventing them. The introduction of blood banking, and the in-
vention of inexpensive and reliable transfusion equipment for
the collection, storage and administration of blood, have increased the availability of blood and plasma.

Today blood and plasma transfusions are almost as common-
place as ordinary sodium chloride and glucose infusions. This
has made possible surgical procedures previously too dangerous to undertake, and has also reduced the frequency of deaths
from hemorrhage. A disadvantage in the use of plasma is that
it may cause homologous serum hepatitis.

Homologous Serum Jaundice

The available data show that the problem of homologous serum hepatitis has not yet been solved. The danger is much greater when pooled plasma is used than when plasma or whole blood derived from a single individual is administered. There is no practicable test to detect carriers of the virus. The ability to transmit the virus may be retained for an indefinite period of time.

Individuals with a history of hepatitis should never be used as donors for blood transfusion, while individuals who have been intimately exposed to the disease should not be used as donors for at least six months. Such blood may be used for preparing plasma or plasma fractions where adequate means for destroying the virus are used. When fresh, frozen or freeze-dried plasma is needed, this should preferably be prepared from blood from a single individual. At the present stage of knowledge, homologous serum hepatitis is a calculated risk which is assumed as part of a blood or plasma transfusion.

State Not Liable as Distributor

It has been held that the State, acting as a distributor of pooled blood plasma, was not liable to the estate of a patient who had contracted fatal homologous serum jaundice through transfusion of pooled blood plasma ordered by the attending physician. The plasma was war surplus, originally procured for the Army and Navy by the American Red Cross. The plasma administered to the patient had been shipped to the local branch of the Red Cross, which stored the material and delivered it untouched and in its original package to a hospital. The court declared that the danger of serum jaundice is well known to the medical profession, and there is no obligation for the State to instruct licensed physicians on the proper application of therapeutic agents in common use.[1]

---

[1] *Parker* v. *State of New York*, 201 Misc. 416, 105 N.Y.S. 2d 735, aff'd 112 N.Y.S. 2d 695, 280 App. Div. 157 (1952).

In another case, the State acted as a distributor of pooled blood plasma, the use of which caused the death of a patient from homologous serum jaundice. The State was held not liable for blood administration by a physician at a hospital.[2]

Transfusion is Not Sale of Blood

Lawsuits have been instituted on the theory that the hospital should be liable on the basis of a commercial transaction for the sale of blood rather than for negligence in its administration. In suing for the sale of unfit blood, the theory is that there was a breach of implied warranty of fitness for the purpose or of the merchantable quality of the blood. This would be a breach of contract action as distinguished from one in negligence in administering contaminated blood. It has been held that furnishing blood to a patient for a transfusion charged for by a hospital does not constitute a sale; the patient has no cause of action for breach of implied warranties of fitness for use or of merchantable quality.

A patient brought an action for damages for personal injuries sustained while at a hospital, when she was given a transfusion of blood which contained hepatitis virus that caused her to contract jaundice. The complaint contained no allegations of negligence, but sought recovery solely upon the theory that the supplying of blood constituted a sale within the meaning of the Sales Act, and as a consequence there attached the implied warranties of fitness for purpose and merchantable quality.

The court ruled that the supplying of blood by the hospital did not constitute a sale, and thus the implied warranties did not attach. To hold that it was a sale would mean that the hospital, no matter how careful, would be held responsible virtually as an insurer. The action was dismissed.[3]

---

[2] *Hidy* v. *State of New York*, 3 N.Y.S. 2d 756, 163 N.Y.S. 2d 986 (1957).

[3] *Perlmutter* v. *Beth David Hospital*, 308 N.Y. 812, 126 N.E. 2d 869, 308 N.Y. 100, 123 N.E. 2d 792 (1955).

A Utah court has held that the furnishing of blood by a hospital at the request of the patient or his doctor for a charge is a part of a service and not a sale. The hospital was not negligent in the procuration, testing and furnishing of the blood transfusion to the patient, who died because of incompatibility of the blood. Nor was the hospital liable on the theory of an implied warranty of fitness for the use for which it was intended.[4]

By suing for a breach of warranty of fitness for use in the sale of blood, the patient may seek to circumvent the hospital's immunity from lawsuits for negligence. This approach was used in a case against a public hospital in the State of Washington.

The patient was admitted for surgery and a routine blood transfusion was ordered. It was alleged that the hospital employees made an incorrect determination of the patient's blood type and that the wrong transfusion was the cause of her death. The court held that the hospital provides blood as part of its service and not as a sale of merchandise. If there was any improper act of omission or commission, the case is in negligence and therefore barred by the immunity statute, even though the complaint attempts to show a breach of warranty.[5]

Blood plasma was administered by hospital employees while the patient was unconscious. The blood plasma used allegedly contained jaundice viruses and other injurious substances, as a result of which the patient became afflicted with homologous serum hepatitis which allegedly caused his death. His administrator sued the manufacturer or processor.

The court dismissed the first cause of action in the complaint which was based upon the alleged breach of warranty in the sale of blood plasma, but stated it was not passing upon the

---

[4] *Dibblee* v. *Dr. W. H. Groves Latter Day Saints Hospital*, 364 P. 2d. 1085 (Utah) (1961).

[5] *Giles* v. *Kennewick Public Hospital*, 296 P. 2d 662 (Wash.) (1956).

question of negligence in the second cause of action until the trial.[6]

California has adopted a statute which provides that the procurement, processing, distribution or use of whole blood, plasma, blood products and blood derivatives for the purpose of injecting or transferring the same is to be considered a service and not a sale.

Express Warranty of Fitness

The question of express warranty, as distinguished from an implied warranty under the Sales Act, was not passed upon in the Perlmutter case. The Perlmutter case was based upon the theory of implied warranty under section 96 of the Sales Act.

In the ordinary case in which the hospital furnishes blood or plasma, concepts of purchase and sale cannot separately be attached to healing materials, such as medicines, drugs or blood supplied by the hospital for a price as part of the medical services it offers. That the property or title to certain items of medical material may be transferred, so to speak, from the hospital to the patient during the course of medical treatment does not serve to make each such transaction a sale. The transfer of the personal property is but an incidental feature of the transaction; it is the service feature that dominates.

In a recent case, a hospital was sued for the death of a patient following a blood transfusion. The complaint alleged that the personnel "warranted to plaintiff" that the blood plasma or whole blood, or whatever substance it was that was injected into plaintiff's intestate, was fit for her and that the said transfusion would not be harmful to plaintiff's intestate.

The court held that at least so far as the complaint itself is concerned, it was the contention of the plaintiff that express warranties were made. It may be that at the trial such express warranties will be unprovable, but that is not a reason to dismiss the complaint until the facts are established at the trial.

[6] *Krom* v. *Sharp and Dohme*, 180 N.Y.S. 2d 99 (1958).

Thus the mere allegation of an express warranty can defeat an effort to dismiss the case without a trial.[7]

Administering Wrong Type of Blood

There are occasions when patients with the same or similar names are in the hospital at the same time and two such persons may require blood simultaneously. Unless everyone concerned is cautious, the requisitions, cross-matching samples or bottles of compatible blood, may be interchanged. Nurses are obligated to make certain that every requisition for blood carries the patient's complete name, accurately spelled, and his hospital number.

A common cause for incompatible blood transfusion is the mislabeling of laboratory specimens drawn from patients. A requisition form for blood should be filled out giving the name and chart number as well as the room. Tubes containing the blood should be clearly labeled with the patient's name and chart number, since there may be more than one individual of the same name in the same ward in the hospital.

A laboratory technician, employed by a hospital in New York State, made a serological test to determine the patient's blood factor, with the result that the patient was transfused with blood of the wrong factor and suffered serious consequences. The court held that the hospital was liable for the errors of the technician. A judgment was awarded to the patient.[8]

In another case, the circulating nurse had come into the operating room with a bottle of blood on which there was a slip inscribed with the name of the patient, type of blood and the name of the doctor. The slip showed that the blood was for another patient, previously operated on. This information on the slip was entirely different from the facts with respect to

[7] *Napoli v. St. Peter's Hospital*, 213 N.Y.S. 2d 6 (1961).

[8] *Berg v. New York Society for the Relief of the Ruptured & Crippled*, 1 N.Y. 2d 499, 135 N.E. 2d 523 (1956).

decedent, yet the registered nurse turned the bottle over to the anesthetist, implying that the blood was intended for the decedent. The anesthetist had a chart showing the type of blood of decedent; he testified that it was his duty to check the blood and that a surgeon does not check blood. He, the anesthetist, did not perform that duty.

The majority opinion of the court affirmed the judgment against the hospital, anesthetist and surgeon, but reduced the amount from $130,000.00 to $90,000.00. The dissenting opinion held that there was no proof of malpractice on the part of the surgeon, for he had the right to rely upon the competency of the anesthetist and the hospital staff.[9]

In a personal injury action, the patient alleged that she entered the hospital for a hysterectomy, and that on the night she entered the hospital she was given a transfusion of mismatched blood, from which she suffered a severe reaction. Thereafter, the operation was performed; on the same day, she was given another transfusion of mismatched blood, resulting in lower nephron nephrosis. During her stay in the hospital, her condition became critical; she was fed intravenously; she remained at home convalescing for a considerable time. Judgment was rendered against the hospital for $17,500.00.[10]

Damages were recovered, under the Federal Tort Claims Act, by a serviceman and his wife for injuries suffered by the wife because of the transfusion of incompatible blood. The wife recovered $40,000.00 for pain, suffering, mental anguish, loss of physical ability to perform household tasks, permanent injury to her kidneys, and permanent rheumatoid arthritis. The serviceman recovered $10,000.00 for loss of the services and companionship of his wife.

The wife had been given a transfusion of 1,000 cc. of blood

[9] *Weiss* v. *Pulrang*, 205 N.Y.S. 2d 274 (1960).
[10] *Glantz* v. *Mt. Sinai Hospital*, Sup. Ct., Queens Co., Conroy, J., N.Y.L.J., June 27, 1957, p. 8, Col. 6.

in connection with a hysterectomy performed at an Army hospital. Her blood had previously been typed as Group O positive. In typing her blood for the transfusion, a hospital technician determined that it was Group B positive. She was transfused with Group B positive blood and developed a hemolytic reaction. Her blood was immediately retyped and it was determined to be Group O positive.[11]

Transfusion of the Wrong Patient

There is one case reported of a transfusion having been given to the wrong patient. She had an operation for the removal of a kidney. After she recovered, an intern and a hospital nurse entered her room and informed her she was to have a blood transfusion. The transfusion was a mistake; it had been ordered for a different patient on the same floor. The intern was a fourth-year medical student fully qualified to administer a blood transfusion. Blood transfusions were ordered only by a patient's attending physician or by a house physician. No such order was given in her case. During the transfusion the patient had a chill and a rising temperature; the procedure was stopped. She suffered severe headaches thereafter, became mentally ill and spent some time in a mental hospital. At the time of the transfusion, she was at, or approaching her menopause; the transfusion was the turning point that caused her subsequent illness.

The hospital was held responsible. The patient was entitled to be protected against trespass and assault, if such acts could be reasonably anticipated. The wrongs were committed by the very persons whom the hospital employed and gave access to the rooms and persons of patients. Their acts constitute liability on the part of the hospital.[12]

---

[11] *Redding* v. *U.S.*, 196 F. Supp. 871 (D.C. Ark.) (1961).

[12] *Necolayff* v. *Genesee Hospital*, 61 N.Y.S. 2d 832, 270 App. Div. 648, aff'd 296 N.Y. 936, 73 N.E. 2d 117 (1947).

Injuries to Blood Donors

It is a common practice for hospitals to obtain a general release from the donor in advance of a donation (Fig. 43, below),

TRANSFUSION RECORD

Donor No. | Amount Drawn | Diluent ______ | Preliminary Grouping ANTI–A ◯ ANTI–B ◯ | Group | Rh

Family Name | First Name | Middle Name | Home Phone | Occupation

Address | City | Zone | State | Sex M F | Age

DONOR'S MEDICAL HISTORY

Malaria ____ Antimalaria Drugs ____ Tuberculosis ____ Fainting Spells ____ Convulsions ____ Rheumatic Fever ____ Blood Infections ____

Undulant fever ____ Epilepsy ____ Heart disease ____ Eczema ____

Glandular Swelling ____ Dyspnoea ____ Venereal Disease ____ Persistent Cough ____ Illness in past three months ____

Jaundice ____ Blood Transfusion Received ____ Recently Pregnant ____ Asthma ____ Hay Fever ____ Diabetes ____

Food last eaten ____ (Date Time) a.m. p.m. Food: ____

Hg. ____ B.P. ____ Pulse ____ Temp. ____ Wgt. ____ Serology ____ Icterus Index ____

Blood Group ____ Veins ____ Hematoma ____ No. punctures ____ Heart ____ Skin ____ Spleen ____

Donor Reaction ____

I hereby certify that this donor appears to be free from diseases transmissible by blood transfusion and is a suitable donor for removal of not more than ____ cc. of blood.

Date ____ Signed ____ M.D.
Examining Physician

DONOR'S AUTHORIZATION TO TAKE BLOOD

I hereby certify that I have truthfully answered the above questions concerning diseases and conditions and give permission to the Blood Bank Service of this hospital, to withdraw up to 500 cc. of blood for the use of the service, and I further release this hospital and each and all of its physicians, nurses, technicians or other members of its staff from any claims which I may have against them relative or incidental to or in consequence of such withdrawal of blood.

Date ____ ____
Signature of Donor or Signature and Relationship of Guardian if Donor is a Minor

Witness ____ Technician ____

RECIPIENT'S RECORD

Family Name | First Name | Physician | Room No. | Hosp. No.

Cross-matching reveals patient and donor compatible:
Yes ☐ No ☐ See laboratory reports. Technician's Signature ____ Date ____

Previous transfusions: Dates ____ Reactions: ____

Indication for this transfusion ____ Date ____ a.m. p.m.

Method: Direct ☐ Indirect ☐ Amt. blood given ____ cc. Amt. saline ____ cc. Amt. dextrose ____ cc.

Reactions: respiratory distress ____ chill ____ nausea-vomiting ____ urticaria ____ shock ____ cyanosis ____ anuria ____ hematuria ____ jaundice ____

Pulse: one hour before ____ one hour after ____ temp. one hour before ____ temp. one hour after ____

To be filled out in triplicate and when donor's blood is to be used all copies should be sent to the patient's medical record. Within 24 hrs. after transfusion, forms should be completed in triplicate sending the two carbon copies back to the Blood Bank and the original remaining on the chart.

FORM E-402 PHYSICIANS' RECORD CO., BERWYN, ILLINOIS - PRINTED IN U.S.A. TRANSFUSION RECORD

FIG. 43 — TRANSFUSION RECORD

reciting the possible risks. Complications such as local hematoma or thrombophlebitis at the venesection site, injuries due to fainting before or after bleeding, and disease states which follow blood donation occasionally give rise to lawsuits. The signing of a release may act as a bar to an action because of the known risks voluntarily assumed by the donor.

For the first time in 1951 a court in New York passed upon the validity of a general release signed by a blood donor in advance of the donation of blood, exculpating the supplier of the blood from any consequences from the giving of the blood "by reason of any matter relative or incidental to such donation of blood." He claimed that he suffered injuries which were not the direct result of the donation of the blood.

The court held that while a blood donor could give a valid release in advance of a donation absolving others from responsibility for harm to him, the release would not apply to those acts of negligence which were not ordinarily attributable to the giving of the blood. Here he fainted and fell after his blood had been extracted. The want of care occurred after his blood had been taken. The court held that the release included only such matters particularly described in the release or those of a similar nature. The donor therefore was entitled to damages.[13]

A telephone company employee was among a group of employees who voluntarily agreed to donate blood to a patient. The blood was drawn from her arm by a nurse employed by the American Red Cross. The donor advised that she had suffered from an anemic condition. It was alleged by the nurse that a test was made to determine the eligibility of the donor for the transfusion. Following the blood donation, the donor became ill. The court held that the tests were made in a careless, indifferent and negligent manner and without regard to the condition of the donor. She was awarded $2,000.00 against the American Red Cross.[14]

Jehovah's Witnesses and Blood Transfusions

Jehovah's Witnesses do not oppose the people's use of trans-

---

[13] *Boll* v. *Sharp & Dohme. Inc.*. 107 N.Y.S. 2d 174 (1951).

[14] *Bowman* v. *American Red Cross*, 241 N.Y.S. 2d 971 (1963).

fusions but allow each one the right to decide for himself what he may conscientiously do. "Jehovah's Witnesses consecrate their lives to God and feel bound by His word, and with these things in view they individually decide their personal course and bear their personal responsibility therefor before God."

The Scriptural objection to blood transfusions which Jehovah's Witnesses present is that God has forbidden the use of blood as a food. According to the quoted Scripture, the administration of blood means that the body is being fed with food, contrary to the Bible.

Another objection raised by the sect is that blood transfusion procedures are hazardous. Their literature points out the occurrence of a number of deaths due to incomplete sterilization of the citrate solution in the bottle, blood being held under refrigeration longer than safety permits, and contaminated blood causing hepatitis.

The religious principles of the Jehovah's Witnesses, like the religious beliefs of all persons, should be respected. Every person has the right, as a matter of law, to say what may or may not be done to his body.

One is not legally obligated to preserve his life or maintain health by submitting to necessary medical care. Such decision imposes no penalty upon the individual so long as the exercise of the right does not endanger the life or health of others.

There is no reported case of a physician having been sued by a Jehovah's Witness who received a blood transfusion, either without his consent or contrary to his express wishes.

In one case a public hospital alleged that where people voluntarily come to the hospital and submit to the jurisdiction of the hospital, they are obliged to do what the hospital thinks is the right thing to do; that in refusing a blood transfusion the patient would be taking his own life, a form of suicide. The court held, however, that there was no precedent for an order requiring an adult patient to accept blood, especially if the patient is completely competent at all times to make the decision. In the case of an infant, the court stated, it will step in as guardian of the child or as guardian of an incompetent and make the decision.[15]

Another recent case involving an adult member of the sect resulted in a court order authorizing a blood transfusion. The patient, a 25-year-old mother, was admitted to the hospital as an emergency patient. The husband said that on religious grounds he would not approve a blood transfusion for his wife, but that if the court ordered the transfusion, the responsibility was not his. The patient was not in a mental condition to make a decision, and the doctors confirmed that the patient would die without blood. Thus, when death without blood became imminent, the hospital was faced with the choice of turning the patient out of the hospital for failure to accept medical treatment, which of course was impossible because of her condition, letting her die in bed, with whatever responsibility that would entail, or administering the blood. The court at the time of the application was unaware of any precise legal precedent for its action, but because of the demonstrated imminence of death from loss of blood from a ruptured ulcer, decided to sign the order to save the patient's life.[16]

In an emergency, should the surgeon in good conscience, in an effort to save the patient's life, risk violation of the patient's prohibition against the use of blood, the patient would have to prove some damage from the transfusion in order to hold the surgeon liable for other than nominal damages.

Objections of Parents on Religious Grounds

Jehovah's Witnesses, the court held in one case, enjoy the constitutional right to freedom of religion and may practice the religion of their choice without interference. The parents

---

[15] *In the Matter of Erickson*, New York, Sup. Ct., Nassau Co., Special Term, Part II, Oct. 1, 1962.

[16] Application of the President and Directors of Georgetown College, USDC — Columbia Circuit, September 19, 1963. (See USDC-DC opinion of Feb. 3, 1964.)

do not, however, have the right to impose upon an innocent child the hazards to it flowing from their own religious convictions. "The welfare of the child is paramount. If medical science requires a blood transfusion to preserve the child's life, the child should not be deprived of life because the mother's religious persuasion opposes such transfusion. The child has a right to survival and a chance to live and the court has a duty to extend its protecting arm to the child. It is of no concern to the court what religious preference the parents may elect."[17]

The rights of religion and parenthood are not beyond limitation, the Supreme Court of Illinois declared in approving the action of a circuit judge in temporarily depriving parents of the custody of their minor child, and subjecting the child, over the parents' religious objections, to a blood transfusion. A guardian was appointed for the eight-day-old infant. The court ruled that the parents were not deprived of their freedom of religion and of their rights as parents, in violation of the Fourteenth Amendment to the United States Constitution.[18]

In a Missouri case the court held that the child is a ward of the court when brought before it to determine the personal rights of the child and the court may order a blood transfusion in the event of the parents' refusal to consent.[19]

The court, in a New Jersey case, ordered a blood transfusion for an unborn child, to be administered upon birth, where the mother's medical history, because of her Rh blood condition, strongly indicated such a transfusion would be needed.[20]

The New Jersey Supreme Court upheld the legal procedure employed by a hospital in an attempt to preserve the life of a three-year-old. The administrator petitioned the local court to grant temporary custody of the child to him so that he could

[17] *Battaglia* v. *Battaglia*, 172 N.Y.S. 2d 361 (1958).

[18] *People ex rel. Wallace* v. *Labrenz*, 411 Ill. 618, 104 N.E. 2d 769 (1958).

[19] *Morrison* v. *State*, 252 S.W. 2d 97 (Mo.) (1952).

[20] *Hoener* v. *Bertinato*, 171 A. 2d 140 (N.J.) (1961).

agree to the transfusion. The court cooperated, but after the transfusion the child died. The parents were offended by the court order and continued to litigate, contending that it represented a violation of their constitutional rights to practice their religion without governmental interference. The trial court was held justified in finding the parents guilty of neglecting their child (thus allowing appointment of a temporary guardian) when they refused to allow the transfusion, even though the safety and efficacy of transfusions are subject to some dispute among physicians.[21]

A provision of Ohio's Juvenile Code authorizes a court, upon the certificate of one or more reputable practicing physicians, to summarily provide for emergency medical and surgical treatment which appears to be immediately necessary for any child concerning whom a complaint or an application for care has been filed, pending the service of a citation upon its parents, guardian or custodian. The court held that this statute, under which an order was made authorizing blood transfusions for a three-year-old child suffering from severe burns, was not unconstitutional as denying, in its application, due process to the child's parents who refused to authorize transfusions because the religious sect of which they were members forbade blood transfusions as violative of certain Biblical injunctions. The court noted that the evidence was undisputed that a transfusion was necessary, and that the best medical opinion held that to deprive the child of a transfusion would have been to risk his life. "When a child's right to live and his parents' religious beliefs collide," the court declared, "the former is paramount, and the religious doctrine must give way."[22]

A divorced mother's continuing custody of minor children was conditioned to eliminate the need for her consent to necessary transfusions of blood or plasma. The court ruled that the

---

[21] *State* v. *Perricone*, 181 A. 2d 751 (N.J.) (1962).

[22] In the Interest of Clark, Ohio Com. Pl., September 22, 1962; opinion by Judge Paul W. Alexander.

mother's religious practices could not be permitted to interfere with the welfare of her children. The father was a licensed physician and surgeon; the mother was a registered nurse. The mother became a Jehovah's Witness and was divorced by the father. The mother was given custody of their three children. The trial court did not remove the children from the custody of the mother, but conditioned her right to custody by requiring immediate written notice to the court if any of the children should be hospitalized, and requiring periodic reports by competent pediatricians.[23]

Elective Procedures

In elective procedures where there is no emergency, an adult patient has the right to impose the condition that no blood be administered (Fig. 44, p. 262; Fig. 45, p. 263; Fig. 46, p. 264; Fig. 47, p. 265). The surgeon in such case may elect whether or not to accept the patient for treatment. If the restriction on the use of blood is unknown to the surgeon until after the patient has been admitted to the hospital, he may decide whether to withdraw as physician, provided that the patient is not in imminent danger and has a reasonable opportunity to secure the services of another physician.

The best procedure, under ordinary circumstances, may be to obtain a release from the patient absolving the hospital and surgeon from liability on account of the patient's refusal to accept a blood transfusion.

Statement of American Hospital Association

It is suggested that the following points receive consideration by hospitals in the case of persons whose religious faith prohibits the transfusion of blood:

1. If the patient is an adult, a written refusal is recommended to absolve the hospital, the physician or physicians, and all other assisting personnel from liability, if any, for the failure to administer blood.

---

[23] *Levitsky* v. *Levitsky*, 190 A. 2d 621 (Md.) (1963).

2. If the patient is legally too young to make his own decisions, the written refusal of the parents, if available, should be secured. (In certain instances courts have in-

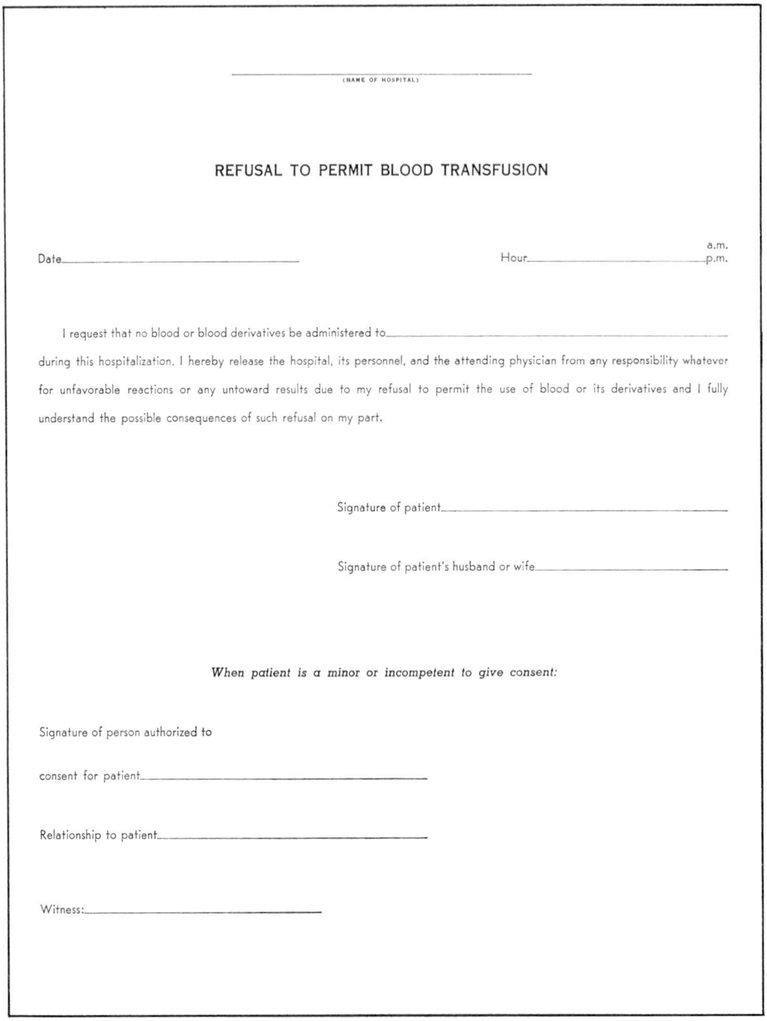

(NAME OF HOSPITAL)

REFUSAL TO PERMIT BLOOD TRANSFUSION

Date_____   Hour_____ a.m. / p.m.

I request that no blood or blood derivatives be administered to_____ during this hospitalization. I hereby release the hospital, its personnel, and the attending physician from any responsibility whatever for unfavorable reactions or any untoward results due to my refusal to permit the use of blood or its derivatives and I fully understand the possible consequences of such refusal on my part.

Signature of patient_____

Signature of patient's husband or wife_____

When patient is a minor or incompetent to give consent:

Signature of person authorized to

consent for patient_____

Relationship to patient_____

Witness:_____

FIG. 44 — REFUSAL TO PERMIT BLOOD TRANSFUSION

tervened to authorize transfusions to minors in spite of the objections of their parents).

3. In emergencies, and where release of the parents of mi-

nors is not obtainable, it would be expected that blood would be administered when medically indicated unless clear and convincing evidence is at hand that the patient,

---

AGREEMENT FOR BLOOD TRANSFUSION

TO: Dr_____and

_____Hospital.

Date:_____19____

1. I hereby request and authorize the administration of a blood transfusion to_____
(INSERT "MYSELF" OR NAME OF PATIENT)
and such additional transfusions as may be deemed advisable in the judgment of Dr._____,
the attending physician, or those he may designate to assist him.

2. It is understood and agreed that the attending physician or his assistant will be responsible only for the performance of their own individual professional acts, and that the blood typing and the selection of compatible blood are the responsibilities of those who actually perform the necessary laboratory tests.

3. It is further understood and agreed that no express or implied warranties were made to the undersigned or anyone else as to the blood or plasma or any other substances used or to be used in connection with such treatment and that the use of such blood or other substances is to be considered a service and not a sale.

4. It is further expressly agreed that I hereby release the Hospital, its personnel and medical staff from all responsibility or liability for the consequences, if any, resulting from the administration of blood, plasma or other substances.

Signature of patient_____

When patient is a minor
Signature of person authorized to
consent for patient_____

Relationship to patient_____

Address_____

Witness:_____

Address_____

City and State_____

FIG. 45 — AGREEMENT FOR BLOOD TRANSFUSION

if conscious, or the parent, if present, would refuse transfusion.

4. Jehovah's Witnesses consider blood derivatives objection-

able, but do not object to the use of blood substitutes.

5. Representatives of Jehovah's Witnesses state, "that a physician who is one of Jehovah's Witnesses may, accord-

---

TRANSFUSION REACTION REPORT

Patient's Name_____ Date_____

Hospital No._____ Room No._____

Doctor_____ Blood Bank Donor No._____

Diagnosis_____

Any history of abortion or pregnancy? If so, when?_____

Patient's temperature at start of transfusion_____ At end_____

Time started_____ Time stopped_____

Amount of blood given_____

SYMPTOMS	Immediate	Late
Chill		
Temperature (Record every 6 hours for 24 hours)		
Dyspnea		
Nausea		
Pain, with location		
Urticaria		
Hematuria, or dark urines		
Shock		
Jaundice		

Additional Information:_____

Signed:_____

FIG. 46 — TRANSFUSION REACTION REPORT

ing to his belief in the Bible, administer blood, if he can conscientiously do so, when required for the patient who has no objections or who does not indicate that he is one of Jehovah's Witnesses, when ordinary use and customary professional practice require it. If he desires to withdraw because of conscientious objection to blood transfu-

INVESTIGATION OF TRANSFUSION REACTION

Patient's Name_____Case No._____

Date and time of reaction_____Room No._____

Amount of blood in returned bottle_____Bottle No._____

RECHECK OF TYPINGS:

                              Anti-A   Anti-B   A cells   B cells   Anti-D

Patient's blood_____

Donor's blood from container_____

Pilot Tube_____

Patient is   Gr   Rh   Donor blood is   Gr   Rh

Appearance of patient's serum (plasma Hb.)_____

Appearance of donor's blood_____

Major crossmatch:

     in saline_____

     in albumin_____

     Indirect antiglobulin test (Coombs)

SPECIAL STUDIES:

_____

_____

URINE: (Appearance and examination for hemoglobin, etc.)_____

_____

CULTURE AND SMEAR:_____

_____

CONCLUSIONS:_____

_____

                                           Signed_____

FIG. 47 — INVESTIGATION OF TRANSFUSION REACTION

sion based on religious scruples, and he may professionally do so without serious hazard to the patient, he may turn the case over to another physician."

6. In view of the foregoing paragraph, it is desirable that provision be made within the hospital for the administration of blood to patients who do not object to its use, in the event that medical staff members are unwilling to administer blood because of their religious beliefs.

chapter 22

RECORDS OF ABORTIONS

W HILE criminal abortions are alien to the hospital, it is not unusual to admit cases of incomplete abortion, accidental or criminal. The abortionist may start the case in his office and advise the patient to go to her doctor or to a hospital when the miscarriage comes on.

For the protection of the hospital, nurses and medical staff, in every case of spontaneous, threatened or inevitable abortion requiring surgical treatment and in all cases of therapeutic and criminal abortions, a careful history should be taken. A meager history may lead to a slanderous accusation that a physician is an abortionist. Intent, a necessary element of the crime of abortion, may be spelled out of the history given. In addition, the patient should be requested to sign a "Release from Responsibility" form on admission (Fig. 48, p. 268).

Recording History and Opinions

Before deciding that the abortion is of criminal origin a competent medical opinion should be secured. That a woman has aborted after an accident or after medical treatment is not of itself evidence of criminal causation, for some women abort habitually. Causes of spontaneous abortion may include malposition or malformation of the uterus, violent exercise, diseases such as tuberculosis or a tumor of the abdominal cavity. An untreated syphilitic mother may bear an immature or premature deadborn infant. The thoroughness with which the record is prepared may ultimately determine the good or bad faith of the physician.

The Consultation Record

Except in an extreme emergency, before any operative procedure is undertaken, all cases of spontaneous, threatened or inevitable abortion should be seen by a member of the active or consulting staff in addition to the obstetrician on service; the written record of consultation (Fig. 12, p. 25) should be made before the uterus is emptied. In therapeutic abortions

RELEASE FROM RESPONSIBILITY
FOR ABORTION

Date ________ 19____ Time ________ a.m. / p.m.

This is to certify that I, ______________________________, a patient

applying for admission to ______________________________ Hospital
believe that I am in a condition of abortion. I hereby declare that neither the attending physician nor any person employed by or connected with the said hospital has knowingly performed any act which may have contributed to the induction of the abortion, and I do hereby absolve said persons from any responsibility or liability for my condition.

Witness ________________ Signed ________________
(PATIENT OR NEAREST RELATIVE)

Witness ________________ ________________
(RELATIONSHIP)

Authorization must be signed by the patient, or by the nearest relative when patient is physically or mentally incompetent.

FORM C-406 PHYSICIANS' RECORD CO., BERWYN, ILLINOIS PRINTED IN U.S.A.

FIG. 48 — RELEASE FROM RESPONSIBILITY FOR ABORTION

the consultant should give his affirmative opinion with a statement of the indications, over his signature, before the procedure is carried out. The consultation must not be a subterfuge for consent or approval.

The mere failure to obtain a consultation, however, is not sufficient to establish guilty intent; additional evidence is necessary to corroborate the claim of the state that the operation was for other than therapeutic purposes. The law requires consultation in Georgia, Maryland, New Mexico and Oregon.

Confidential Communications Concerning Abortions

Communications made to a physician or a nurse with respect to an abortion will be held not privileged if they were not connected with diagnosis or treatment. Among them may be a request made by a woman to a physician to commit the abortion; a communication from one physician to another made to secure the aid of the latter in performing the operation; or where the physician is consulted by the seducer concerning the possibility of committing the abortion.

Abortion Defined Medically

Medically, an abortion is the expulsion of the fetus before the child is viable; that is, any time before the end of the sixth month. According to some authors, expulsion of the fetus during the first three months is termed abortion; from this time to viability it is termed immature delivery or miscarriage, and from the period of viability to that of maturity it is defined as premature delivery.

Abortion Defined Legally

Abortion is the act of miscarrying or producing young before their natural time, or before the fetus is perfectly formed and lacking the power to live independently of its mother.

The statutes defining the crime of abortion provide that whoever, with the intent of producing the miscarriage of any pregnant woman or of any woman, unlawfully administers or causes to be given to her any drug or noxious substance whatsoever, or unlawfully uses any instrument or means whatever, with such intent, shall be guilty of the offense.

Most statutes specifically exempt those abortions performed to save life. It is for the jury to determine, in a prosecution for the criminal abortion, whether it was spontaneous or induced; whether, if intentionally induced, the act was medically justified or criminal and whether the abortion injured health or destroyed life.

Unlawful Inducing of Abortions

The physician recording the patient's history in case of abortion or suspected abortion should note whether instruments were used, the type of instruments, by whom used, in what manner and for what purpose; what drugs were prescribed and administered and by whom also should be noted.

The statutes impose criminal liability not only upon those who administer the drug or substance, but also upon all who aid, abet, advise or prescribe for the same, unless necessary to preserve the life of the woman.

All persons who assist in an illegal operation are equally guilty. A physician was convicted of the crime of abortion, even though it was not shown that he himself handled the instruments used. The act of aiding or assisting is no less criminal than the actual use of the instrument.

Generally, the woman consenting to an abortion is not regarded as an accomplice to the crime.

Therapeutic Abortions

Not all abortions are illegal. An abortion may be indispensable to save the mother in eclampsia, pulmonary disease, severe cardiac disease, nephritis and in other cases. There are no hard and fast rules as to the type of disease.

Therapeutic abortion may be defined, medically, as the deliberate termination of pregnancy prior to the period of fetal viability, because continuation of the pregnancy endangers the life or health of the mother or because the fetal hazard is markedly increased.

The medical indications for therapeutic abortion may be ovular, gynecological or systemic, the latter directly related to, or unrelated to, pregnancy. Whatever the medical indication suggested, there is always the question: Is the proposed abortion legal? The legal definition of therapeutic abortion is to be found in the exceptions provided in the statutes which define criminal abortion.

Except when done for therapeutic reasons (Fig. 49, below),

THERAPEUTIC ABORTION

Date ____________________

This is to certify that we, the undersigned husband and wife, declare that we, each and both of us, have been thoroughly instructed as to the effect of the proposed operation upon ____________________, wife of ____________________, and consent to the performance of the operation. We further agree that this operation is necessary for the protection of the wife's life and well-being. We absolve ____________________ Hospital and her attending physician from any responsibility for the wife's present condition or any condition that may result therefrom.

____
WIFE

____
HUSBAND

Signature Witnessed:

By ____________________

By ____________________

This completed form must be accompanied by consulting physician's report of examination and recommendation for termination of pregnancy.

FORM C-419 PHYSICIANS' RECORD CO., BERWYN, ILLINOIS - PRINTED IN U.S.A. (APPROVED BY CALIFORNIA HOSPITAL ASSOCIATION FORM CHA-4) THERAPEUTIC ABORTION

FIG. 49 — THERAPEUTIC ABORTION

preferably certified to by two or more reputable medical practitioners, the procedure is a criminal act. That the patient has consented to the operation does not make the procedure lawful, for any operation not required on medical grounds and which inflicts bodily injury is in itself a criminal act. Unless the nurse and physician can prove justification for the abortion, they may be convicted of the crime of unlawfully producing a miscarriage.

Whether an abortion is therapeutic or criminal may be a medicolegal question. To overcome the presumption that the physician acted in good faith, the prosecution must show by competent medical testimony that the abortion neither imminently nor potentially imperiled life. The defendant physician himself or through expert testimony then must show the therapeutic necessity. The jury will determine whom the credible evidence favors and to what extent.

Legal and Medical Indications for Therapeutic Abortions

What diseases or conditions in a pregnant woman are indications for a therapeutic abortion is a matter for medical testimony; honest differences of opinion may exist among practitioners and in the medical literature on the subject. Good judgment would therefore demand that the physician have at least one consultant in the case. A consultation is required in those cases in which a procedure is to be performed to interrupt a known or suspected pregnancy.

Medical therapy has so improved that few afflictions justify therapeutic abortion. The use of antibiotics has rendered almost unnecessary the interruption of pregnancy because of intractable pyelonephritis; the vomiting of pregnancy may be overcome by intravenous glucose and parenteral vitamins and in selected cases by psychotherapy. On the other hand, interruption may be justified in some cases of severe cardiorenal vascular disease, cardiac disease, pulmonary disease, urologic, neurologic and psychiatric disorders, and possibly some other medical conditions.

From a legal standpoint, it would appear a safe procedure to judge each case on its own merits, employ consultant service and base the ultimate need for interrupted pregnancy on the ground that death or serious impairment of health may reasonably be expected to follow if there is no abortion.

Religious Viewpoints

From the Catholic point of view, in all pregnancies whether normal or ectopic, it is illicit to kill the mother in order to save the child, or to kill the child in order to save the mother. The indirect loss of one life, resulting from an attempt to save the other, is morally justifiable, provided the physician does what he can to save both lives.

Direct abortion is a direct killing of an unborn child, and it is never permitted, even when the ultimate purpose is to save the life of the mother. Neither eclampsia, nor hyperemesis gravidarum, nor any other condition of pregnancy constitutes an exception to this prohibition.

Every procedure whose sole immediate effect is the termination of pregnancy before viability is a direct abortion. An abortion is said to be indirect when the interruption of the pregnancy is the undesired but unavoidable effect of a procedure immediately directed to some other good purpose (e.g., the stopping of hemorrhage or the removal of cancer). Granted that an abortion is indirect, it may be permitted for a sufficiently serious reason (e.g., when the procedure is really necessary to save the life of the mother), because in this case all the conditions of the principle of the double effect are applicable.

Operations, treatments and medications during pregnancy which have for their immediate purpose the cure of a proportionately serious pathological condition of the mother are permitted, even though they indirectly cause an abortion, when they cannot be safely postponed until the fetus is viable.

No procedure primarily designed to empty the uterus is permissible unless the physician is reasonably sure that the fetus is already dead or detached: procedures primarily designed to stop hemorrhage (as distinguished from those designed to empty the uterus) are permitted insofar as they are necessary, even to the extent of risking an abortion. In this case the abortion would be indirect.

Among orthodox Jews it is considered a criminal act to interrupt pregnancy after the fortieth day of gestation. However, to destroy the fetus to save the mother is not only permissible but is obligatory. The Protestant view approves the principle of birth control, but considers that the nontherapeutic abortion in general is sinful and abhorrent to right-minded people.

chapter 23

CONSENT FOR STERILIZATION
AND ARTIFICIAL INSEMINATION

STERILIZATION is the rendering of an individual unable to reproduce offspring by the closure of the tubes which carry the germ cells. In the female, these are the oviducts, known also as the salpinges or Fallopian tubes; the operation of closure is known as salpingectomy. The ovaries are not organically altered and menstruation continues normally. Sterilization can be accomplished also by irradiation or removal of the ovaries, or by removal of the uterus. In the male, the vas deferens on each side transmits the spermatozoa; the surgical procedure of blocking them is referred to as a vasectomy. Salpingectomy and vasectomy have become established as the terminology generally employed by surgeons.

Vasectomy and castration are to be distinguished; the former does not incapacitate the patient, as it is possible by a further operation to restore his reproductive powers. Vasectomy appears to have no untoward physical effect on the male organs; some men state that potency has increased following the procedure. Vasectomy does not cause hormone imbalance, alter personality or render the subject less competent to earn a livelihood or lead a normal life.

Legal Considerations

From a legal standpoint, sterilization has been defined as a procedure (surgical or otherwise) undertaken for the purpose of making one incapable of reproduction. The procedure should be distinguished from a case in which sterility results as a by-product of an operation for cure or alleviation of disease; e.g., panhysterectomy for cure of cancer in the female; bilateral orchidectomy for the purpose of inhibiting the spread of prostatic carcinoma in the male.

The law is concerned with sterilization, because the state has an interest in the perpetuation of its people through the bringing forth of children. Connecticut,[1] Kansas,[2] and Utah,[3] by statute, have declared operations for the purpose of destroying the power to procreate to be unlawful unless the same shall be medical necessity. In Utah, an unlawful sterilization is a felony, while in Iowa and Kansas such operations are misdemeanors. Connecticut, Indiana, Mississippi and Virginia prohibit nontherapeutic sterilization.

Criminal Liabilities

While castration may not be named specifically in a criminal statute as a crime, it may come under the definition of a mayhem, which is defined as the offense of depriving a person by violence of any limb, member or organ or causing any mutilation of the body. An older definition describes the crime as unlawfully depriving another of the use of such members as may render him less able in fighting, or disables the tongue, or puts out an eye, or slits the nose, ear or lips. The mayhem may be classed as an assault and battery in the statute.

Reasons for Sterilization Operations

A common reason advanced for a sterilizing operation is therapy. The whole or an important part of the reproductive system is excised in order to preserve the life or health of the patient. An example of this in the male is an orchidectomy to

---

[1] Gen. Stat. of Conn. ch. 200, sec. 4183.

[2] Gen. Stat. of Kan., 1919, ch. 76, sec. 76-155.

[3] Utah Code Anno., sec. 64-10-12.

reduce the spread of cancer in the prostate gland. Objections rarely are offered to this operation when it is undertaken after consultation with a specialist and with the express consent of the patient as well as that of his wife, if he is married.

Another example, in the female, is the excision of the diseased uterus or portions of the Fallopian tubes for the prevention of future pregnancies. From the legal point of view, such an operation is permissible when a physician after consultation has declared that it is necessary for the preservation of the patient's health. Where the purpose of the sterilization is therapeutic, the gynecologist should seek consultation with an obstetrician, neurologist or psychiatrist.

There are some indications for therapeutic sterilization upon which most medical men agree: among these are severe forms of heart disease, active pulmonary tuberculosis, severe kidney disease, severe diabetes, certain forms of insanity (dementia praecox, manic depressive psychosis), feeble-mindedness of the familial type, Huntington's chorea, hereditary optic atrophy, existing malignant tumors which may be further stimulated by pregnancy, aneurysm of large vessels, recurrent severe toxemia of pregnancy of the eclamptogenic or nephritic type, extreme contracted pelvis which makes Cesarean at term contraindicated or hazardous, and the repeated birth of monstrosities if there appears to be a strong hereditary tendency.

There is another group of conditions about which there may be divergence of opinion. This includes milder forms of heart disease and nephritis, inactive pulmonary tuberculosis, mild diabetes, psychoneurosis and past psychoses of various forms.

Various combinations of physical or mental defects, which if taken alone would not be sufficient to justify sterilization, may collectively be serious enough to warrant the procedure. Thus, a moderately contracted pelvis and cardiac disease, or a moderately severe diabetes in one who has had a malignant breast tumor removed, might justify sterilization.

Legal Control of Nontherapeutic Sterilization

Although sterilization laws may differ from state to state, one principle may be accepted as almost universal; that nontherapeutic sterilizations are prohibited.

Economic conditions which make the birth of additional children burdensome create no legal justification for such operation. However, in one case, it has been held in California that a nontherapeutic sterilization is legal. In that case, subsequent to the performance of a vasectomy upon the plaintiff, the plaintiff's wife became pregnant and he became the father of a child. The plaintiff sued the defendant physician for malpractice and breach of contract. The operation was performed solely for the convenience of the couple who wanted no more children. Neither the doctor nor the plaintiff challenged the legality of the nontherapeutic sterilization. Finding neither negligence nor breach of contract, the court held in favor of the defendant doctor, stating:

"Admittedly there is no statutory prohibition in California against sterilization as such, with consent, and it is legally recognized, although there are other states in which this particular operation is regulated.

"California recognizes sterilization in mental defectives and mentally deficient persons under the Health and Welfare Code as well as in the Penal Code for certain crimes under Section 645. In other words, it is not like an operation which is prohibited and unlawful, and there is no judicial or legislative announcement of public policy against sterilization as such, with the consent of the husband and wife, although in some states of the Union there is a prohibition against such an operation except where it is medically required."[4]

This position of the court is contrary to an opinion rendered by a former Attorney General of California and the dicta ex-

---

[4]*Corman* v. *Anderson*, Los Angeles Superior Court, California, No. 701, 588, (Nov. 16, 1960).

pressed in a 1943 California case, *Wiley* v. *Wiley,* 139 P. 2d 950; but in accord with a 1957 Pennsylvania case, *Shaheen* v. *Knight,* 11 D.C. 2d 41. In his opinion, the Attorney General of California indicated that a sterilization of convenience involves the crime of mayhem for which consent is no defense. In the *Wiley* case, the court assumed, without discussion, that sterilization without medical necessity is a wrongful act.

North Carolina, in 1963, following in the footsteps of Virginia, which in 1962 became the first state to enact such legislation, has adopted a statute authorizing voluntary sterilization of humans for non-medical reasons with appropriate provisions protecting the physician performing the procedure after a thirty-day "cooling-off" period.

Both the Virginia and North Carolina statutes prescribe a rather stringent procedure which must be followed if the physician seeks to take advantage of the liability protection afforded by the law. Virginia's law does not distinguish between therapeutic and non-therapeutic procedures, while North Carolina's statute provides that the new law shall not affect "therapeutical sterilization laws."

In four other states (Connecticut, Kansas, Montana and Utah) statutes which have been on the books for a number of years provide that it is illegal to sterilize any person for other than eugenic or therapeutic reasons. As to the law on this subject in other states, there appears to be sharp disagreement between medical-legal experts.

Prevention of Procreation of the Unfit (Eugenic)

Twenty-nine states have enacted legislation that provides for sterilization of the socially inadequate.[5] The law designates the classes of persons to which it applies, who may be included

---

[5] Alabama, Arizona, California, Connecticut, Delaware, Georgia, Idaho, Indiana, Iowa, Kansas, Maine, Michigan, Minnesota, Mississippi, Montana, Nebraska, New Hampshire, North Carolina, North Dakota, Oklahoma, Oregon, South Carolina, South Dakota, Utah, Vermont, Virginia, Washington, West Virginia, Wisconsin.

in one of five groups: feeble-minded, epileptic, habitual criminals or moral degenerates. Such statutes apply to the enumerated classes of defective persons confined in specified institutions.

In some states the statutes have expanded compulsory sterilization to include those who would probably become wards of the state; objection is made that punishment is inflicted on the unfortunate for an economic reason.

Conditions for Valid Consent

The circumstances in which a person may give valid consent to a sterility operation are not defined by law with precision. The voluntary sterilization of a resident of the state, on showing of good cause, is permitted in Delaware, Iowa, Maine, North Carolina, North Dakota and Vermont.

Consent is valid if the operation is for (1) the relief or cure of some existing disease, or (2) safeguarding the life of the woman when pregnancy, because of some existing disease or defect, would endanger her life. Consent may also be valid if the operation is required to prevent the birth of diseased or defective offspring when some existing transmissible disease or taint renders that result reasonably likely to follow conception. State law must be consulted.

A written consent from the patient (Fig. 50, p. 281), his parent or guardian if he is a minor, and from the spouse also if the patient is married, should be obtained after a disclosure of all the facts and medical grounds for the operation.

Consent of Husband for Operation on Wife

A wife in full possession of her faculties may determine for herself whether she shall submit to such an operation. The husband may not withhold necessary medical assistance to his wife by failing to give consent to an operation upon her. Nevertheless, as a matter of good public relations the husband's consent should be sought, for the absence of his authorization may point to a lack of good faith on the part of the wife or physician. Consultation to justify medical necessity for the operation is a precaution in every case.

STERILIZATION PERMIT

Date_____ Hour_____.M.

I hereby authorize and direct Doctor_____ and assistants of his choice to perform the following operation upon me at_____Hospital:

_____and to do any other procedure that his (their) judgment may dictate during the above operation. It has been explained to me that I may (or will probably) be sterile as a result of this operation, but no such result has been warranted. I understand that the word "sterility" means that I may be unable to conceive or bear children, and in giving my consent to the operation have in mind the possibility (probability) of such a result. I absolve said doctor, his assistants and the hospital from all responsibility for my present condition or any condition that may result from said operation.

Signed _____

Signature Witnessed:

By_____.

By_____

I join in authorizing the performance upon my wife (husband) of the surgery consented to above. It has been explained to me that as a result of the operation my wife (husband) may be sterile.

Signed _____

Signature Witnessed:

By _____

By _____

C-441   PHYSICANS RECORD CO., BERWYN, ILLINOIS - PRINTED IN U.S.A.   STERILIZATION PERMIT
(APPROVED BY CALIFORNIA HOSPITAL ASSOCIATION FORM CHA-7)

FIG. 50 — STERILIZATION PERMIT

Therapeutic Sterilization of the Husband

A man for whom sterilization is required is exposed to a lesser operative risk than a woman, for the tubes that carry his germ cells pass closer to the surface of his body. The operation, which is simpler, can be performed under local anesthesia. Since vasectomy is less complex for a man than a sterilization operation is for a woman, some married couples prefer the former, even though the primary object may be for the protection of the wife's health.

Religious Attitudes on Sterilization

Apart from the law there are also moral and religious objections to contraceptive sterilization. If such operations are permitted in a hospital, the religious persuasions of the patients should not be overlooked.

Sterilization of a female is licit if a pathological condition of the organ renders it necessary for the preservation of the patient's life or health, but it is illicit if the purpose of the operation or treatment is to prevent the inconveniences or dangers of childbearing. The purpose must be to aid the present state of the patient's health, and not be directed toward preventing her from conceiving in the future.

Civil Actions for Sterilization Operations

A few civil actions for damages have been recorded as a result of sterilization operations or negligent treatment unintentionally causing sterilization.

The wife of a man who had been emasculated by the malpractice of a physician sued him for having deprived her of potential motherhood. The court denied her compensation on the ground that the damages were too remote to be ascertainable.[6]

A man who submitted to an operation sued the doctor who had stated that he would be made sterile; the wife had given birth to another child. The court held that he could not recover damages from the physician; a physician does not guarantee

---

[6] *Landwehr* v. *Barbas*, 268 N.Y. 547, 241 App. Div. 769 (1935).

infallible results; no damage could be shown from the birth of a child. Consent is a shield against civil liability if the operating physician can show that the sterilization was performed in accordance with proper methods.[7]

In another case, a husband failed to give consent to a hysterectomy performed upon his wife who was a patient in a private mental hospital. The physician was held liable for the unlawful operation performed without consent.[8]

After two births had necessitated cesarean sections, the second involving an abdominal rupture and a toxic condition, the physician obtained the consent of the patient to tie the tubes and render her sterile. However, he failed to sterilize her, making another operation necessary. There was proof, said the court, from which a jury could find that the doctor contracted to do a sterilizing operation but failed to perform it, to the patient's damage. The damage was the need for a second operation and the expenses.[9]

In an English case, a woman became pregnant and delivered a stillborn child after an operation for sterilization. The surgeon had advised the operation because the woman had a weak heart. He decided not to use the usual techniques of sterilization because of the heart condition, but to use a less reliable method. The woman, however, did not keep an appointment to visit the outpatient clinic. The court ruled that the surgeon was not negligent in failing to warn the woman that there was a slight risk of pregnancy and to advise her to use contraceptives; it was impractical for the surgeon to give the advice in the hospital ward, since a number of the nurses and patients were Roman Catholic who, on conscientious grounds, would have objected to the giving of such advice. In the light of present medical opinion and practice, the court ruled that the sur-

[7] *Christenson* v. *Thornby*, 255 N.W. 620 (Minn.) (1934).

[8] *Pratt* v. *Davis*, 224 Ill. 300, 79 N.E. 562 (1906).

[9] *West* v. *Underwood*, 132 N.J.L. 325, 40 A. 2d 610 (1945).

geon did not fall short of professional standards. He was held not liable for the expense of a further sterilization operation which the woman underwent.[10]

Consent for Artificial Insemination

In one out of every three children resulting from artificial insemination, the donor is not the husband of the woman impregnated. In homologous insemination, the donor is the husband; the offspring is considered the legitimate issue of the couple. In heterologous insemination, the donor is one other than the husband of the woman, and the offspring is of questionable legitimacy, even though the husband may consent to the procedure. Little can be said, therefore, of the medicolegal aspects of artificial insemination, especially in the absence of legislation and because of the paucity of legal decisions.

The wife should consent in writing to the procedure as well as the husband. The donor should consent in writing to the unrestricted use of the semen he supplies and should certify that he will not attempt to ascertain the identity of the husband and wife involved. Written consent of the donor's wife should be secured as well. Permission for the physician to use his best judgment in selecting the donor should be given.[11]

Legal Decisions on Artificial Insemination

In a case in New York, the wife asked the court to determine her husband's right to visit the minor child of the two parties. It was conceded that she was artificially inseminated, with his consent, and that the child was not of his blood. The court held that the child had been potentially adopted or semi-adopted by the husband and that he was entitled to the same rights of visitation as those acquired by a foster parent who has for-

[10] *Waters* v. *Park, The Lancet,* Vol. II, No. 7195, p. 204 (Queens Bench Division, July 14, 1961).

[11] *Medicolegal Forms with Legal Analysis,* Law Department, American Medical Association, 1961.

mally adopted the child, if not to the same rights to which a natural father would be entitled under the same circumstances. Further, that the situation was no different from that involving a child born out of wedlock who is made legitimate by the marriage of the interested parties. Accordingly, he was granted the right to visit the child at specified times.[12]

In an Illinois case, in 1954, the court ruled that a "test tube" baby born of artificial insemination was illegitimate when the donor was a third party. The court also held that the wife who had been inseminated from a third party was guilty of adultery, irrespective of the husband's consent or otherwise. But if the husband is the donor, artificial insemination does not violate public policy and is not adultery.[13]

The husband and the wife, in a 1963 case in New York, agreed that she would be artificially inseminated with the semen of a third party donor. Both signed the consent to have this done; in addition the husband promised to pay all the expenses. He also signed a waiver of liability and for medical and/or surgical treatments. As a result of the artificial insemination a child was born. The court held that although the husband was liable for the support of the child, the child was "born out of wedlock" and must be construed to be an "illegitimate child."[14]

---

[12] *Strnad* v. *Strnad*, 190 Misc. 786, 78 N.Y.S. 2d 390 (1948).

[13] *Doornbos* v. *Doornbos*, 12 Ill. App. 2d 473, 139 N.E. 2d 844 (1956).

[14] *Gursky* v. *Gursky*, 242 N.Y.S. 2d 406 (1963).

chapter 24

AUTOPSY CONSENTS

THE first record of an autopsy in North America is one in
Salem, Massachusetts, in 1639. During the next few dec-
ades in the Colonies a number of such examinations were conducted chiefly for medicolegal reasons. The rise of medical
schools, the increase in the number of physicians, and the recognition in medical circles of the need for knowledge of the
human body based upon dissection resulted in an increased
number of postmortems.

Autopsies, necropsies and postmortem examinations are syn-
onymous terms. Autopsies are scientific procedures, the purpose of which is to establish with all possible accuracy the
cause of death; to determine the nature and cause of the pathological processes involved, and to acquire reliable information
concerning the nature and cause of disease. The ultimate objective is to add to the sum total of our knowledge concerning
the diseases from which the patient suffered and in this way
to improve the health of mankind.

Today, the percentage of autopsies is one of the best indices
of the standard of medical practice in a hospital. The Joint
Commission on Accreditation of Hospitals desires that autopsies be performed on the bodies of at least 20 per cent of the
persons dying within the hospital, and the American Medical
Association for approval of an intern training program requires an autopsy rate of at least 25 per cent of deaths occurring within the hospital.

Who May Pronounce the Patient Dead

Death is said to be the cessation of all vital functions without capability of resuscitation. Only a person licensed to practice medicine is qualified to pronounce a patient dead, except that an unlicensed intern may do so in some states. A nurse has no such legal authority, nor the right to fill out and file a death certificate; her responsibility ends with noting the time the person apparently ceased to breathe, if she is in attendance at that time, and notifying the attending doctor or a staff member. A hospital without an intern or resident staff should insist that all patients receiving medical attention be assigned to a member of the attending staff.

Persons authorized to pronounce death are generally enumerated in state and local statutes.

The Death Certificate

Inasmuch as the issuing of a burial permit depends upon the presentation of a properly executed death certificate, the complete reporting of deaths is assured except in those cases where a body is disposed of illegally. The law specifies who may sign a death certificate and on what form, indicates the circumstances under which a death shall be reported to the medical examiner or coroner, and states the procedure by which a burial permit may be obtained.

The properly filled out death certificate may become valuable to the survivors for insurance and inheritance purposes. As community statistics, much information is derived from the complete and accurate registration of deaths with respect to age, sex, race, location of residence and occurrence, occupation and other pertinent facts.

When a death certificate is rejected because the certified cause of death is ambiguous or improper, the hospital must assume responsibility for the resulting delay. This inconvenience to the family and the funeral director will certainly result in a deterioration of the hospital's public relations.

Rights in Dead Bodies

The common law does not regard a dead human body as property which may be sold, nor as an asset of the estate of the deceased. For the same reason, at common law, a person could not make an agreement whereby he disposed of his body after death, so as to violate the right of his wife or relatives to bury the body. The established rule, however, is that although there can be no property right in a dead body in a commercial sense, there is a quasi-property right to the extent of investing the nearest relatives with the right to bury their dead.

For the purpose of preservation and burial, a surviving spouse or next of kin, in the absence of a different disposition by will, has the right to possession of the dead body. The wishes of a decedent in the matter of the disposition of his remains are paramount and in some jurisdictions this right is confirmed specifically by statute.

Damages for Unlawful Autopsies

It is a rule of law, as held in an action for an unauthorized autopsy, that a person mutilating a body, without the consent of those entitled to possession, is liable for injury to the feelings of the next of kin resulting from such unlawful act, even though no money damage is alleged or proved.[1] The courts recognize that an act of indignity upon the dead body may entitle the kindred to substantial damages.

The damages awarded are never for injury done to the body as a piece of property, but for the injury to the feelings and the mental suffering of the living from the illegal act. In a case against the State of New York, a widow sought to recover for an unlawful autopsy upon the body of her deceased husband, and for failure to replace the brain, heart and other organs. In giving a judgment of damages for the widow, the court could

---

[1] *Beller* v. *City of New York*, 269 App. Div. 642, 58 N.Y.S. 2d 112 (1945).

see no justification for the autopsy; the unauthorized post-mortem and dismemberment were held to have injured her feelings. Proof of pecuniary loss was not essential to recover damages. The sum of $1,000.00 was awarded as the reasonable settlement for damages.[2]

Securing Permission for Autopsy

The necropsy authorization in some states need not be in writing, but for the protection of hospital and pathologist none should be performed with only verbal permission, except under unusual circumstances. One willing to give oral consent some-times refuses to sign a permit; in such case the person secur-ing the consent should sign a statement as to the circum-stances, indicating the name, address and relationship of the individual giving oral permission. A witness to the verbal au-thorization should sign the statement.

Administrative Responsibility for Autopsy

Proper authorization for postmortem examination is of the utmost importance. Staff members enthusiastic about a case may seek to obtain permission from any relative present. The administrator or some person in an administrative capacity should review each case, for it is his responsibility and that of his institution to exercise due care to the end that laws and regulations governing the performance of autopsies are ob-served.

Necropsy authorizations are consents for the institutional officers to perform autopsies, which are actually done by the pathologist; he should see that the forms have been properly signed and approved and note the limitations to the consents. Where the pathologist serves on a salaried basis, he may be considered an employee or agent of the hospital. He does the autopsy at the direction of the administration. If the autopsy proves unauthorized, both the hospital and the pathologist may

---

[2]*Gould* v. *State of New York*, 181 Misc. 884, 46 N.Y.S. 2d 313 (1944).

be liable for civil damages; in certain states, the physician may be subject to criminal penalties or disciplinary action.

As a rule the consent is attached to the report of autopsy and made part of the medical record. The pathologist who is not a member of the regular staff of the hospital may request that the permit be kept in the files of the pathology department.

In the zeal to obtain permission for autopsy, no one should make any promises which cannot or will not be kept. If limitations are accepted, these must be adhered to strictly. To do otherwise is inexcusable, constitutes a betrayal of the family's confidence, and may lead to a lawsuit. As a general rule, it will be found that unreasonable restrictions need not be promised. The relative who gives consent will usually permit an adequate postmortem examination.

Whenever an extensive dissection is necessary, every effort should be made to cooperate with the embalmer in proper restoration of the body before its delivery. At the conclusion of the autopsy a responsible member of the pathology department should review the body to check the condition in which it is to be delivered to the funeral director.

Use of Telegraph or Telephone Consent

The use of telegraph or telephone to obtain consent would have certain disadvantages if it became necessary to prove the identity of the sender. The telegram may have originated by a telephone call to the telegraph office or by a written request, perhaps destroyed by the company. If a dispute should arise as to the right to give consent or as to identity, difficulty in proving handwriting and relationship may follow. Having another person listen in on a telephone extension is of doubtful value; neither the speaker nor the so-called witness may be able to identify the distant voice. Before one can testify to such telephone conversation, it would be necessary to indicate that he recognized the voice of the person who had been called as belonging to that person.

Although the use of telegraph or telephone to obtain consent may be more or less precarious, as a practical and very necessary expedient this method is used by many hospitals, particularly if patients come from long distances and are unaccompanied by relatives or friends. If these media for communication were not resorted to, the hospital would lose an appreciable number of autopsies. The risk is a calculated one in the interests of practicality, as it is in commercial transactions which daily are consummated by telegraph, letter or telephone. Many hospitals realize the objections from a strictly legal standpoint, but feel that the use of standard media of communication in the community would be regarded as the application of "reasonable care" and good faith, sufficient to constitute a valid legal defense against the rare possibility of a lawsuit.

In Connecticut, Indiana, Kentucky, Pennsylvania and the City of New York, telegraphic permission for autopsy is specifically authorized by statute.

Limitations on Autopsies

A common form of authority for autopsy gives the relationship to the deceased of the person giving consent, and authorizes such examination of the body and of its tissues as may be necessary to determine the cause of death (Fig. 51, p. 292). It provides for a witness and the signature of the person consenting. Any restrictions should be specifically noted on the form.

The one who has the right to permit an autopsy also has the right to restrict it. A note of such limitation should be made on the necropsy permit and the pathologist notified. However, a consent which authorizes examination to ascertain the cause of death impliedly permits the removal of organs necessary for microscopic examination, provided no tissue is retained. It is important that the consent specifically include a provision permitting the retention of diseased tissue or organs.

Limitations on the authorization must be observed to prevent lawsuits. To minimize the proposed size of the incision may be a mistake; it may give rise to the claim that there was misrepresentation as to the extent of the necropsy. Whatever arguments are advanced or proposals made, they should be truthfully and tactfully presented.

AUTHORIZATION FOR AUTOPSY

Date________________ 19____ Time__________ a.m. p.m.

I, ______________________________, bearing the relationship of ______________________, to

______________________________ recently deceased in ______________________________
(NAME OF PATIENT)

Hospital, hereby authorize Dr. ______________________________ and such persons as he may designate, to perform a

COMPLETE.............☐ HEAD only..............☐ TRUNK only.............☐

postmortem examination on the body of the deceased, and to remove and retain such organs, or parts of organs and tissues as may be necessary for further study to determine the cause of death, and to advance medical knowledge and progress. It is understood that due care will be taken to avoid mutilation or disfigurement of the body.

Witness______________________ Signed______________________
(NEAREST OF KIN)*

Witness______________________ ______________________
(RELATIONSHIP)

*For the purpose of this authorization the surviving spouse shall be considered the next of kin. In the absence of a surviving spouse, the next of kin shall be identified in accordance with the applicable state law.

FORM C-401 PHYSICIANS' RECORD CO., BERWYN, ILLINOIS PRINTED IN U.S.A.

FIG. 51 — AUTHORIZATION FOR AUTOPSY

Religious Objections to Autopsies

Nowhere in the Bible, in the Talmudic or post-Talmudic writings, is there evidence that postmortem examinations are prohibited by the Jewish law. According to traditional interpretations, which are not necessarily accepted by all Jewish groups, autopsies and transplantations of organs are permitted only in those cases where the decedent gave consent.

There is no definite statement by the Catholic Church which can be construed as prohibiting autopsies; autopsies have been encouraged when it appeared that benefit would accrue from them. Similarly, there appears to be nothing in the writings of the Protestant clergy to point to a prohibition on autopsies.

Persons to Give Consent for Autopsy

The basis of an action for damages for the mutilation of a dead body has developed through the duty of burial by the nearest relatives and their right to its possession intact for that purpose. The right to maintain an action for the willful mutilation of a corpse must be determined by the individual who has the right of custody of the body for burial.

The surviving spouse is first in line for such custody and has the primary right to give or to withhold consent. Either widow or widower may maintain an action for the unlawful mutilation of the body of the spouse. A widow who was living with her husband at the time of his death has a right to possession of the husband's body for burial, which is paramount to the right of next of kin.

Where there is a surviving spouse entitled to consent to autopsy, the authorization of neither the adult children nor the brothers and sisters of the deceased is valid.

The words "next of kin" generally do not include a widow or widower but those who are related in proximity of blood and who inherit. "Next of kin" is the person or persons in the nearest degree of relationship by blood; such kinsmen are usually defined by the statute designating who is entitled to inherit the property of the deceased if he died without a will.

Of importance in determining who has the right to give consent to the necropsy may be the circumstances surrounding the life of the decedent and the acceptance of responsibility for burial. The ordinary rights which exist by reason of close ties of blood or marital relationships may be forfeited through the conduct of such relatives, to be supplanted by more distant kin who have manifested a close interest in the decedent.

California amended its law in 1963 to provide that a physician may perform an autopsy if the decedent prior to his death authorized it in his will or other written instrument or upon receipt of written authorization from any person representing himself to be either (1) the surviving spouse; (2) a surviving child or parent; (3) a surviving brother or sister; (4) any other kin or person who has acquired the right to control the disposition of the remains; (5) a public administrator; or (6) a coroner or other authorized public officer. The amended law specifically provides that a physician is not liable for performing an autopsy in accordance with such authorization unless he has actual notice that the representation is untrue at the time the autopsy is performed. If the authorization for an autopsy is contained in a will, the autopsy may be performed regardless of the validity of the will or of the fact that the will may not be offered for or admitted to probate until a later date.

A new Idaho statute authorizes any physician to conduct a post-mortem examination of the body of a deceased when consent has been given by whichever one of the following assumes custody of the body for the purposes of burial: father, mother, husband, wife, child, guardian, next-of-kin, or in the absence of any of the foregoing, a friend or a person charged by law with the responsibility for burial. If two or more persons assume custody of the body, the consent of one of them shall be deemed sufficient.

A 1963 West Virginia law contains provisions similar to the California and Idaho statutes. Like the Idaho statute it does not specifically exempt the physician from civil liability in the event that he mistakenly relies on an authorization given by an unqualified party.

Separation by Abandonment of Spouse

In a technical sense the word "abandonment" is the relinquishing of a right to which one is entitled. Desertion of one spouse by the other is the cessation of cohabitation and a wrongful refusal on the part of the spouse charged with the desertion to live with the other.

Abandonment or desertion of the decedent by the surviving

spouse results in a waiver of the right of the survivor. Waiver can also be inferred from the disinterest of the surviving spouse.

Where the wife of her own volition is not living with her husband at the time of his death or refuses to assume the trust incident to her right, a waiver of that right is implied and the right immediately descends to the next of kin. The right of the spouse must be promptly asserted, or the right to possession of the body for burial will be held to have been waived in favor of the next of kin.

Separation by Agreement of Spouses

There are also separations by agreement between a husband and wife contemplating their living separate and apart. Written separation agreements may be approved by the court and a decree of separation granted based on such agreement.

In the case of a separation by mutual agreement, it may not be feasible to show the abandonment of one spouse by the other, but it may be possible to establish a relationship of complete disinterest in one another, or a waiver otherwise of the right to grant or deny consent.

Effects of Judicial Separation

There is a difference in the rights of parties to a marriage in separations due to abandonment or desertion and those resulting from a judicial separation.

A judicial separation is the granting of a decree or judgment by a competent court of the right of one spouse to live apart from the other and of the rights of property and the custody of their children, without divorce.

The decree acts as a mere temporary limited divorce *a mensa et thoro* (from bed and board), leaving all the other marital rights and obligations in full force during the life of the parties and subject to the complete restoration of the marital status by reconciliation. It does not end the marriage relation, but merely suspends certain of their marital rights and obligations, such as cohabitation, until they come together again as husband and wife.

The fact that the court has authorized the parties to the marriage to live apart temporarily would not appear to cause a forfeiture of the right of the surviving spouse to consent or refuse to authorize an autopsy. There would have to be shown some other facts in the relationship of the parties to warrant the conclusion that interest by the surviving spouse in the deceased was abandoned.

When Spouses Have Been Divorced

A marriage is dissolved only by the death of one of the parties, or by the judgment of a court of competent jurisdiction decreeing a divorce of the parties. The word "divorce" imports a dissolution of the marriage relation between husband and wife, in which there is a complete severance of the tie by which the parties were united; the marriage relation is as absolutely destroyed as if dissolved by death. It is an absolute divorce *a vinculo matrimonii* (from the bonds of matrimony) as distinguished from a judicial separation *a mensa et thoro* (from bed and board).

Divorce between the spouses terminates their legal relationship, so that upon the decease of one, the other has no right in the disposition of the body or to consent to autopsy.

However, a husband against whom has been entered only an interlocutory decree of divorce, which is a decree made pending a final judgment of divorce, is not divorced within the definition of the term "divorced."

Adult Children of Deceased Parent

There appears to be generally an equal right to give consent for autopsy among surviving adult children, in the absence of a living spouse, provided the children have not alienated themselves from the deceased by unwillingness to support, a lack of affection or interest in the parent, or other conduct which might constitute a forfeiture of the right. Whether the consent of only one child or the oldest child or the one taking care of the burial is sufficient is a matter of state statute or judicial interpretation of who is entitled to that right.

Minor Children of Deceased

If no surviving parent exists, minor children of sufficient maturity who are the next of kin have the right to consent to necropsy on the deceased parent.

Rights of Mother of Deceased Child

The courts are not in agreement as to whether the consent of the father alone, without that of the mother, is sufficient to authorize an autopsy on a deceased child. The test is to examine the state statutes as to whether both parents are charged with the support of a minor child, whether one or both parents are made next of kin or whether the father alone is deemed such; also who is under a duty to provide burial, and whether such parent can pay the cost.

A widow may recover for an unlawful autopsy upon the body of her unmarried minor son, as well as for an unlawful autopsy upon the body of her adult unmarried son who resided with her. Where the father is deceased, a mother may recover for an unlawful autopsy on her unmarried daughter.

When Father Has Preference

Where by statute the father is made next of kin of his child to the exclusion of the mother, he is preferred to the mother. The fact that the mother is entitled equally with the father to the estate of the deceased child has no bearing; it is the father's duties to the child which are determinant.

Parent May Forfeit Right

The wishes of parents and near relatives concerning their deceased are not lightly set aside at the instance of strangers to the blood or of distant relatives. There are exceptions which arise out of such circumstances as would deprive a natural guardian of the child's custody.

When a divorce is granted, the court makes provision for the guardianship, support and education of the minor children, and may modify such order when circumstances are such as to render a change proper.

Brothers and Sisters of Deceased

While the widow is living, the brothers and sisters of the deceased have no rights in the body and may not bring an action for its willful mutilation. However, if the widow has yielded her right of disposition of the remains or has been estranged from the deceased in his lifetime, she forfeits her right to give or deny consent for autopsy.

Executors and Administrators as Such Have No Control

According to the weight of authority, executors and administrators, as such, may not recover damages for the unlawful mutilation of a dead body. The fact that the administrator must pay the funeral expenses as the first of debts does not make him the legal custodian of the remains. However, if the legal representative of the estate is also the relative entitled to possession of the body for burial, the spouse or next of kin, as such, may bring an action for unlawful mutilation.

Under the statutes the right to administration of the estate is that, first, of the surviving spouse. To such survivor also belongs the right of control of the body for interment; a waiver of the right to administer the estate does not include a waiver of such burial right.

Authorization by Statute

The rights of hospitals, where the persons legally entitled to custody of the body are unknown, are such rights as are given by statute. Most states have adopted "anatomical acts" which provide that the bodies of persons dying in hospitals, prisons or other public institutions, and which have to be buried at

public expense, shall be surrendered to regularly established
medical or dental schools for the purpose of the advancement
of science.

In the main, the statutes are similar, providing for the delivery of the corpse to a medical or dental school in the state
authorized to confer the professional degree or to teach medicine, anatomy or surgery, or to any university in the state
having a medical preparatory or post-graduate course.

A specified time must elapse subsequent to the patient's
death before the body may be surrendered or autopsied at the
hospital. A reasonable effort must be made to communicate
with relatives; if they cannot be found, friends should be
sought. A friend claiming the corpse for burial may be required to present an affidavit stating the facts of his friendship and that he assumes the cost of burial. Unless such affidavit is made, the hospital need not deliver the corpse.

Autopsies in Insurance Cases

Certain life insurance policies exclude from coverage "accidental injury, disability, dismemberment or death caused directly or indirectly, wholly or partly, by disease in any form,
fits, vertigo, mental infirmity or bacterial infection," etc. The
standard autopsy clause reads: "The Company shall have the
. . . right and opportunity to make an autopsy in case of death
where it is not forbidden by law." If the cause of death is in
dispute, the services of a pathologist may be necessary.

The standard statutory insurance provisions that an insurer
may examine the person of the insured and, if not forbidden
by law, make an autopsy in case of death, are in force in Arizona, California, Connecticut, Delaware, District of Columbia,
Illinois, Indiana, Iowa, Kansas, Maryland, Michigan, Minnesota, New Hampshire, New Jersey, New York, North Carolina,
Pennsylvania, South Dakota, Tennessee, Vermont, Washington, West Virginia, Wisconsin and Wyoming.

Demand for autopsy must be made by the insurer within a

reasonable time after death. Courts are averse, under ordinary circumstances, to ordering disinterment for autopsy for insurance purposes. The autopsy surgeon chosen to do the necropsy should secure the consent of the person authorized by law to give it, not necessarily the beneficiary of the policy, or in the alternative, an agreement from the insurer to hold him harmless if a claim is made for unlawful autopsy.

Medical Examiner's and Coroner's Cases

The office of coroner is an ancient one, and came with the common law to this country from England. In the United States the coroner is an elective county officer. His powers and duties here are what they were at common law, except as they have been modified by our statutes. At common law, the coroner was required to hold an inquest before a coroner's jury to seek information and evidence in case of death by violence or other undue means, and thus to prevent the escape of the guilty.

The coroner's office in some states has been abolished and that of medical examiner substituted. The right to autopsy exists for both coroner and medical examiner by statute. The medicolegal autopsy is not only for the purpose of determining the cause of death, but also to decide whether it was due to natural causes or otherwise. Such an autopsy differs from the ordinary hospital post mortem in that it is primarily concerned with whether the death was suicidal, accidental, homicidal or due to natural causes. The coroner's autopsy may not be held except as incidental to an inquest. Such autopsy needs no consent of the family of the deceased. The coroner may summon witnesses to the inquest, select a jury, listen to evidence, determine the cause of death and even find that the person came to his death at the hands of a certain named person.

In most of the states where the office of coroner functions, the law does not require him to be a physician. Even in many large cities, neither medical nor legal qualifications are required of one seeking the office of coroner. The local mortician is the coroner in some counties. A state might be well served by having a central medicolegal laboratory with toxicologists, pathologists and other experts available for regional or local work, in place of the coroner system.

Hospital Cases for Coroners or Medical Examiners

The coroner or medical examiner investigates deaths involving violence or suspicious circumstances. If ascertaining the cause of death requires facts other than those obtained by questioning, an autopsy may be necessary. In medicolegal autopsies, a great deal of detail is often required, not usually true of the ordinary autopsy.

Reporting of deaths to the medical examiner or coroner is usually required by law if the death is considered wholly or in part the result of accident, suicide or homicide; if abortion or poisoning is alleged, or if the death is closely associated with or allegedly caused by a therapeutic substance, procedure or operation. Included in this last category will be deaths under anesthesia, in the operating room, and following transfusion; deaths following the administration of arsenicals; such diseases as agranulocytosis, aplastic anemia and homologous serum jaundice. Deaths occurring after a short stay in a hospital (before a reasonable clinical diagnosis has been made), deaths that are unusual, entirely unexpected, or in which criminal or civil actions are likely to follow, are all reportable.

It is a criminal offense to conceal from the medical examiner's or coroner's office any case which properly belongs under his jurisdiction. It is similarly a criminal offense and civilly actionable for one to report a case to the medical examiner's or coroner's office fraudulently, for the sole purpose of obtaining an unauthorized autopsy. There may be legitimate doubt as to whether a case is properly one to report. In such cases, the medical examiner or coroner on duty in the area where the hospital is located, should be consulted. A record should be made of the discussion with him, and this should be incorporated in the hospital chart for future reference.

The medical examiner or coroner is given the right by law to use his judgment as to whether or not he will perform the autopsy. He may perform the autopsy, or in cases in which criminal action or civil litigation is not likely to follow, he may permit the hospital to solicit consent. If this effort to get authorization is successful, he may permit the pathologist to perform the autopsy under his supervision, or he may declare that the case reported is not one for his office, in which event the hospital must issue the certificate without delay, either with or without autopsy.

Transplantation of Tissues and Organs

Medical science has developed methods which enable physicians to remove tissue from persons immediately following death and to use the tissue for living persons to replace or rehabilitate tissues or even organs (Fig. 52, p. 303) of the human body, such as kidneys or the eyes.

The transferring of tissue as a life-prolonging or life-saving measure has acquired general acceptance by the medical profession. Autologous transplantation of tissue, i.e., from one part of the individual to another, as skin, bone, cartilage has met with success. Homologous transplantation of tissue from one individual to another, as corneal grafts, is also practiced. Advances in methods of tissue storage enable vessel transplantation to be performed. The transplantation of bone tissue to a patient may be done from a donor who has required chest surgery.

The use of skin grafts for patients who have suffered extensive skin losses, particularly burns, has been practiced for years, but the grafts used were autografts; that is, they were from patients' own bodies. There was still considerable loss of life and long convalescence because only a limited amount of skin could be obtained. Therefore, it was natural that the prac-

tice of using skin from another person (homografting) was
developed. Postmortem homografts may be obtained from pa-

DONOR'S AUTHORIZATION FOR REMOVAL OF ORGAN

I, the undersigned, hereby authorize_____Hospital to remove

_____from my body after death,

SPECIFY ORGAN(S)

for the purpose of using such organs for transplantation to another person, if possible.

Dated:_____   Signed:_____

Witness:_____

- -

AUTHORIZATION OF PARENTS OF INFANT FOR REMOVAL OF ORGAN

We, the undersigned, parents of_____, an infant,

do hereby authorize_____Hospital and its physicians to remove

_____from the body of our child

SPECIFY ORGAN(S)

upon his decease for the purpose of transplantation to another child, if possible.

Dated:_____   Signed:_____

Witness:_____   Relationship:_____

                                             Signed:_____

                                             Relationship:_____

- -

AUTHORIZATION OF NEXT OF KIN OF ADULT FOR REMOVAL OF ORGAN

The undersigned, being next of kin of_____

deceased, hereby authorize(s)_____Hospital to remove_____

from the body of said decedent for the purpose of transplantation to another person, if possible.   SPECIFY ORGAN(S)

Dated:_____   Signed:_____

Witness:_____   Relationship:_____

                                             Signed:_____

                                             Relationship:_____

FIG. 52 — DONOR'S AUTHORIZATION FOR REMOVAL OF ORGAN

tients soon after death and used with success in the same manner as fresh homografts.[3]

---

[3] BRADLEY, F. R., BROWN, J. B., FRYER, M. P., and ZAYDON, T. J., "Skin Bank Stores
Postmortem Homografts," *Hosp.*, 31:54, January 16, 1957.

Banks for the storage of skin, arteries, cartilage, bone, eyes and blood depend upon the hospital's needs and the availability of material. Since the organs and tissue to be stored must be removed almost immediately after death, it is imperative that arrangements for securing organs and tissue be consummated before death. Consent for the use of tissue or organs of a deceased person, such as kidneys (Fig. 53, below) (Fig. 54, p.

AUTHORIZATION FOR KIDNEY TRANSPLANT (ADULT)

The undersigned, hereby authorizes and requests Dr._____

and whomever he may designate as his assistants to perform a kidney transplant upon me at _____Hospital.

I understand that the Hospital will try to obtain a normal kidney from whatever source is available and will surgically transplant this kidney into my abdomen; that my diseased kidney(s) will be removed subsequently if the doctors are satisfied that the transplanted kidney is functioning properly.

I understand that there may be a greater risk of infection than in other types of surgery, and that my body may reject the transplanted kidney. I also understand that my prognosis is poor at this time and the Hospital and doctors ave made no representation nor given assurances as to the success or result of this procedure.

I consent to the administration of such anesthetics as are necessary and I authorize the hospital to dispose of any tissue or parts surgically removed in accordance with its accustomed practice.

I hereby certify that I have read and fully understand the above **Authorization for Kidney Transplant**, the reasons why the above named surgery is considered necessary, its advantages and possible complications, if any, as well as possible alternative modes of treatment, which were explained to me by Dr._____

Date:_____   Signed:_____

Witness:_____

FIG. 53 — AUTHORIZATION FOR KIDNEY TRANSPLANT (ADULT)

305) or eyes for corneal grafts, may come either antemortem from the prospective donor or postmortem from the next of kin; living donors generally are a limited source of tissue to be used for therapeutic purposes. If any great amount of tissue is to become available for homografts or certain other purposes it must come from the bodies of deceased persons.

Legal Control of Transplantations

Many states have specific statutes that permit persons to

donate their bodies or parts of their bodies for medical use. These laws specifically authorize donations of bodies or body parts by the deceased prior to death. The statutes often require that the instrument of donation be executed with certain legal formalities and, in some instances, provide that it be filed as a matter of public record. Statutes also provide that a donation is effective immediately at death, even if contained in a will,

AUTHORIZATION FOR KIDNEY TRANSPLANT (INFANT)

We, (names of parents)_____

of (address)_____who are

the parents of_____an infant presently

hospitalized at _____ Hospital, do hereby authorize and request Dr._____
and whomever he may designate as his assistants to perform a kidney transplant upon our child named above.

We understand that the Hospital will try to obtain a normal kidney from whatever source is available and will surgically transplant this kidney into our child's abdomen; that our child's diseased kidney(s) will be removed subsequently if the doctors are satisfied that the transplanted kidney is functioning properly.

We understand that there may be a greater risk of infection than in other types of surgery, and that our child's body may reject the transplanted kidney. We also understand that the prognosis is poor at this time and the Hospital and doctors have made no representations nor given assurances as to the success or result of this procedure.

We consent to the administration of such anesthetics as are necessary and we authorize the hospital to dispose of any tissue or parts surgically removed in accordance with its accustomed practice.

We hereby certify that we have read and fully understand the above **Authorization for Kidney Transplant**, the reasons why the above named surgery is considered necessary, its advantages and possible complications, if any, as well as possible alternative

modes of treatment, which were explained to us by Dr._____

Date_____   Father's Signature_____

Witness_____   Mother's Signature_____

FIG. 54 — AUTHORIZATION FOR KIDNEY TRANSPLANT (INFANT)

and regardless of the validity of the will in other respects. The need for prompt action to preserve parts of the body for future use accounts for this type of legislation.

The donation statutes usually describe the eligible recipients of bodies or body parts as institutions which preserve, store, and use bodies and parts for medical purposes. The donation is not invalidated even if no recipient is named, so long as the body is made available to a worthy recipient; some statutes do not deal at all with the recipients.[4]

New laws revising or facilitating the gift of human bodies, eyes and other tissue were adopted in 1963 in Connecticut, Florida, Indiana, Nevada, South Carolina and South Dakota, and New Jersey, in addition to states which already have some form of legislation, such as Alabama, Alaska, Arizona, Arkansas, California, Colorado, Georgia, Illinois, Iowa, Kentucky, Louisiana, Maine, Maryland, Michigan, Minnesota, Missouri, Montana, Nebraska, New Mexico, New York, North Carolina, North Dakota, Oklahoma, Oregon, Pennsylvania, Tennessee, Texas, Washington, West Virginia, Wisconsin, and the Commonwealth of Puerto Rico.

---

[4] HERSHEY, N., "Obtaining Consent for the Use of Body Tissues," 63:105, *Am. J. Nurs.*, August, 1963.

chapter 25

MEDICAL STAFF ORGANIZATION

ONE of the most important responsibilities of the trustees constituting the governing board of a hospital is the selection of a competent medical staff. The governing board has a moral, if not legal, responsibility for the conduct of the professional staff in the care of patients in the hospital. Court decisions hold that the governing board is charged with the duty of appointing qualified practitioners of medicine, although the actual recommendations are made by the medical staff.

Patients of the hospital are protected against unqualified practitioners, through the certification of physician specialists by the various specialty boards. Within the hospital there is usually a tissue committee or some other group, whose function is to measure the performance of staff physicians, thus assuring year-round safeguards against unauthorized, unnecessary or improper treatment. Little is left to the lay governing board, except to approve the recommendations of the medical board which examines into the qualifications of applicants to the staff.

Responsibilities of Governing Board

The governing board of the hospital through the medical staff bylaws should establish the organizational structure of the medical staff. In turn the medical staff must also develop recommendations for the governing board in preparing bylaws, rules, and regulations for the efficient administration of its affairs and a sound plan for self-government.

The bylaws should provide for the method of selection of physicians, tenure and practice privileges; officers of the medical staff; chairman and secretary of each clinical department; standing and special committees; regular and special meetings, with adequate record of minutes and attendance; procedure for amendment of bylaws; and rules and regulations for the care of patients.

Liaison between the governing board and the medical staff is usually provided through regular meetings of a joint conference committee consisting of equal numbers (generally three) of members of the medical staff and the governing board, including the hospital administration.

In the area of evaluating the quality of hospital medical care most trustees are least informed. Since most board members are as a rule business and professional people from diverse fields, they consider themselves better qualified to understand financial and administrative matters.[1]

Of utmost importance to the board's proper discharge of its responsibility for hospital medical care is the appointment and maintenance of a superior medical staff. Final action on original medical staff appointments, modifications thereof, annual re-appointments, and termination of appointments are nondelegable functions of the board, although action is taken after receiving medical staff recommendations.

Exclusion of Unqualified Practitioners

The trustees of voluntary hospitals have both the right and the duty to exclude undesirable and unqualified medical practitioners from staff membership or from treating patients therein. The trustees of the hospital may exclude a physician who has not had acceptable medical training, and may adopt rules and regulations for the admission and qualifications of medical staff members. No reason need be given by the board

---

[1] SUTTON, F. G., "Taking the Guesswork Out of Medical Care Evaluation," *Trustee*, 16: 1-6, Oct. 1963.

of trustees of a voluntary hospital for the rejection of a physician's application for staff membership, nor can the courts compel a disclosure of the reason for the rejection, nor question the trustees' judgment.

The governing board may require, as a condition of membership on the medical staff, that physicians comply with ethical standards. A license to practice medicine by itself does not entitle a physician to hospital privileges. The law does not require a voluntary hospital to furnish its services and accommodations to every one who applies, whether patient or physician. There can be no absolute right in individuals to claim the benefit of its privileges. There must be discretion vested in the trustees to make selection from applicants with regard to accommodations available. The trustees acting as the governing board may reject one who has some trivial ailment, and accept another whose needs are greater. This is not illegal discrimination depriving a person of his rights; nor is it deemed such discrimination, if from a large number of physicians the trustees select members of the visiting staff with regard, not only to their medical skill, but also to their adaptability to the rules and discipline of the institution.[2]

Rights of Physicians

A physician's appointment to a hospital staff and the privileges extended to him cannot be abrogated arbitrarily, unless the bylaws of the hospital so provide. If the appointment is made in accordance with the bylaws such designation and the rights that go with it constitute a contract. This contract may not be breached by the trustees, except for cause, and then only after a hearing and an opportunity to be heard. The physician has no legal remedy if he is removed as prescribed by the bylaws, to which he has agreed upon becoming an appointed member of the medical staff.

---

[2] *Van Campen* v. *Olean General Hospital*, 210 App. Div. 204, 205 N.Y.S. 554, aff'd 239 N.Y. 615, 147 N.E. 219 (1924).

Demotion in grade during the annual tenure cannot be made unless the physician is given a hearing pursuant to the bylaws. Violation of this right may give rise to an action for damages or to an injunction requiring his restoration, unless good cause for such demotion can be shown. Promotion, of course, increases the physician's benefits and may be made at any time. At the expiration of the physician's appointment, he may be promoted, demoted or dropped entirely from the staff without notice, although the fair procedure would be to notify him sufficiently in advance so that he may make other plans for the hospitalization of his private patients.

Even though the bylaws of a hospital medical staff provided for a hearing if a recommendation for reappointment is not given, this provision did not bar the Board of Governors of the hospital from denying reappointment without a hearing. The court found that the Board of Governors had an unrestricted right to grant or deny appointment or reappointment of doctors to the hospital staff, and that the staff organization and its committees had authority only to recommend that a doctor be reappointed or not. Therefore, it said that it did not have to decide whether the doctor had been given a proper hearing.[3]

Despite provisions in a hospital's constitution permitting enjoyment of "off service" privileges by a staff doctor after he has reached retirement age, the board of trustees of the hospital had authority to deny reappointment to a surgeon who had reached the age limit established by the constitution. It also had the right to deny him "off service" privileges, which includes the care of his private patients in the hospital.[4]

The Supreme Court of New Jersey held that a physician may recover damages from a hospital if the trustees maliciously interfere with his status as a member of the hospital medical staff. The court said that although a trustee of the hospital

[3] *Weary* v. *Baylor University Hospital*, 360 S.W. 2d 895 (Tex.) (1962).

[4] *Leider* v. *Beth Israel Hospital Association*, 182 N.E. 2d 393, 227 N.Y.S. 2d 900 (N.Y.) (1962).

has a qualified privilege to make statements concerning the doctor's qualifications for reappointment, the privilege is lost if the statements are made with malice.[5]

Trustees' Liability for Acts of Medical Staff

Control of the selection of the medical staff by the governing board is legally significant even in states which grant immunity to hospitals for injury to patients. Many of the states which extend exemption to hospitals for the medical acts of physicians impose liability if it can be proved that the trustees were negligent in the selection of the physician. It is equally negligent to retain incompetent practitioners.

The general rule is that a trustee is not liable for the negligence of the servants or agents of the hospital which results in injuries to patients, unless it can be shown that the trustee directed, or controlled, or took part in the negligent act.

No liability will be imputed to the trustees for the malpractice of a physician who has been appointed house surgeon after his competency had been passed upon by the medical board. There are no reported cases in which trustees of a voluntary hospital have been held liable for injuries to a patient. The liability, where it exists, is that of the corporation operating the hospital or that of the individual responsible for the injury. To hold a trustee personally liable, it must be shown that he acted in the particular case in a capacity unrelated to his function as a trustee of the hospital.

Appointments in Public Hospitals

Public hospitals are more limited by state and local laws and by hospital bylaws and rules than voluntary hospitals in restricting the rights of physicians to practice therein.

Court decisions appear to establish the rule that duly licensed physicians are entitled to medical staff courtesy privileges in a public hospital. The public hospital is regarded as an

---

[5] *Raymond* v. *Cregar*, 185 A. 2d 856 (N.J.) (1962).

"open hospital" in which the courtesy medical staff consists of physicians who attend their private patients, and who do not desire to become members of the active medical staff or who are not eligible. However, they may practice only general medicine and surgery unless they are appointed to the active medical staff. All physicians, irrespective of their staff status, who use the facilities of a public hospital, may be required to comply with its reasonable rules and regulations.[6]

The issuance of a license to practice medicine and surgery does not give the holder thereof the right per se to practice in a public institution. Reasonable rules and regulations may be adopted as well as standards or qualifications for those who wish to serve in the hospital; these should be general and not arbitrary or discriminatory; they should be clear and not vague, ambiguous or uncertain. It is perfectly reasonable to require that in order to perform major surgery, the physician be a diplomate in surgery.

The authority of the governing board is controlled by state law or the statute which provides for the establishment of the hospital and the authority of the governing board. Rules and regulations adopted by the governing body must promote efficiency in the operation of the hospital. They must be such as are necessary for the hospital better to carry out the duties and obligations it owes to the public.

Any public hospital, having adopted reasonable rules and regulations governing the practice of medicine or surgery, cannot arbitrarily deny a regularly licensed physician or surgeon the right to practice in such hospital as long as the practitioner stays within the law.

Denial of Reappointment

It is the right of the governing board to reappoint members of the medical staff upon recommendation of the medical board

---

[6] *Alpert* v. *Board of Governors of Fulton City Hospital*, 238 App. Div. 542, 145 N.Y.S. 2d 534 (1955).

or medical staff, as the constitution or bylaws may provide. Rarely does the governing board reappoint or appoint one who has been disapproved by the medical board or staff. While the governing board may refuse to make a reappointment, no such action should be taken without giving reasons. In fact, no appointment, denial of reappointment or cancellation of membership should occur without consulting the appropriate medical group in the hospital.

Bylaws usually provide that appointments to the medical staff are made for a period of one year or until the end of the fiscal year of the hospital. One advantage of annual appointments is that it allows the elimination of the unethical and unfit without the need of a hearing. The failure to reappoint is less drastic than the cancellation of an appointment. There may be good enough reason at times, however, to require the immediate termination of a doctor's hospital privileges.

Hearings for Disciplinary Action

Before taking action against a member of the medical staff of a voluntary hospital, it is customary and proper to accord him a hearing unless the bylaws provide for summary dismissal. While the courts will not substitute their judgment for that of the governing board, they will look into the record to see whether the proceeding has been in accordance with the constitution and bylaws, whether the charges are substantial and whether the physician has had fair notice and an opportunity to be heard.

The same formality is not necessary in connection with the reappointment of members of the medical staff. To deny reappointment at the termination of the annual term, the governing board need give neither notice nor hearing to the physician.

On all matters affecting members of the medical staff or their care of patients, the medical board stands in the relation of technical advisor to the governing board; lay trustees of the hospital are not competent to judge the professional abilities of the physicians. Hearings concerned with the disciplining of physicians therefore should be left to the medical board which, after investigation, forwards its recommendations to the governing board for final decision.

The governing board may provide in the bylaws for the expulsion of a staff member without a hearing, but such a rule is rarely adopted. The usual practice is to arrange for charges and a hearing. If the bylaws specifically state that notice is mandatory, the physician cannot be deprived of membership without proper notice to him and an opportunity to be heard.

The bylaws may provide that written charges against staff members shall be referred to the executive committee for investigation and recommendations, after which a vote of the staff shall be taken without discussion. A two-thirds vote by secret ballot may be prescribed for the suspension or dismissal of a member. He must be notified in writing of such contemplated action within a specified time prior to the vote.

Committees of Medical Staff

To expedite certain functions of the medical staff, the following committees generally are established:

Executive Committee. This committee consists of officers of the medical staff and, in addition, two or three members of the active medical staff to be elected at the annual meetings.

Credentials or Qualifications Committee. The president or chairman of the medical staff appoints three to five members to serve on this committee. Its purposes are to regulate requirements for permission of physicians to work in the hospital, investigate and appraise the credentials of all applicants for membership on the medical staff, and make recommendations on medical staff appointments, promotions, and privileges to do major surgery.

Medical Records Committee. The three to five members of this committee, appointed by the president or chairman of the medical staff, endeavor to promote the medical records' standards of the hospital. They are concerned with the facilities, personnel and procedures in producing good medical records. The committee reviews the medical records to assure they are properly written and of scientific quality, that is, that each record contains sufficient data to justify the diagnosis and warrant the treatment. Members of this committee meet frequently and work closely with the medical record librarian. A report on the condition of medical records should be made at each meeting of the medical staff.

Program Committee. This committee's function may be performed by the executive committee itself or by a special committee of three to five members appointed by the president or chairman of the medical staff. Its members are responsible for the preparation of programs for medical staff meetings when there is a review and analysis of professional work.

Tissue Committee. This committee serves as an effective control of surgery and is now a requirement of the Joint Commission on Accreditation of Hospitals. It is comprised of the pathologist, a surgeon, a gynecologist when possible, and other members. Its chief function is to review all tissues removed at surgery reported normal or with pathology and to justify the operation and the adequacy of the treatment needed.

Joint Conference Committee. Generally, three to five members of the medical staff and an equal number of the governing board constitute this committee, with the administrator as an ex-officio member. They function as a liaison between the medical staff and the governing board by deliberating on matters of mutual interest and concern.

chapter 26

OPERATING ROOM
RESPONSIBILITY

THE purpose of the operating room is to provide patients with a suitable and safe environment for the performance of operative procedures. Within the operating room may be found surgical, anesthesia and nursing services, each closely dependent upon the other. The objectives of the operating room nursing service are to provide high quality support to the surgeons during operative procedures and to promote coordination of functions between nursing, surgical and anesthesia staffs. It is in the operating room that the bases of many lawsuits originate from such mishaps as anesthesia accidents, lost sponges, blood transfusion errors, broken surgical needles and other hazards.

One of the problems in such lawsuits is the determination of who is at fault. The team in the operating room may consist of surgeons, anesthesiologists or anesthetists, interns, residents, nurses and others. To fix responsibility is a difficult matter for the patient on the basis of his own testimony, because in most cases he is unconscious at the time he sustains the injury.

However, it is common practice for the attorney representing the patient to ascertain, if possible, from the medical chart or from other sources, the names of the persons participating in the operation in order that they may be included as defendants in the lawsuit. The procedure of examination before trial is followed to question personnel who were present in the operating room as to the facts surrounding the accident.

Records Before Surgery

Every hospital should have a regulation or policy to the effect that no patient, unless an emergency or time does not permit, should go under surgery unless the medical record is written and accompanies him to the operating room. This is evidence of preoperative study so necessary for an accurate diagnosis, carefully established, confirmed so far as possible, and recorded before operation.

A policy, such as the above, should be established by the medical staff and approved by the governing board of the hospital. The evidence of preoperative study of the case will obviate errors in diagnosis and operative procedures. There is no doubt that a thorough preoperative study, as evidenced by a good medical record, will, in certain instances, be responsible for saving lives.

From the preoperative study of recorded data and examination, the surgeon estimates the degree of risk involved in the operation. If he concludes it is not adequate, he will administer supportive treatment, such as rest, saline or blood transfusion and other appropriate measures. No patient should be operated upon, unless an emergency exists, without estimating the risk in relation to his ability to stand the strain of the operation to which he is subjected.

In case a patient comes to the operating room without the medical record being written up and there is no emergency, the operating room supervisor should have the authority to cancel the operation and send the patient back to the ward, provided, however, that further delay will not be detrimental to the patient. In this circumstance, the supervisor should confer with the surgeon concerned and point out to him the policy to which he subscribed as a member of the medical staff. She may also seek the advice of the chief surgeon or a competent resident.

It is incumbent on her to report the instance immediately to her superior officer, the director of nursing, who, in turn, should take the matter up with the administrator and he will follow through on it as far as is necessary.[1]

Responsibility for Negligence

The complex organization of the operating room team may make it difficult to establish individual responsibility for injury to a patient. Depending upon the relationship existing at the time of an incident, the nurse herself may be liable, or the hospital may be liable as her general employer, or the surgeon as her special employer if the nurse is functioning under his control.

Whether the hospital is liable for the negligence of the surgeon or nurse may depend on their relationship to the hospital, on the nature of the hospital, and on the law of the state.

If the surgeon is not an employee or agent of the hospital and the nurse was not negligent, there is no liability on the hospital for the failure, for example, to remove a sponge.

While a nurse is a general employee of the hospital, for particular purposes she may become a special employee of the surgeon. The use of the word special in this sense relates to an individual designated to perform a specific function. Her negligence becomes imputable to the operating surgeon on showing that he had complete control and supervision over her acts during the operation.

In legal phraseology, the term imputed means attributed vicariously; that is, an act, fact or quality is said to be imputed to a person when it is ascribed or charged to him, not because he is personally cognizant of it or responsible for the particular

---

[1] MacEachern, M. T., "Records Before Surgery," *Trustee*, June 1955.

act, but because he has control over another person for whose acts or knowledge he is responsible.

A person is considered an employer when he has the right to control and direct the individual who performs the services, not only as to the result to be accomplished, but also as to the means to be used. The individual subject to such direction is an employee.

When one receives treatment by a nurse furnished by the hospital, but who is under the direct supervision of the surgeon, the nurse acts as the agent of the doctor. The hospital is not liable for her negligence while she serves under his direction. Neither is the hospital responsible for the doctor's negligence.

There are circumstances in which it is difficult to decide whether the nurse was acting as agent or employee of the physician or of the hospital. Such situations may have to be submitted to the jury for decision or become a question of law.

Insofar as the functions of a nurse are medical in character, the same rules as to proof of malpractice apply to her as to physicians and surgeons. In the case of a nurse, malpractice would consist of the failure to use that degree of skill and learning in caring for a patient which is customarily used by nurses in the same community in a similar situation.

If the alleged neglect relates to matters which are reasonably within the ken of the average layman, the jury may determine the culpability of the person charged therewith without the aid of experts. If it relates solely to the exercise of judgment in the application of skill and learning, proof of the negligence must be given by experts. The function of a surgical nurse in the operating room as to her duty to check on the removal of instruments is not outside the knowledge of laymen and need not be proved by expert evidence.

It is a matter of common knowledge that no special skill is required in counting instruments; under some circumstances proof of custom is some evidence of what should be done and may assist in the determination of what constitutes due care; it does not conclusively establish the standard of care.

Duties of Nursing Personnel

The nurse in charge of the operating room division is responsible for the administration and supervision of nursing service in the operating rooms. The title of the nurse in charge may vary from operating room supervisor, assistant director of nursing service, department head or head nurse to clinical instructor. She directs the work of her staff and coordinates their activities with those of the surgeons, anesthetists and auxiliary workers. She must do everything possible to prevent injury to the patient, including the elimination of explosion hazards and supervision of the use of aseptic techniques. The training of all newly assigned nursing service personnel in the policies and procedures approved by the medical board for the care and safeguarding of the patient is a primary responsibility of the nurse in charge.

As in other areas of the hospital, the nurse in charge is expected to delegate some of her responsibilities. She remains accountable if the person she assigns is not qualified to carry out the delegated activity.

Operating Room Nurses

The operating room nursing staff may consist of professional nurses, student nurses, practical nurses and auxiliary personnel.

The designation of a professional nurse as head nurse in charge of a particular operating room or unit depends on the size of the department and the organization of the staff. She may have both professional and auxiliary workers to whom she delegates various activities in the operating room.

The auxiliary personnel may include surgical technical aides, orderlies, nursing aides and ward clerks. These lay workers are trained on the job for specific activities to be performed under the supervision of the professional nurse. The head nurse remains responsible for any activity she may delegate that is beyond the scope of the nonprofessional worker.

Control Exercised Over Nurse

The liability of the surgeon or hospital may hinge on the degree of control exercised over the actions of the nurse by the one or the other. In order to determine responsibility, the attorney for the plaintiff may include the hospital, surgeon and nurse as defendants. If the negligence of the nurse is proved, it then becomes a matter of deciding whether the nurse was acting as agent of the surgeon, the hospital or the patient.

Some lawsuits involve not only the question of whether the surgeon had control over the nurse in the operating room, but also whether the act was merely routine or specifically directed by the doctor.

The nurse's responsibilities preceding an operation may include seeing that the operating room is cleaned, instruments sterilized and available, drapes ready and the patient placed on the operating table. All these are administrative or ministerial functions performed by the nurse as an employee of the hospital before the doctor comes into the room.

There are other nursing acts which may be part of the patient's medical care at the direction of the physician. The application of hot-water bottles may be a medical or therapeutic act, done not as a routine matter in all operative procedures but for the surgeon to decide. The surgeon's responsibility does not begin at the exact moment when he starts to make an incision in the body, but includes the preoperative application of hot-water bottles in the operating room and under his eyes.[2]

Relationship of Intern and Resident

In determining whether the intern or resident is the agent

[2] *Benedict* v. *Bondi, et al.*, 122 A. 2d 209 (Pa.) (1956).

of the attending physician, the essential test is whether he is subject to the latter's control or right of control with regard not only to the work done but also to the manner of performing it.

Where the hospital assigns the intern to the attending physician for a special purpose, the test is whether he remains subject to the control of the hospital or to the physician whom he is to assist. In some cases he may be in the employ of both hospital and attending physician; it is then for the jury to decide whether for the negligent act alleged he was the special servant of the attending physician and the general servant of the hospital.

It is not a tenable argument for the surgeon to allege that the hospital is liable for the acts of the intern provided to him, just as it is for the medications, nurses, operating room facilities, and the like. Supplying mere mechanical implements or medicines is not in the same category as furnishing the services of an intern at the surgeon's request to assist him in the discharge of a duty which he has undertaken to perform. Since the acts of the intern are subject to the surgeon's control and supervision, it would be immaterial whether the hospital supplied the intern's services to the surgeon or whether they were obtained in some other manner.

Liability of Attending Surgeon

While the operating surgeon does not have control of every single act of his collaborators, he will be liable for the act complained of if he directed or knew of the existence of such negligent conduct and had a chance to remedy it but failed to do so.

The absence of the attending surgeon from the operating room is by itself no legal negligence, unless he has assigned an inexperienced resident to the case or has failed to give proper instructions. In such case he may be held jointly liable with the resident for the poor result. The mere presence of the attending surgeon in the operating room does not relieve the resident of responsibility for his own misconduct. To permit an inexperienced resident to perform major surgery may cast liability upon the hospital; the institution is obligated to furnish competent medical attention for its patients. However, a hospital resident may practice without supervision or direction if he undertakes to perform only those surgical procedures for which he has had sufficient experience and skill.

As a general rule, it may be stated that both nurse and surgeon are under a duty to use all reasonable efforts to ascertain that no foreign substances remain in the patient's body after the operation. Leaving a foreign substance in a patient's body following surgery is so inconsistent with due care as to raise an inference of negligence.

Although the failure to remove all sponges after the operation raises an inference of negligence, the surgeons may show that under the stress of the emergency the occurrence was unavoidable.

Where a sponge was left in the abdomen of an infant patient, both the operating surgeon and the hospital where the operation was performed were held liable. The court held that the evidence was sufficient to permit the jury to find that both the surgeon and the "scrub nurse" were negligent. It said that the surgeon was responsible for his own negligence and the hospital was liable for the negligence of the nurse. It also said that it was within the discretion of the trial court to find that the award to the father was excessive.[3]

Accounting for Sponges

Resourceful operating room procedures are a measure of caution, but the number and variety of lost sponges, pads and other foreign bodies are proof that methods of prevention are not infallible. Sponge count technique varies with the type of nursing procedure and operative team set-up in the hospital.

---

[3] *French* v. *Fischer*, 362 S.W. 2d 926 (Tenn.) (1962).

Regulations are generally adopted to govern procedures in the operating room. While the existence or absence of specific rules is not conclusive on the issue of due care, yet from their non-existence one may infer neglect.

A number of hospitals, medical school-affiliated, which provide residency training programs in general surgery and in the surgical specialties, adhere to a policy which specifically excludes a sponge count by the nurse. Such hospitals teach (1) that the surgeon alone is responsible for everything connected with the operation, including seeing that no foreign body is left in the patient; (2) that the surgeon cannot delegate any part of this responsibility to an assistant or to a nurse; (3) that a sponge count by the nurse dilutes the surgeon's responsibility to the patient, to the detriment of good surgical care.

They point out in support of their stand that neither the American College of Surgeons nor the Joint Commission on Accreditation of Hospitals requires a hospital to adhere to a sponge count procedure.

Reliance on Nurses' Count

When the surgeon is sued for malpractice in that a sponge was negligently left in the patient, he is permitted to show the rule in the hospital for the nurse to count the used sponges, to announce that all sponges are accounted for and his reliance on such report. These facts and others may be considered by the jury in determining whether the surgeon or nurse exercised reasonable care.

Reliance on the nurse's count, though commonly accepted by the medical profession as a routine practice, is not conclusive evidence that it is reasonable or due care. In Arkansas, Kentucky, Minnesota, and Wisconsin the usual custom of counting the sponges by a nurse before and after the operation and reliance upon that custom is some evidence, but not conclusive, that the surgeon was not negligent. Pennsylvania places the burden on the physician to overcome the presumption of negligence where the sponge is left in the body of the patient. Under the Massachusetts rule, which is an exception to the general holding, it is sufficient to prove that it was customary for the assisting nurses or attendants to keep count of the sponges, to absolve the surgeon.

Removal of Drains and Tubes

It is a matter of common knowledge that due care is lacking if surgical instruments or medical supplies are not removed before an incision is closed. Direct proof of the failure to remove the foreign substance is not necessary if the evidence leads to the inference that the material was overlooked.

Drainage tube cases are different from other foreign substance cases, for the patient claims a specific negligent act such as the improper fastening of the tube, causing it to slip into the body cavity.

Much can be done by an alert nurse to prevent some of the unfortunate results which occur from slipped drains. While the nurse's chance of being made a defendant is relatively less than that of the surgeon, she is nevertheless charged with the duty to observe the patient's condition and to note whether he is in distress. If the patient tampers with the drainage tube and such inference results in injury to him, neither the physician nor the nurse has violated any duty.

Some situations require the patient to prove by expert testimony that the surgeon or nurse was negligent, while other cases cast the burden on the defendant to show by expert proof that the treatment rendered was proper. There are instances when the patient may prove his case without expert testimony.

Broken Surgical or Hypodermic Needles

While needles do not often break during a procedure, such accidents do occur. The breaking of a hypodermic needle of itself is not negligence; the patient must prove negligence and that such conduct was the proximate cause of the injury.

If in the course of a procedure the nurse has knowledge that a needle has been broken, the question arises as to whether the patient should be notified of the occurrence and how soon. The nurse need not give immediate notice to the patient, nor does the surgeon have to attempt to remove it at once. On the other hand, neither nurse nor physician may keep permanently silent and do nothing about the matter. A policy of waiting in silence indefinitely may constitute negligence.

As a matter of law, the patient may be entitled to an explanation as to how the needle was caused to be broken or to have been left in his body. He may show what precautions should have been taken by the operating room nurses to account for all the needles used during the operation.

When a needle is broken it becomes a matter of medical judgment whether the particle should be probed for or an x-ray taken to locate its exact position. In the event that a nurse breaks off part of a hypodermic needle while giving the patient an injection, the matter of removal should be left to the discretion of a physician. Failure to x-ray promptly may be malpractice as may continuing to probe when probing threatens to push the needle in farther.

chapter 27

MEDICAL MALPRACTICE

MEDICAL records play an important part in the trial of malpractice cases against physicians and hospitals. Such records in the modern hospital have the safeguards of trustworthiness and are useful in establishing whether or not there has been malpractice. The record may be the means either of disproving a lack of due care or it may prove the existence of negligence in treatment.

Actions in malpractice against physicians have increased in recent years; this may be due partly to the gradual disappearance of the family doctor, traditionally the friend and confidant of his patient. The modern trend toward impersonal efficiency, while it has undoubtedly raised the standards of the profession, has forced the physician's attainments to stand largely in the light of scientific merit, unprotected by the armor of friendship.

One who sues a physician for malpractice has to overcome certain peculiar difficulties. He may have been unconscious or otherwise unaware of what was happening to him; he may be unable to assign specific acts of negligence or omissions as the cause of his condition. Moreover, the well-known reluctance of physicians to testify against their colleagues may make expert proof of negligence onerous or impossible. The law gives the physician the benefit of every favorable presumption. These problems, among others, must be solved in the ordinary malpractice case before the patient may recover damages.

Duties of the Physician

The law does not hold the physician or surgeon liable for every untoward result which may occur in treatment; it requires only that he have the learning and skill of physicians in good standing in the same locality and that he use ordinary care and diligence in applying that learning and skill. Whether he has done so in a particular case is generally a matter for expert testimony, for negligence will not be presumed; it must be affirmatively proved.

The physician is not required to possess extraordinary learning and skill. However, he is bound to keep abreast of the times; departure from approved methods in general use, resulting in injury to the patient, will render him liable no matter how good his intentions may have been.

A physician is not obliged to treat any patient, nor on terms which are not suitable to him. The fact that no other physician is available to the patient at the time of need does not place him under legal compulsion to aid the person. However, once he has agreed to serve the patient, no matter by whom summoned, a physician-patient relationship is commenced, with its attendant rights and obligations.

Malpractice Defined

Negligence when applied to the professions is called malpractice and is defined as the doing of some act which a reasonable and prudent person would not do, or the failure to do some act which such a person should or would do. The standard of prudent conduct is not defined by law with precision, but is left to the determination of a judge or jury.

Such negligence may be common law negligence, which is based largely on decisions and opinions in prior cases and are used as precedents to guide in the determination of new cases. There is also statutory negligence, wherein negligence is defined by the legislatures. In addition, there is criminal negligence, a third type which arises when the act done or omitted is a violation of a penal statute, and carries with it a penalty of fine, imprisonment, or loss of a right or privilege, such as the license to practice the profession.

The term "malpractice" has a broad connotation and is employed generally to designate "bad practice," sometimes called "malapraxis," in the treatment of a patient.

Malpractice is (1) the failure of a physician or surgeon in the treatment of a patient to possess and employ that reasonable degree of learning, skill, and experience which ordinarily is possessed by others of his profession; or (2) his failure to exercise reasonable and ordinary care and diligence in the exertion of his skill and the application of his knowledge; or (3) his failure to exert his best judgment as to the treatment of the case entrusted to him; or (4) his failure to bestow such reasonable and ordinary care, skill, and diligence as physicians and surgeons in the same neighborhood in the same general line of practice ordinarily have and exercise in like cases.

Negligence, as the term is applied in the general law of negligence, refers to an inadvertent act or omission resulting in injury. The term malpractice involves, in addition to negligence, an ignorant or willful departure from approved medical practice, for which the patient's remedy in either case is an action for damages against the physician.

Failure To Cure Is Not Malpractice

The physician who accepts a patient must go beyond a thorough and careful examination of the patient. If more than one diagnosis is suggested from the history and symptoms, he is under a duty to make a differential diagnosis, using such exclusionary tests as prevail among medical men of average learning, judgment and skill in that or similar communities.

A doctor may expressly contract with a patient to cure him or not to charge him for treatment. In such an agreement, which is not against public policy, the physician is bound by the ordinary rules of contract. Should he abandon the patient during the course of treatment, although with no injury to the patient, he will be liable for breach of contract. Where he specifically or impliedly warrants a cure, he becomes an insurer of the result. For the breach of contract the patient is entitled to recover what he has paid and to collect for whatever damages he can prove arose out of the breach of contract.

The allegation of a breach of contract generally is used when the patient in an action for malpractice seeks to avoid the shorter statute of limitations and to take advantage, if possible, of the longer time limitations placed on contract actions.

No malpractice can be presumed generally from the results of treatment, nor does the fact that the outcome was not as favorable as the patient expected indicate a want of proper care. The fact that the patient has failed to make a complete recovery raises no presumption of a lack of proper skill and attention and the physician is not held liable.

Doctrine of *Res Ipsa Loquitur*

Res ipsa loquitur (the thing speaks for itself) is merely a short way of saying that, so far as the court can see, the jury from their experience as men of the world may be warranted in thinking that an accident of the particular kind does not happen except in consequence of negligence, and that therefore there is a presumption of fact, in the absence of explanation or other evidence which the jury believe, that it happened as a result of negligence.

There are instances in which a patient is incapable of knowing exactly what happened while he was undergoing treatment. This is usually true in the operating room. The surgeon, nurses, technicians, and others perform a variety of tasks while the patient, under anesthetic, cannot see, hear, or feel what is occurring. The application of the rule of *res ipsa loquitur* in such a context follows from the recognition of this basic fact by the court and its belief that the defendant (usually the surgeon) has better access to the evidence of what actually happened than does the patient.

Not every state has the rule of *res ipsa loquitur* and, in states that do recognize it, its scope and effect vary considerably. The objection to the rule by physicians and their insurance companies is obvious. Often they cannot present any substantial evidence to explain the accident and injury, and most cases that go to the jury on a *res ipsa loquitur* theory are decided in favor of the patient.

There is little doubt that legal rules, including *res ipsa loquitur*, are misused or poorly applied at times. Misuse or misapplication of *res ipsa loquitur* in some situations, however, should not blind us to the many occasions upon which its application serves justice.[1]

The *res ipsa loquitur* doctrine does not apply, for example, when a patient has an allergic reaction to a local anesthetic, because the reaction is an element beyond the control of the physician.[2] In a California case, however, the jury was allowed to decide whether the factual situation was such that (1) the untoward result was of a kind which ordinarily does not occur in the absence of someone's negligence, (2) it was caused by an agency or instrumentality within the exclusive control of the surgeon, and (3) it was not due to any voluntary action or contribution on the part of the plaintiff.[3]

A jury was permitted to hold a surgeon liable for an unexplained chemical burn in the operating room while the patient was undergoing surgery. It was found that the surgeon had exclusive control or the duty to exercise control over the use of the phenol solution during the operation.[4]

While the testimony of experts concerning the standard in

---

[1] HERSHEY, N., "Res Ipsa Loquitur," *Am. J. Nurs.;* 63:101, Nov. 1963.

[2] *Mogensen* v. *Hicks,* Sup. Ct., 110 N.W. 2d 563 (Iowa) (1961).

[3] *Cho* v. *Kempler,* 2 Cal. Rptr. 167 (1960).

[4] *Jensen* v. *Linner,* 108 N.W. 2d 705 (Minn.) (1961).

the profession and a deviation therefrom is not always necessary for the application of *res ipsa loquitur,* there are cases where one cannot say that the occurrence ordinarily bespeaks negligence.[5] A physician or surgeon should not be burdened with the task of explaining every unfortunate result occurring from honest and necessary efforts to cure or relieve human ailments and injuries, but a presumption or inference may arise when, during the course of his efforts, there is an unusual fact or omission which, in the ordinary experience and knowledge of laymen, does not or should not occur when ordinary care is exercised.[6]

The first requisite for the use of the doctrine is that it must be within the common knowledge of the layman that such an injury does not ordinarily occur without negligence. In malpractice cases, because the layman is unfamiliar with the intricacies of medical practice, the jury is ordinarily incompetent to supply the standard by which to measure professional medical conduct without the aid of expert testimony. In such case, when the plaintiff fails to present expert testimony to establish a standard of care, it is proper for the court to grant judgment for the defendant.[7]

Responsibility for Unexpected Drug Reactions

That the use of a drug brings unexpected reactions is no proof of the physician's malpractice if he has used due care and skill in its administration; he is not expected to anticipate unusual and unnatural effects. Personal idiosyncrasies of the patient cannot be predicted in the ordinary case.

The mere fact, for example, that an unidentified liquid is placed in an organ as sensitive as the eye followed by pain and inflammation is not, without other evidence, sufficient to warrant an inference by a jury that its use was improper. In one

---

[5] *Toy* v. *Rickert,* 146 A. 2d 510 (N.J.) (1958).

[6] *Worster* v. *Caylor,* 110 N.E. 2d 337 (Ind.) (1953).

[7] *Renrick* v. *City of Newark,* 181 A. 2d 25 (N.J.) (1962).

case, a patient was under treatment for a genitourinary infection; he developed what appeared to be an inflamed throat and eyes, which the physician diagnosed as acute pharyngitis and acute conjunctivitis caused by some form of pathogenic streptococci. The physician proceeded with penicillin therapy after the patient stated he did not know if he had ever had any penicillin. The condition of the patient became worse and he eventually suffered the loss of sight of one eye and impairment of vision of the other. There was conflicting evidence as to whether the penicillin treatment was the cause of the injury; the inquiry as to the patient's allergy was adequate under the circumstances. The jury decided in favor of the physician.[8]

A patient who received a tetanus antitoxin injection became ill with serum poisoning. He testified that though he received other injections, he had never suffered from any allergic effects. He also stated that the hospital doctor had administered a scratch test prior to the injection, which indicated no hypersensitivity. All this established the application of good medical practice on the part of the hospital doctor. According to the plaintiff's own medical testimony a percentage of allergic reactions to tetanus antitoxin is to be expected though they are usually of a temporary nature.[9]

Use of Experimental Treatments and Drugs

Certain methods of treatment have the general acceptance of the profession; others may be experimental in nature. A physician experimenting with an untried drug may be liable for untoward results. (Fig. 55, p. 334).

Principles governing clinical research have been developed gradually over the years by numerous research institutions, hospitals and medical or allied groups. In order to conform with ethical standards three requirements must be satisfied

---

[8] *Johnston* v. *Brother*, 12 Cal. Rptr. 23 (Calif.) (1961).

[9] *Gorlin* v. *Master Contracting Corp.*, 180 N.Y.S. 2d 84 (1958).

according to the American Medical Association prior to human experiments: (1) the voluntary consent of the person on whom the experiment is to be performed, (2) the danger of each experiment must be previously investigated by animal experimentation and (3) the experiment must be performed under proper medical protection and management.[10]

The American Hospital Association's policy statement emphasizes that hospital authorities, along with nurses and phar-

AUTHORIZATION FOR TREATMENT WITH DRUG
UNDER CLINICAL INVESTIGATION

I hereby authorize________________________Hospital and my attending physician and his assistants to treat________________________
with the drug or preparation presently identified as________________________
____
for the following condition________________________
____

It has been explained to me by Dr.________________________that the safety and usefulness of the drug in the treatment of patients for the above condition are now being investigated for the purpose of providing further evidence of its safety and usefulness.

I understand that no representations have been made to me of beneficial results nor has there been any guarantee, either express or implied, that I will be cured or that treatment with the said drug will be successful.

I voluntarily consent to treatment with the drug and release the hospital and aforesaid physicians from liability for any results that may occur.

Date________________ Signed________________________
Address________________________
Witness________________ Relationship to patient________________________

FIG. 55 — AUTHORIZATION FOR TREATMENT WITH DRUG UNDER CLINICAL INVESTIGATION

macists engaged in administering, compounding and dispensing investigational drugs, should have available to them basic information on actions, uses, side effects, symptoms of toxicity, and dosage and dosage forms.[11]

[10] Report of Judicial Council, American Medical Association, J.A.M.A., 132:1090, 1946.

[11] Statement of Principles Involved in the Use of Investigational Drugs in Hospitals, Council on Professional Practice, *Hospitals*, J.A.H.A., 31:106, Dec. 1, 1957.

The Drug Amendments of 1962

Congress enacted the Drug Amendments of 1962 on October 10, 1962 when the President signed S. 1552. The effective date of the new law generally is May 1, 1963. It is necessary now for the drug manufacturer to establish that a new drug is both safe and effective before it can be marketed. The law does not apply to drugs which were commercially used or sold in the United States before the day of the enactment of the new law.

The Food and Drug Administration can require, either by regulation or specific order, that the applicant for drug clearance keep records and reports of clinical experience and other information concerning the drugs. A new drug is defined, in general, as one which is not generally recognized among qualified experts as safe for use under the conditions for its labeling. If the drug is generally recognized by experts to be effective for the conditions for which it is intended, it is not a new drug. But if the claims have no general recognition as being already established, a new drug application must be filed to establish the validity of such claims.

The Secretary of the Federal Food and Drug Administration may exempt drugs intended for investigational use by experts qualified by scientific training and experience to investigate the safety and effectiveness of drugs. Before any clinical testing is undertaken, the manufacturer or the sponsor of the investigation is required to submit to the Secretary reports of preclinical tests (including tests on animals). An agreement must be signed by the investigators that patients to whom the drug is to be administered will be under his personal supervision, or under the supervision of investigators responsible to him, and that he will not supply the drug to any other persons for administration to human beings.

Records are to be maintained and reports made to the Secretary as prescribed by him as to the results obtained in the investigational use of such drug. The manufacturer, or the sponsor of the investigation, is to require the experts using such drugs for investigational purposes to certify to such manufacturer or sponsor that they will inform any human beings to whom such drugs are being administered that such drugs are being used for investigational purposes, and will obtain the consent of such human beings or their representatives to such administration, unless it is deemed not feasible or, in their professional judgment it is contrary to the best interests of such human beings. These reports need not be submitted directly to the Secretary by any clinical investigator.

Skill and Care Required of Specialists

By preference or training, many physicians have devoted themselves to the study of one particular organ, or to a specialty. One holding himself out as having special knowledge and skill in the treatment of a particular disease is bound to bring patients employing him as a specialist that degree of skill and learning ordinarily possessed by physicians in that community who devote special study to such organ or disease.

The rule that the standard of skill must relate to that of the locality in which the specialist practices or to similar localities is frequently omitted. However, the duty imposed by law upon a physician who is, or holds himself out to be, a specialist is measured by a higher standard than that applicable to a general practitioner.

The various speciality examining boards such as for Internal Medicine, Anesthesiology, Radiology, Pathology, Orthopedic Surgery, Pediatrics, etc., are used frequently to establish the qualifications of the physician as a specialist.

Proof to Establish Malpractice

In the average case, malpractice is difficult to prove, because the physician knows what has been done and its significance; the patient must judge chiefly by the results.

It is not sufficient to show by medical testimony that the ailment might or could have resulted from the alleged cause.[12] The accused doctor is entitled to have his treatment of the patient tested by the rules and principles of the school of medicine to which he belongs. If he renders the treatment with ordinary skill and care in accordance with his school of practice, he is not answerable for bad results.

There are no fixed standards for measuring the qualifications of the medical witness as an expert. He must have knowledge of medical custom in the same or similar vicinities, and of practice under the conditions of the particular case or what is usually and customarily done by physicians under circumstances similar to those which confronted the defendant.

Through expert testimony the jury is able to determine not only whether the defendant possessed and exercised the requisite degree of skill and care, but also whether he followed common or ordinary practice in the care of the patient.

Expert testimony, however, may not be necessary in a case in which it is alleged the operation was performed without consent, or where an autopsy is done without legal authorization, or there is an invasion of the right of privacy, a betrayal of professional confidence, libel, false imprisonment, breach of contract to cure, or in cases in which the defendant has made an admission of lack of skill or of negligence.

Defenses by the Physician

Every person is bound to use due care for his own safety and welfare, and if it appears that a person's own negligence has contributed to his injury, he may not recover damages, despite the fact that the person responsible for the injury was negligent. "Contributory negligence" hence may be pleaded as a defense by the physician where the negligence of the patient has been an active or contributory cause of the injury. A pa-

---

[12] *Eubanks* v. *Piedmont Natural Gas. Co.*, 198 F. Supp. 522 (D.C.W.D., SC) (1961).

tient must prove that he conformed to the reasonable directions of his physician and that his own conduct did not contribute to the injury.

There are relatively few cases in which the defense of contributory negligence is asserted, because the patient is usually inactive at the time of treatment and places himself completely in the hands of the physician.

In some jurisdictions, contributory negligence cannot defeat an action for malpractice, but serves only to mitigate damages. In such states, (Arkansas, Mississippi, Nebraska, South Dakota and Wisconsin) contributory negligence has the effect of reducing the amount of damages which may be recovered by the patient.

Another defense to a malpractice action, which should not be confused with contributory negligence, is that of assumed risk, based on the legal doctrine that if one voluntarily enters into an arrangement which he knows involves a probable risk, he cannot recover for an injury which results from such risk.

It is necessary, however, that the patient be made aware of the risk and that he agrees to it as a possible hazard. Such a defense might be applicable in a case in which an investigational drug is used, or an infection is contracted by a patient as a result of the use of pooled blood plasma, or he is exposed to x-ray to locate a broken hypodermic needle.

The doctrine of assumption of risk presupposes that the medical treatment was carried out with proper care and without negligence; the patient does not assume that there will be negligence when he has no reason to anticipate such negligence.

Another defense which can be asserted is that the suit is barred by the statute of limitations. These statutes vary from state to state as to the time prescribed within which the particular type of lawsuit must be brought. The question of when the statute begins to run often determines the date when the cause of action should be barred; the statute may provide that the statute begins to run at the time the injury was or should have been discovered by the patient, or the time when the treatment was completed. The fraudulent concealment from the patient of the malpractice may postpone the tolling of the statute. In the case of minors or where the defendant is absent from the state, the running of the statute may be postponed.

"Good Samaritan" Statutes

"Good Samaritan" legislation is designed to exempt physicians (and frequently others) from civil liability for any negligent acts or omissions arising out of rendering medical aid or treatment at the scene of an accident or emergency.

The first "Good Samaritan" law was enacted in California in 1959. Eight states had adopted similar statutes by the end of 1961. In 1962, five additional states had enacted this type legislation. During 1963, there was more activity in "Good Samaritan" proposals. Twelve states, Connecticut, Indiana, Maryland, Michigan, Montana, Nevada, New Hampshire, New Jersey, New Mexico, Ohio, Pennsylvania and Tennessee adopted for the first time a "Good Samaritan" statute. California's and South Dakota's laws were extended to protect nurses, while Oklahoma now affords civil immunity to anyone rendering emergency care.

chapter 28

HOSPITAL LIABILITY

LIABILITY is the general rule for negligent or tortious conduct; immunity is the exception. Human beings ordinarily are responsible for their own careless actions; they must respond also in damages for negligent injury inflicted by their agents and employees.

The tort which generally affects hospitals is called "negligence." The word has been defined as the omission to do something which a reasonable man, guided by those considerations which ordinarily regulate human affairs, would do, or the doing of something which a prudent and reasonable man would not do.

However, one of the things that makes it difficult to understand the law applicable to hospitals for injuries to patients is that each state has its own decisions or statutes for exempting the hospital or holding it liable. The result has been not only confusion, but also opposite decisions on the same facts in many of the states. It is therefore necessary to know the fundamental principles which determine liability and how they are applied in the various jurisdictions.

To begin with, hospitals have been classified according to three categories: public, charitable and private institutions. Public hospitals which are governmental agencies usually are not liable. Generally speaking, charitable hospitals are relieved in a number of states of responsibility on various theories, but held responsible in others. On the other hand, private or proprietary hospitals which are operated for profit ordinarily are liable for the misconduct or neglect of their employees which causes injury to a patient.

Theories for Exemption

Historically, the immunity of nonprofit or voluntary (charitable) hospitals in this country for injuries to patients has been based on a statement in an English case, decided in 1864, that "to give damages out of a trust fund would not be to apply it to those objects which the author of the fund had in view, but would be to divert it to a completely different purpose."[1]

In this country, the first court to adhere to the "trust funds" doctrine of exemption was the Supreme Court of Massachusetts, in 1876.[2] Since then the courts have pointed out in a number of decisions that the trust funds rule is not only unjust to the injured patient, but it also is illogical. If the trust funds theory is reasonable it should exempt such an institution from all liability, either to a patient, an employee or a stranger; but in most jurisdictions that have adopted this doctrine, the exemption does not apply when the injury is inflicted on an employee or a stranger.

Another theory for exemption is that of "waiver," which holds that one accepting the bounty of a charitable institution impliedly waives any claim against it for the negligence of its employees: "One who accepts the benefit either of a public or a private charity enters into a relation which exempts his benefactor from liability for the negligence of its servants in administering the charity."[3]

A further theory for immunity is that it is against public policy to hold the charity liable for the negligence of employees

[1] *Feoffe's of Heriot's Hospital* v. *Ross*, 12 Clark & Fin. 507, 8 Eng. Reprint 1506 (1846).

[2] *McDonald* v. *Massachusetts General Hospital*, 120 Mass. 432, 21 Am. Rep. 529 (1876).

[3] *Powers* v. *Massachusetts Homeopathic Hospital*, 120 Mass. 432, 21 Am. Rep. 529 (1876).

who were selected with due care.[4] It is argued that such hospitals perform a quasi-public function in ministering to the sick without pecuniary profit to themselves; the patient who accepts the services of such an institution, if injured therein by an employee, must look for redress to such employee alone.[5]

An additional doctrine is the rule of *respondeat superior,* which literally means let the superior respond. It is asserted that in ordinary business an employer is responsible for the acts of his employee. However, that is not true of the hospital when it cannot control the act of its employee as, for example, where a nurse in the operating room becomes subject to the direction of the operating surgeon. In such case, the hospital, although it is the employer, does not control the acts of the nurse, hence the rule of *respondeat superior* is not extended to hold the hospital responsible.

Evolution of Liability of Charitable Hospitals

The early cases on the liability of charitable hospitals were decided in the days when hospitals were established and supported mainly by benefactions. The courts sought a legal basis to protect these institutions against money judgments which would cripple their functions. However, the dire prediction that hospitals would cease to exist or that their operations would be hamstrung if judgments against the corporations were permitted has not been borne out by time or experience.

The law on the immunity, partial immunity or nonimmunity from liability of organizations not-for-profit, which maintain and operate hospitals, has never been what might be described as "settled." The subject has been discussed, talked about and ruled on by numerous courts in the nation with many varied and divergent results during the past fifty years.

---

[4] *Taylor* v. *Flower Deaconess Hospital*, 104 Ohio St. 61, 135 N.E. 287 (1922); (Ohio now restricts exemption from liability to nonpaying patients.) See *Avellone* v. *St. John's Hospital*, 165 Ohio St. 467, 136 N.E. 2d 410 (Ohio) (1956).

[5] *Morrison* v. *Henke*, 165 Wis. 166, 160 N.W. 173 (1936) (full liability of hospitals fixed in 1961 by decision in *Kojis* v. *Doctors' Hospital*, 107 N.W. 2d 131).

Prior to 1942 only two or three courts had rejected the immunity of charities outright. In that year a devastating opinion by Judge Rutledge in the Court of Appeals of the District of Columbia reviewed all the arguments in favor of immunity and demolished them so completely as to change the course of the law. It has been followed by a flood of decisions holding that a charity is liable for its torts to the same extent as any other defendant.[6]

One of the cases that has had a salutary effect on the whole question of liability of charitable hospitals is the New York case of *Bing* v. *Thunig,* decided in 1957, in which the Court of Appeals held that "the conception that the hospital does not undertake to treat the patient, does not undertake to act through its doctors and nurses, but undertakes instead simply to procure them to act upon their own responsibility, no longer reflects the fact. Present-day hospitals, as their manner of operation plainly demonstrates, do far more than furnish facilities for treatment. They regularly employ on a salary basis a large staff of physicians, nurses and interns as well as administrative and manual workers, and they charge patients for medical care and treatment, collecting for such services, if necessary, by legal action."[7]

Status of Exemptions and Liabilities

The doctrine of full liability has been adopted by the following states, even though there had been prior rulings of immunity or qualified immunity: Arizona (1952), California (1951), District of Columbia (1942), Iowa (1950), Kentucky (1961), Michigan (1960), New York (1957), Ohio (1956), and Wisconsin (1961).

In the following states when the question of liability arose for the first time, the courts held that charitable hospitals were fully liable for the torts of their employees: Alaska (1952),

---

[6]*President and Directors of Georgetown College* v. *Hughes,* 130 F. (2d) 810 (1942).

[7]*Bing* v. *Thunig,* 2 N.Y. 2d 656, 143 N.E. 2d 3 (1957).

Delaware (1951), Florida (1940), Minnesota (1920), Montana (1961), New Hampshire (1939), North Dakota (1946), Rhode Island (1879), but overruled by statute in 1956, Vermont (1950).

Charitable hospitals have been held liable only to paying patients in Alabama (1915), Idaho (1956), Mississippi (1951), Oklahoma (1938), Washington (1953), and Utah (1938).

There are a number of states which abrogate immunity from tort liability to the extent that the charitable hospital is covered by a liability insurance policy: Arkansas (1950), Colorado (1939), Georgia (1961), Illinois (1950), Kansas (1959), Louisiana (1950), Maryland (1956), New Jersey (1960) limited to $10,000.00 by statute, and Tennessee (1938).

Charitable immunity exists and has been affirmed in Arkansas (1959), Connecticut (1961), Indiana (1924), Kansas (1961) by statute, Maryland (1959), Massachusetts (1876), Missouri (1961), Nebraska (1955), Nevada (1955), North Carolina (1953), Oregon (1944), Pennsylvania (1961), South Carolina (1914), Texas (1955), Vermont (1950), Virginia (1959), West Virginia (1953), and Wyoming (1916).

To the extent that the injury to the patient occurred in the course of conducting a commercial activity which is unrelated to the institutional charitable purpose, immunity will not be recognized: South Carolina (1959).

Decisions on Charitable Hospital Liability

ALABAMA — Liable to paying patient. *Tucker* v. *Mobile Infirmary Assn.*, 68 So. 4, 191 Ala. 572 (1915). No reported court decision involving charity patients although the Tucker case may be interpreted to indicate full liability.

ALASKA — Full liability. *Moats* v. *Sisters of Charity,* 13 Alaska 546 (1952) ; *Tuengel* v. *Sitka,* 118 F. Supp. 399 (1954).

ARIZONA — Full liability. *Ray* v. *Tucson Medical Center,* 230 P. (2d) 220, 72 Ariz. 22 (1952).

ARKANSAS — Immune from liability to nonpaying patients except for negligence in the selection and retention of employees. *Arkansas Midland R. Co.* v. *Pearson*, 135 S.W. 917, 98 Ark. 399 (1911) ; *Helton* v. *Sisters of Mercy of St. Joseph's Hospital*, 351 S.W. 2d 129 (1961).

CALIFORNIA — Full liability. *Malloy* v. *Fong*, 232 P. (2d) 241, 37 Cal. (2d) 356 (1951) ; Section 1714 California Civil Code.

COLORADO — Execution under a judgment rendered against a charity in a tort action cannot be levied on property which is part of the charitable trust. *St. Mary's Academy* v. *Solomon*, 238 P. 22, 77 Colo. 463 (1925). Liability within limits of insurance coverage. *O'Connor* v. *Boulder Colorado Sanitarium Assn.*, 96 P. (2d) 835, 105 Colo. 259 (1939).

CONNECTICUT — Immune from liability except for negligence in the selection and retention of employees. *Hearns* v. *Waterbury Hospital*, 33 A. 595, 66 Conn. 98 (1895) ; *McDermott* v. *St. Mary's Hospital*, 133 A. (2d) 608 (1957) ; *McEvoy* v. *Hartford Hospital*, 173 A. 2d 357 (1961).

DELAWARE — Full liability. *Durney* v. *St. Francis Hospital*, 83 A. (2d) 753 (1951).

DISTRICT OF COLUMBIA — Question of liability not authoritatively decided. Dicta expressing full liability in Court of Appeals decision. *President and Directors of Georgetown College* v. *Hughes*, 130 Fed. (2d) 810, 76 App. D.C. 123 (1942). A trial court held that hospital is immune from liability for injuries sustained by a patient through the negligence of its nurses where there is no claim that they were negligently selected by the hospital or that hospital itself was negligent. *White* v. *Providence Hospital*, 80 F. Supp. 76 (1943).

FLORIDA — Liable to paying patients. *Nicholson* v. *Good Samaritan Hospital*, 199 So. 344, 145 Fla. 360 (1941). No reported cases involving charity patients although the doctrine of full liability is dicta in *Wilson* v. *Lee Memorial Hospital,* 65 So. (2d) 40 (1953).

GEORGIA — Liable for negligence in selecting and retaining employees; execution on a judgment recovered for such negligence is not limited to nontrust assets. Liable to paying patients for negligence of employees even though they have been selected with due care but judgment can be executed only from income derived from paying patients or insurance. *Morton* v. *Savannah Hospital,* 6 S.E. 887, 148 Ga. 438 (1918) ; *Cox* v. *DeJarnette,* 104 Ga. 664, 123 S.E. (2d) 16 (1961).

HAWAII — No reported cases.

IDAHO — Liable to paying but not to nonpaying patients. *Wheat* v. *Idaho Falls Latter Day Saints Hospital,* 297 P (2d) 1041 (1956).

ILLINOIS — Liable within limits of liability insurance and other nontrust assets. *Moore* v. *Moyle,* 92 N.E. (2d) 81, 405 Ill. 555 (1950) ; *Fairall* v. *Sisters of Third Order of St. Francis,* 14 CCH Neg. Cases 2d 1405 (1963).

INDIANA — Immune from liability to charity and paying patients unless hospital failed to exercise reasonable care in selecting and retaining employees who committed tort, in which case there is no immunity. *St. Vincent's Hospital* v. *Stine,* 144 N.E. 537, 195 Ind. 350 (1924).

IOWA — Full liability. *Haynes* v. *Presbyterian Hospital,* 45 N.W. (2d) 51, 241 Iowa 1269 (1950).

KANSAS — By statute (1959) immune, except as to insurance coverage.

KENTUCKY — Immune from liability to paying and nonpaying patients. *Mullikan* v. *Jewish Hospital Assn. of Louisville,* 348 S.W. 3d 930 (1961).

LOUISIANA — Immune from liability. *Jordan* v. *Touro Infirmary,* 123 So. 726 (1922). But immunity of assured unavailable as defense by insurer. *Stamos* v. *Standard Accident Ins. Co.,* 199 F. Supp. 245 (1954).

MAINE — Immune from liability. *Jensen* v. *Maine Eye & Ear Infirmary,* 78 A. 898, 107 Me. 408 (1910).

MARYLAND — Immune from liability. *Howard* v. *South Baltimore General Hospital,* 62 A. (2d) 574 (1948). Exception: liability within limits of insurance coverage (provided by statute) ; *Gorman* v. *St. Paul Fire & Marine Ins. Co.,* 121 A. (2d) 812 (1956) ; *Cornelius* v. *Sinai Hospital of Baltimore, Inc.,* 148 A. 2d 567 (1959).

MASSACHUSETTS — Immune from liability. *McDonald* v. *Massachusetts General Hospital,* 21 Am. Rep. 529, 120 Mass. 432 (1876).

MICHIGAN — Full liability. *Parker* v. *Port Huron Hospital,* 105 N.W., 2d 1 (1960).

MINNESOTA — Full liability. *Mulliner* v. *Evangelischer Diakonniessenverein,* 175 N.W., 699, 144 Min. 392 (1920).

MISSISSIPPI — Liable to paying patients. *Mississippi Baptist Hospital* v. *Holmes,* 55 So. (2d) 142 (1951). Liable for negligence in the selection and retention of employees. *Mississippi Baptist Hospital* v. *Moore,* 126 So. 465, 156 Miss. 676 (1930).

MISSOURI — Immune from liability. *Dile* v. *St. Luke's Hospital,* 196 S.W. (2d) 615, 355 Mo. 436 (1946) ; *Schute* v. *Missionaries of LaSalette Corp.,* 13 CCH Neg. Cases 859 (1961).

MONTANA — Full liability. *Howard* v. *Sisters of Charity of Leavenworth,* 193 E. Supp. 191 (1961).

NEBRASKA — Immune from liability. *Cheatham* v. *Bishop Clarkson Memorial Hospital,* 70 N.W. (2d) 96, 160 Neb. 297 (1955) ; *Muller* v. *Nebraska Methodist Hospital,* 70 N.W. (2d) 86, 160 Neb. 279 (1955).

NEVADA — Immune from liability to nonpaying patients. *Springer* v. *Federated Church of Reno,* 283 P. (2d) 1071 (1955). No reported cases involving paying patients.

NEW HAMPSHIRE — Full liability. *Welch* v. *Frisbie Memorial Hospital,* 9 A. (2d) 761, 90 N.H. 337 (1939).

NEW JERSEY — Limited liability by statute to $10,000.00.

NEW MEXICO — No reported court decisions.

NEW YORK — Full liability. *Bing* v. *Thunig,* 143 N.E. (2d) 3, 163 N.Y.S. (2d) 3 (1957).

NORTH CAROLINA — Immune from liability. *Williams* v. *Union County Hospital Assn.,* 75 S.E. (2d) 308, 237 N.C. 395 (1953). Exception: liable for negligence in selection and retention of employees. *Williams* v. *Randolph Hospital Inc.,* 75 S.E. (2d) 303, 237 N.C. 387 (1953).

NORTH DAKOTA — Full liability. *Rickbeil* v. *Grafton Deaconess Hospital,* 23 N.W. (2d) 247, 73 N.D. 525 (1946).

OHIO — Full liability. *Avellone* v. *St. John's Hospital,* 135 N.E. (2d) 410 (1956).

OKLAHOMA — Liable to paying patients. *Sisters of the Sorrowful Mother* v. *Zeidler,* 82 P. (2d) 996, 183 Okla. 454 (1938). No reported cases involving charity patients.

OREGON — Immune from liability. *Gregory* v. *Salem General Hospital,* 153 P. (2d) 837, 175 Ore. 464 (1944).

PENNSYLVANIA — Immune from liability. *Gable* v. *Sisters of St. Francis,* 75 A. 1087, 227 Pa. 254 (1910) ; *Weeks* v. *Children's Hospital of Philadelphia,* 200 F. Supp. 11 (1961).

RHODE ISLAND — Immune from liability by statute. General Laws, Section 7-1-22 (1956). *Fournier* v. *Miriam Hospital,* 175 A. 2d 298 (1961).

SOUTH CAROLINA — Immune from liability. *Lindler* v. *Columbia Hospital,* 81 S.E. 512, 98 S.C. 25 (1914) ; *Eiserhardt* v. *State Agricultural & Mechanical Society,* 111 S.E. 2d 568 (1959).

SOUTH DAKOTA — No reported cases.

TENNESSEE — Full liability but damages not recoverable out of trust property. *Vanderbilt University* v. *Henderson,* 127 S.W. (2d) 284, 23 Tenn. App. 135 (1938).

TEXAS — Immune from liability. Exception: liable for negligence in selection and retention of employees. *Jones* v. *Baylor Hospital,* 284 S.W. (2d) 929 (1955) ; *Killen* v. *Brazosport Memorial Hospital,* 364 S.W. 2d 411 (1963).

UTAH — Liable to paying patients and probably also to nonpaying patients. *Sessions* v. *Thomas D. Dee Memorial Hospital,* 78 P. (2d) 645, 94 Utah 460 (1938).

VERMONT — Full liability. *Foster* v. *Roman Catholic Diocese of Vermont,* 70 A. (2d) 230, 116 Vt. 124 (1950).

VIRGINIA — Immune from liability. *Weston* v. *Hospital of St. Vincent,* 107 S.E. 785, 131 Va. 587 (1921). Exception: liable for negligence in selection and retention of employees. *Norfolk Protestant Hospital* v. *Plunkett,* 173 S.E. 263, 162 Va. 151 (1934) ; *Memorial Hospital* v. *Oakes,* 200 Va. 870 (1959).

WASHINGTON — Liable to paying but not to nonpaying patients. *Pierce* v. *Yakima Valley Memorial Hospital,* 260 P. (2d) 765 (1953). Liable for negligence in selection or retention of employees. *Canney* v. *Sisters of Charity,* 130 P. (2d) 899, (1942).

WEST VIRGINIA — Immune from liability. *Meade* v. *St. Francis Hospital,* 74 S.E. (2d) 405, 137 W. Va. 834 (1953). Exception: liable for negligence in selection or retention of employees. *Roberts* v. *Ohio Valley General Hospital,* 127 S.E. 318, 98 W. Va. 476 (1925).

WISCONSIN — Full liability. *Kojis* v. *Doctors' Hospital,* 107 N.W. 2d 131 (1961).

WYOMING — Immune from liability to nonpaying patients. *Bishop Randall Hospital* v. *Hartley,* 160 P. 385, 24 Wyo. 408 (1916). No reported cases involving paying patients.

Federal Tort Claims Act

It is a general rule of law that neither the Federal Government nor a state is liable for injuries resulting from the negligence of governmental employees unless there is a statute imposing liability. The same rule applies to the political subdivisions of the state.

This principle of law is based on the old English common law, which held that the king could do no wrong. In the newly created United States Government, the sovereignty formerly vesting in the king was vested in the federal and state governments. The immunity which had protected the king was transferred to our government and its units.

The Federal Tort Claims Act was passed in 1946, after nearly thirty years of congressional consideration. By its provisions the Federal Government assumes the obligation to pay damages for the misfeasance of employees in carrying out its functions.

Prior to such Act the Federal Government was immune from any claim against it for damages unless special authorization was given by Congress in each individual case. The Act now makes the United States liable for "tort claims, in the same manner and to the same extent as a private individual under like circumstances" (28 U.S.C. sec. 2674). Although the Act waives immunity from suit for certain specified torts of federal employees, it does not assure all aggrieved persons of damages for injuries caused by such employees.

The Federal Tort Claims Act excludes from coverage "any claims arising out of assault, battery, false imprisonment, false arrest, malicious prosecution, abuse of process, libel, slander, misrepresentation, deceit or interference with contract rights" (28 U.S.C.A. Sec. 2680 (h)).

The Act also provides that the federal district courts are to have "exclusive jurisdiction of civil actions on claims against the United States, for money damages, accruing on and after January 1, 1945, for injury or loss of property, or personal injury or death caused by the negligent or wrongful act or omission of any employee of the Government while acting within the scope of his office or employment, under circumstances where the United States, if a private person, would be liable to the claimant in accordance with the law of the place where the act or omission occurred." (Sec. 1346 (b)).

The phrase "employee of the government" includes members of the military or naval forces of the United States and persons acting on behalf of a federal agency in an official capacity (28 U.S.C. sec. 2671).

Application to Servicemen and Dependents

Since the enactment of the Federal Tort Claims Act by Congress, there have been a number of suits brought by servicemen against the United States Government. In ruling upon these suits, the federal courts have made a distinction between service-connected injuries and injuries unrelated to service. Where the injuries are service-connected or arise out of military activity, the serviceman may not sue the Government under the Act.

Veterans are entitled to treatment in Veterans Administration hospitals irrespective of whether the condition is service-connected or not. However, if the veteran is treated for a non-service incurred condition and is injured at the hospital, he may recover damages under the Act.

The Government has waived its immunity with respect to civilians for the acts and omissions of members of the Armed Forces in the performance of their duties. Toward civilian patients the Government is subject to the same liability and to the same extent that private employers are held responsible under state law for the acts and omissions of their employees.

Relatives of servicemen, if injured during the course of treatment, come within the coverage of the Federal Tort Claims Act; the question of whether the injury is service-connected is not involved.

Under Army regulations sick wives of enlisted men in the Armed Forces may be admitted to Army hospitals when suitable facilities for hospitalization are available.

Negligence of Public Hospitals

About half of the state courts in the United States adhere to the basic proposition that the state and its political sub-divisions are immune from damage actions arising from tort claims, unless the state legislature has accepted liability or the courts find the activity was a proprietary function.

All activities performed by any government unit within the powers assigned by the legislature are governmental. Of these governmental functions some are recognized as being more customarily performed by private industry and, when these activities produce revenue or profit, they have been termed "proprietary." There is no hard and fast rule for the determination of what is a governmental or a proprietary function.

The acceptance of liability by states is of comparatively recent origin. The legislatures of about one-half the states have agreed to waive the immunity of state hospitals from liability to patients; a few states have a constitutional provision against suing the state; other states seem to be silent on the subject.

A county is a subdivision of a state, created by statute; its obligations and liabilities are prescribed by statute. Unless there is express legislative consent, the county is not liable to persons injured by the negligent act of its employees, since it is protected by the doctrine of sovereign immunity.

There are conflicting decisions as to whether a county hospital, in accepting paying patients, assumes liability for negligence of its employees. The majority attitude appears to be that receiving payment for services from patients able to pay does not change the charitable nature or immunity of the institution; such payments are held to be applied to defraying the operating expenses of the institution.

Other courts hold that the liability of the county depends upon whether the operation of the hospital is considered a governmental or a proprietary function. The purpose is governmental which has for its objective the promotion of the public health, safety, morals, general welfare, security, prosperity and contentment of the inhabitants of a given political subdivision. However, activities from which the county derives a pecuniary benefit are considered proprietary.

The rule that a municipal corporation is immune to suit for negligence in the performance of a governmental function, but is liable when fulfilling a function of a proprietary character, obtains in some of the states.

Care for the indigent sick is a governmental function. The fact that a city hospital has some pay patients does not mean that as to them it is exercising a proprietary function. The nature of the function is not changed from patient to patient. A proprietary hospital would not become a governmental operation because it admitted a few charity patients, and the converse is true. The fact that patients who can pay, or who pay in part, may be admitted, as long as the admission of indigents is not impeded, does not change the nature of the operation.

The liability of a city hospital may depend on whether its maintenance under the statute is permissive rather than mandatory.

The courts have not as readily reversed their ruling on the immunity of governmental hospitals as they have in the case of voluntary institutions. Legislative action usually is required to eliminate governmental immunity once that policy has been established. However, there is a trend by recent court decisions in some states or by legislative enactment to limit or remove the immunity. Governmental agencies usually may avail themselves of insurance coverage against liability.

Liability of Proprietary Hospitals

The liability of a private or proprietary hospital is based upon the rule of *respondeat superior,* under which the master is held liable for the wrongs of his servant, occurring within the scope of his employment.

It is recognized by the courts that the obligations of a private hospital to prevent injuries to patients are more onerous than those of public or charitable institutions. When a private hospital is sued, the test of liability is the same as for any other private corporation; namely, whether the employee exercised ordinary care at the time of injury. It matters not that the hospital exercised due care in selecting the employee if he was negligent in the performance of the act.

A private hospital is under the duty to exercise such reasonable care in protecting the patient as his condition, which is known to the hospital through its nurses, may require. The extent and character of the duty is that degree of care, skill and diligence used by hospitals generally in the community and required by the express or implied contract of the undertaking. Such a hospital, however, is not an insurer of its patients against injury inflicted by themselves; the supervision is required to be only in proportion to the ailments of the patient which render him incapable of looking after his own safety.

Those administering such a hospital are obliged to have such training and skill as will enable them to exert ordinary and reasonable care in the treatment of a patient. The hospital will be held responsible for the knowledge it should have ascertained of the patient's condition by the proper exercise of such requisite skill and training. This implied knowledge, coupled with actual knowledge which the hospital possesses, is the basis for applying the rule of "foreseeability."

Ordinary factors to be considered within the scope of foreseeability are the mental and physical condition of the patient, the dangers afforded by his surroundings and the conduct of the patient both before and after admittance to the hospital. The last named factor, however, does not necessarily burden the hospital with the duty to investigate the patient's past history, but refers to the facts given to the hospital at the time of admittance.

In the case of a delirious or deranged patient or one likely to become so, the hospital's duty of reasonable care and attention extends to safeguarding him from dangers due to his mental incapacity. This comprehends any danger which the surroundings would indicate to physicians and nurses of the prudence, competence and experience ordinarily possessed by persons similarly engaged.

Although a private hospital is not liable for the negligence of nurses selected by patients, nor for the acts of medical care performed by its nurses when these acts are done under the direction of the attending doctor, such a hospital is responsible to a patient for the negligent acts of its nurses, in the performance of their routine duties.

A private hospital generally does not undertake to furnish more than facilities and personnel for the care and treatment of patients. If the hospital has agreed to provide medical treatment for a fee, as distinguished from merely furnishing facilities, it may be held liable for damages resulting from improper treatment. A physician employed by a private hospital to treat patients for a fee charged by the hospital is not an independent contractor and the hospital is liable for his malpractice under the doctrine of *respondeat superior*.

INDEX

INDEX

A

Abortion
abortionist, 267
accidental, 267
accusations, 267
admission, 267
Catholic viewpoint, 273
confidential communications, 269
consent of woman, 270
consultation record, 268
consulting staff, 268
criminal, 267, 269, 270
dead infant, 267
drugs, 270
emergencies, 268
good faith, 272
history of, 267
incomplete, 267
inevitable, 267, 268
instruments, 270
intent to commit, 267
Jewish viewpoint, 274
legal definition, 269
medical definition of, 269
medical indications, 270, 272
medical proof, 272
medical therapy, 272
obstetrical service, 268
operative procedures, 268
premature delivery, 269
Protestant viewpoint, 274
release, 268
religious viewpoints, 273
spontaneous, 267, 268
statutes, 269, 270
therapeutic, 267, 273
threatened, 267, 268

Administrative Negligence,
See: Hospital Liability

Admissibility of Records,
See: Evidence

photostatic copies, 91
records on appeal, 91, 92
rules and regulations, 82
Uniform Business Records as
Evidence Act, 59
X-rays, 59

**American Association of Medical
Record Librarians**
accreditation by, 8
approved schools, 8
basic legal principles, 9
Code of Ethics, 9, 10
education, 8
examinations, 8
librarians, 8
membership, 8
professional pledge, 9
protection of records, 10
registration of librarians, 8
retention of records, 47
technicians, 8

American Hospital Association
accident report form, 80
Committee on Safety report, 81
experimental drugs, 334
incident reports, 80
insurance form, 47
Jehovah's Witnesses,
See: Jehovah's Witnesses
record retention, 52, 53

American Medical Association
clinical research, 333, 334
medical report form, 94, 95
Principles of Medical Ethics, 146

Amputated Parts,
See: Tissue and Organs

Anesthesia,
See: Physicians

Artificial Insemination
consent, 284

donor, 284
heterologous, 284
homologous, 284
legal decisions on, 184–285
legitimacy of offspring, 284–285
obligations of father, 284–285
rights of natural father, 284–285

Assault and Battery,
 See: Operations Without Consent

Autopsies
accidental deaths, 300
administrative responsibility, 289
administrator of estate, 298
adult children's rights, 296
anatomical acts, 298, 299
brothers' rights, 298
burial certificate, 287
confidential communications, 77
consents, 288, 289, 292
coroners, 294, 300–302
criminal penalties, 290, 301
damages, 290, 293
death certificates, 287
definition of, 286
dental schools, 299
desertion effects, 295
disposition by will, 288, 294
divorce of spouses, 296, 298
executor's rights, 298
father's rights, 297
forfeiture of rights, 294, 295, 297
forms, 289, 292
friends' rights, 294, 299
funeral directors, 290
homicidal deaths, 300
insurance cases, 299
intern training, 286
Joint Commission requirements,
 286
judicial separation, 295
limitations on, 290, 292
medical examiners, 300–302
medical schools, 299
minor children, 297
mother's rights, 297

mutilation of body, 288, 293
next of kin's rights, 293
operating room deaths, 301
organs, *See:* Tissue and Organs
pathologist, 290
percentage of, 286
pronouncing death, 287
records of, 290
religious objections, 292
removal of organs, 291
reporting deaths, 301
retention of tissue, 291
rights in dead bodies, 288
rights of hospitals, 298
separation of spouses, 294, 295
sister's rights, 298
statutory authorization, 298
suicidal deaths, 300
surviving spouse's rights, 288
telegram consent, 290, 291
telegraph consent, 290, 291
tissue, *See:* Tissue and Organs
unlawful, 288
verbal permit, 289

B

Blood Banks,
 See: Blood Transfusions

Blood Transfusions
American Red Cross, 248, 256
blood banking, 247
California Statute, 251
donors, 248, 255, 256
express warranty, 251
Federal Tort Claims Act, 253
hepatitis, 247, 248
homologous serum jaundice, 247,
 249
implied warranty of fitness, 249,
 250
incompatible blood, 253
intragroup incompatibilities, 247
Jehovah's Witnesses,
 See: Jehovah's Witnesses
merchantable quality, 249
mislabeling, 252

mismatched blood, 253
plasma, 247, 248, 250
pyrogenic reactions, 247, 248
release by donors, 256
requisitions for, 232
Rh factor, 247
Sales Act, 249, 251
sale of blood, 249, 250
sources of error, 247
state as distributor, 249
test for carriers, 248
whole blood, 248
wrong patient, 254
wrong type of blood, 252

Broken Hypodermic Needles,
See: Operating Room

C

Charitable Hospitals,
See: Hospitals

Confidential Communications
abortions, *See:* Abortions
admissibility, 173
autopsies, 77
chiropractors, 78
common law status, 74, 75
dentists, 78
drugless healers, 78
duration of, 77
elements of, 75, 76
examinations, 77
Hippocratic Oath, 74
incident reports, 80
medical ethics, 74
mental healers, 78
names and addresses, 82
names of physicians, 92
nature of, 73
nurses, 78-80
partners of physicians, 78
physicians, 73
privileged communication, 153
psychoanalysts, 78
psychologists, 78
purpose of, 75

records as, 153
statutes for, 75, 82, 100–102
tax cases, 82, 83
treatment, 77
veterinarians, 78
waiver, 100, 173
worksheets, 82

Consent for Autopsy,
See: Autopsies

Consent for Minors,
See: Operations Without Consent
adult siblings, 237, 238
age, 236, 237, 239
blood transfusions,
See: Blood Transfusions
contracts, 236, 240
court order, 237, 240, 241
custody of minors, 236
definition of minor, 236
emancipation, 236, 237, 239
emergency, 237, 241
guardian, 236, 237, 240, 241
guiding principles, 236, 237
immature minor, 237
Jehovah's Witnesses,
See: Jehovah's Witnesses
marriage, 236, 237, 240
maturity, 236, 238
operations, 236
parents, 237, 240
ratification, 238
students, 239
unauthorized operation, 238
unmarried minor, 239
vaccination, 241

Consent for Treatment,
See: Operations Without Consent
anesthesia, 232
assault and battery, 234
blanket consents, 229
blood transfusions,
See: Blood Transfusions
cardiac catheterization, 234
cobalt irradiation, 234
contents of, 227, 228

emergencies, 230, 231
exploratory treatment, 235
form of, 229
identification of patient, 228
informed, 227, 232, 233, 234
Joint Commission on Accreditation
    of Hospitals, 227
legal requirements, 229, 231
major surgery, 282
minor surgical procedures, 231, 232
nature of operation, 228, 229
necessity of, 229, 233
oral, 229
procedures requiring, 231
shock therapy, 233
signature of patient, 87, 228
sterilization, *See:* Sterilization
telegram, 230
telephone, 230
witness, 228, 231
written, 229, 231, 232

Courts,
    See: Trials

administrative agencies, 105, 107,
    110
appeal, 109
circuit, 108
county, 108
district courts, 106, 108
federal judicial system, 106
federal trade commission, 107
jurisdiction of, 105
justice, 108
justice of the peace, 109
municipal, 108
state judicial system, 108
supreme court, 107, 109
surrogates, 109
types of, 105

D

Dead Bodies,
    See: Autopsies

Defenses,
    See: Malpractice

Documents,
    See: Evidence

as evidence, 138, 140
authentication, 140, 152
best evidence rule, 138
business entries rule, 151
certification, 140
hearsay rule, 151, 152
hospital records, 138
private, 140
public, 140
parol evidence rule, 138
secondary evidence, 139
tissue committee reports, 151
unattested, 141

Drugs,
    See: Experimental Drugs

E

Eugenic Sterilization,
    See: Sterilization

Evidence
admissibility, 133, 166, 169, 173
admissions against interest, 175
authentication, 140
best evidence rule, 138
books of account, 141
burden of proof, 133
business records, 134, 151, 160
certification, 140, 180
circumstantial, 129
competency, 135
correspondence, 182
demonstrative, 130
diagnoses, 168, 175–177
direct, 129
dying declarations, 136
entries in regular course of busi-
    ness, 141, 152
exhibits, 192
facts and circumstances, 129
federal rule, 161, 166
financial records, 181
hearsay, 134, 135, 151, 169, 170

hospital records, 134, 138, 152, 153, 166
incident reports, 130
indirect, 129
judicial notice rule, 131, 140
laboratory tests, 178
malpractice, 133
maternity, 135
medical books, 141, 142
medical opinions, 168, 175–177
narrative statements, 170, 171, 172
New York rule, 161
non-medical facts, 168
nurses' notes, 179, 180
parol evidence rule, 139
personal injury cases, 177
photographs, 141, 164
photostats as, 162
physicians' records, 182–184
presumptions of law, 131
prima facie case, 133
primary evidence, 170
private documents, 140
privileged communications, 153
proof required, 167
psychiatric opinions, 177, 178
public documents, 140
real, 130
relevancy, 133, 135
res gestae rule, 135, 136, 174
res ipsa loquitur, 132
rules of, 129
secondary, 139
self-serving declarations, 136, 137, 174
Shop-Book Rule, 141
social service, 182
statutes on, 152, 166
testimony, 130
tissue committee reports, 151, 153
Uniform Business Entries rule, 165
X-rays, 159, 160

Examination Before Trial,
    See: Legal Proceedings

Experimental Drugs
agreement of investigators, 335
American Hospital Association policy, 334
American Medical Association rules, 333, 334
application for clearance, 335
clinical research, 323
consents for, 334
dosage forms, 334
Drug Amendments of 1962, 335
drug reactions, 332–334
Federal Food and Drug Administration, 335
manufacturer of, 335
records and reports, 335, 336
sponsor of investigation, 335
treatments, 333

Expert Evidence,
    See: Medical Experts

F

Federal Tort Claims Act,
    See: Hospital Liability

G

Governmental Hospitals,
    See: Hospital Liability

H

Hospital Liability
Army regulations, 351
charitable, 340, 342
city hospitals, 353
classification of hospitals, 340
county liability, 352
dependents, 351
evolution of, 342, 343
exemptions, 340, 341, 343–349
Federal Government, 349
Federal Tort Claims Act, 349–351
governmental functions, 352
immunities, 341, 342, 343–349, 352
insurance coverage, 353
liabilities of states, 352

medical treatment, 355
municipal corporations, 353
negligence, 340
non-service-connected injuries, 351
private, 340
proprietary functions, 352
proprietary hospitals, 353–355
public, 340, 352
public policy theory, 341
respondeat superior theory doctrine, 342, 355
service connected injuries, 351
servicemen, 351
state immunity, 352
subdivisions of state, 352
tortious conduct, 340
trust funds theory, 341
U. S. Government, 349–351
veterans, 351
waiver theory, 341, 351

I

Infants,
   See: Consents for Minors

J

Jehovah's Witnesses
adult patient, 257
American Hospital Association, 261
appointment of guardian, 259
blood transfusions, 256, 257
consent of husband, 258
consents, 257, 258, 263
Constitutional rights, 259, 260
court order, 257, 260
divorced mother, 260
elective cases, 261
emergency cases, 258, 260
literature of, 257
minors, 258, 259, 260, 262
parents' objections, 258, 262
proof of damages, 258
reaction report, 264, 265
refusal of, 257
release from patient, 261
religious principles, 257, 259, 265

Scriptural objections, 257
written refusal, 261, 262

**Joint Commission on Accreditation
   of Hospitals**
accreditation, 44
autopsies, 286
bylaws and regulations, 155, 156
forms for records, 32, 33, 227
intern training program, 286
preservation of records, 47
short forms, 34
sponge counts, 324
standards for accreditation, 2, 3,
   43
standards for medical records, 3, 4
summaries of records, 35
survey, 43
tissue committees, 144, 149
work sheets, 147

L

Lawsuits,
   See: Legal Proceedings

Legal Proceedings
admission of facts, 118
answers, 113, 114
attorneys, 113
bill of particulars, 113, 116
breach of contract, 112
civil action, 113
commissions, 117
complaint, 113, 114
counterclaim, 115
damages, 113
declaration, 113
defendant, 113
defenses, 115
depositions, 117
examination before trial, 116, 117
general release, 112
interrogatories, 117
judgment after trial, 112
judgment by default, 112
jurisdiction, 114
memorandum of law, 119

motions, 116
notice of trial, 118
nuisance settlement, 111
parties, 113
petition, 113
plaintiff, 113
pleadings, 113
reply, 115
respondent, 113
service of papers, 114
settlements, 112
stipulation of discontinuance, 112
subpoena, 113, 118
summons, 112, 113, 114
torts, 112, 113
trial by jury, 112
verdict, 112
witnesses, 118

M

Malpractice,
    See: Physicians

abandonment of patient, 330
assumed risk defense, 338
clinical research, 333
common law negligence, 328
contracts to cure, 329, 330
contributory negligence, 337, 338
criminal negligence, 328, 329
defenses of physician, 337
defined, 328, 329
Drug Amendments of 1962, 335
drug reactions, 332, 333
duties of physician, 328
experimental drugs, *See:* Experimental Drugs
expert testimony, 337
failure to cure, 329
general practitioner's skill, 336
Good Samaritan statutes, 339
medical records, 327
medical witnesses, 337
proof of, 336, 337
res ipsa loquitur, 330, 331, 332
specialist's skill required, 336

specialty examining boards, 336
statute of limitations, 338, 339
statutory negligence, 328

Medical Experts
cross-examination, 142
opinions, 141, 142, 337
psychiatrists, 142
x-ray films, 159

Medical Information
abstracts, 86, 90
addresses, 93
admission dates, 93
age, 93
approval of physician, 86
assignments, 86
attorneys, 86, 95, 96
authorization of patient, 87
consent form, 86
control of, 84, 85
convalescent homes, 86
date of birth, 93
deceased patients, 90
diagnosis, 93
discharge dates, 93
employers, 86, 102, 103
examination by patient, 100
governmental agencies, 104
guardian's consent, 90, 92
hospitals, 86, 103
insurance carriers, 86, 97, 98
lien laws, 96, 97
medical staff, 93, 94
mental patients, 92
minors, 88, 90
names of physicians, 92, 93, 95, 96
notary public, 87
photostatic copies, 91
private patients, 86
professional information, 93, 94
proofs of illness, 97
required by law, 94
research, 93
semi-private patients, 86
signature of patient, 87

social agencies, 104
study, 93
witness to signature, 87

Medical Records,
   See: Records
abstracts, 50
accidents, 11
admission sheet, 11
anesthesia, 29, 30
authentication, 20, 165
card summaries, 50, 51
completion of, 37, 38, 45
confidential communications, 173
consultations, 5, 27
contents, 5–7
corrections, 32, 42
delay in recording, 45, 46
deceased physicians, 57, 58
discharge summary, 7, 10
drugs, 30
early medical records, 4, 5
examination by attorney, 100
examination by family, 100, 101
examination by patient, 100, 101
fees, 91
final diagnosis, 7
graphic chart, 20
history, 5, 13, 44, 170
incomplete, 36, 37
laboratory reports, 28
laboratory tests, 178
negligence cases, 11
nurses' notes, 17–20, 56, 57
objective findings, 24
operating room, 29
operations, 27, 30
ownership, 84
pathology, 28
personal injury cases, 117
photostatic copies, 91, 153, 161, 162
physical examination, 5, 22, 30, 45
physician's orders, 16, 18
physicians' signatures, 30–32, 42
primary evidence, 170

progress notes, 7, 23, 30
provisional diagnosis, 5, 44
psychiatric opinions, 177, 178
public hospitals, 180, 181
radiologists' reports, 26
removal from hospitals, 44
retention of, 54–57
specialists' report, 25
standards, 1, 2, 43
standing orders, 30
statutes of limitation, 66, 67
summary, 7, 30, 35
tissue reports, 6
treatment, 6, 7
Uniform Business Entries rule, 165

Medical Records Committee
committee composition, 314, 315
disciplinary action by, 39, 43
functions, 38, 44
incomplete records, 39, 43
medical staff bylaws, 38, 39
reports of, 39
revision of forms, 147
staff meetings, 39
suspension of privileges, 40, 41, 43

Medical Record Personnel
American Association of Medical Record Librarians, 8, 9, 43
as witness, 168, 169, 170
code of ethics, 9, 10
custodian, 169
education, 8
eligibility, 8
Joint Commission, 43
librarian, 7
medical record science, 7
pledge, 9
standards, 9
technician, 8, 43
testimony, 169

Medical Staff
appointments, 308, 311, 313
certification of specialists, 307, 312

constitution and bylaws, 313, 314
credentials committee, 314
demotion in grade, 310
disciplinary action, 313, 314
ethical standards, 309
executive committee, 314
governing board responsibility, 307
illegal discrimination, 309
joint conference committee, 308, 315
license to practice, 309, 312
medical board, 312, 313
medical records committee, 314
medical staff bylaws, 34, 307, 309
meetings, 308
officers, 308
"open" hospitals, 312
organization, 307
privileges, 308, 310
program committee, 315
promotion, 310
public hospitals, 311, 312
reappointments, 308, 313
record of minutes, 308
rights of, 309, 310
rules and regulations, 308, 312
special committees, 308
specialty boards, 307
standing committees, 308
state law, 312
tenure, 308
termination of appointments, 308, 310, 313
tissue committee, 315
trustees' liability, 311
trustees' responsibility, 307
unqualified practitioners, 308, 309
utilization committees, 146, 147

Microfilming
as evidence, 162
business entries rule, 162
destruction of original record, 163
primary evidence, 163
proof of process, 163
record preservation, 47, 48

reproduction from, 162
use of, 51, 52
x-rays, 66

N

Negligence,
    See: Malpractice
Nurses
bedside record, 34
graphic chart, 20
Joint Commission, 18
Manual of Nursing Procedure, 81
notes, 17, 19, 181
observations by, 19
personal injury cases, 19
physicians' visits, 19
retention of notes, 56, 57
telephone orders, 18

O

Operating Room
administrator, 318
anesthesia accidents, 316
attorneys, 316
auxiliary personnel, 320
blood transfusion errors, 316
broken surgical needles, 316, 325, 326
control over nurse, 321
counting instruments, 319
director of nursing, 318
drains, 325
emergencies, 317
examination before trial, 316
foreign substances, 323
hospital liability, 318
hot-water bottles, 321
interns, 321, 322
lawsuits, 316
lost sponges, 316
medical chart, 316, 317
names of personnel, 316
nurse in charge, 320
nurse responsibility, 318, 319
nursing duties, 316, 318, 320
operating room supervisor, 317

preoperative studies, 317
regulations, 324
residents, 321, 322, 323
rules in, 317
scrub nurse, 323
sponge count technique, 323
sponges, 323, 324
surgeon's obligations, 317, 318, 321, 322
tubes, 325
x-ray, 320

Operations Without Consent,
    See: Consent for Minors
    See: Consent for Treatment

assault, 242, 243
auxiliary operations, 244
battery, 242, 243
Cesarean sections, 245
consent of husband, 244, 246
damages, 242
emergencies, 244-246
fraudulent consent, 243
implied consent, 244
Oklahoma statute, 246
Organs, *See:* Tissue and Organs
postmortem Cesarean section, 246
unauthorized operation, 242
unrelated conditions, 244
viability of infant, 246
wrong operation, 243

P

Photographs, 209-217
as evidence, 141, 164
authorization for, 209, 211, 212, 214, 215
case history, 213
clinical, 212, 213
commercial purposes, 209, 213, 214
contracts, 214
exhibits, 213
identification of, 164
medical journals, 213, 214
motion pictures, 216
news interest, 210

ownership, 216, 217
patient's record, 211
postmortem, 213
proof of trauma, 164
publications, 213
research, 213
right of privacy, 201
scientific purpose, 215
slides, 213
specimens, 213
teaching, 213
television, 216
unclothed females, 212
x-ray films, 215

Physicians
anesthesia, 28, 30
as witnesses, 183
confidential communications,
    See: Confidential Communications
consultation reports, 27
deceased, 57
discharge summary, 22
expert opinions, 24
Federal shop book rule, 184
house officers, 30
laboratory reports, 28
legal protection, 22
malpractice, *See:* Malpractice
names of, 92
narrative histories, 25
office memoranda, 184
operating room reports, 29
order sheet, 16
pathology reports, 28
private medical records, 182-184
professional services, 183
progress notes, 23
radiologist's interpretations, 26
records of deceased, 183
report of operation, 27
responsibility for errors, 23
signatures, 30
specialists' reports, 25, 26
written reports, 184

Privacy

attorneys' visits, 203-208

clinical demonstrations, 200

consent for pictures, 198

consent for teaching purposes, 201

death ends, 197

hospital associations, 199

insurance investigators, 203

interviews, 198

laymen, 201, 202

medical teaching, 200, 201

motion pictures, 216

newspaper publicity, 197

photographs, 196

press codes, 199

press relations, 196, 197-199

private patients, 200

prominent persons, 195, 196, 209

public relations, 197

radio media, 199

right of, 195, 203

semi-private patients, 201

solicitation of patients, 208

state laws, 196, 200

television, 199, 216

U.S. Public Health Service rules, 203

visitors to patient, 202, 203

waiver of right, 203

Property

abandoned, 224, 225

bailee, 218

bailment, 218, 222

bailor, 218

care of, 218

cash handling, 220, 222

clothes list, 219, 220

constructive bailment, 223

conversion, 223

crime to keep, 226

deceased patients, 223, 224

delivery of, 220

dentures, 220

finder of, 226

forms, 219, 220

hospital charges, 222

innkeepers, 219

insurer of, 219

jewelry, 220

legal process, 219

liability for loss, 219

limitation of liability, 219

lost, 224

misdelivery of, 224

mislaid, 224, 226

private duty nurses, 220, 222

safekeeping of, 218, 219

sale of, 225

R

Records,

See: Medical Records

abstracts, 50

adequacy of, 38

anesthesia report, 29

authentication, 20, 36

autopsies, 290

bedside, 34

completion of, 35, 37

control program, 48, 49

corrections of, 32

defined, 1

discharge summary, 35

incomplete, 37

index cards, 50

laboratory reports, 28

nurse's bedside, 34

operating room reports, 29

photostatic copies, 91

preservation, 47, 48

privileged communications, 100

roentgenograms, 47

short stay, 33

signatures of physicians, 30, 31

summary sheet, 31, 35

transfusion reactions, 264, 265

trustees' responsibility, 36

use of, 32, 49

S

Statute of Limitations
  breach of contracts, 68, 69
  effect of, 66, 67, 69, 70
  Federal Tort Claims Act, 72
  malpractice cases, 67, 68, 338
  minors, 71, 72
  nurses' notes, 57
  postponement of, 70, 71
  record preservation, 53, 54
  records of minors, 54
  x-ray preservation, 64, 65

Sterilization
  California law, 278
  cancer, 276, 277
  castration, 275, 276
  civil actions for, 282–284
  compulsory, 280
  Connecticut statute, 279
  consent for, 280, 281
  criminal liabilities, 276
  definition of, 275, 276
  economic reasons, 278
  eugenic, 279, 280
  husband's sterilization, 281, 282
  Kansas law, 279
  legal considerations, 275
  legal control, 278
  medical indications, 277
  minors, 280
  Montana law, 279
  nontherapeutic, 278
  North Carolina law, 279
  panhysterectomy, 276
  reasons for, 276
  religious attitudes, 282
  salpingectomy, 275
  statutes on, 276, 279
  therapeutic, 277
  Utah law, 279
  vasectomy, 275
  Virginia law, 279

Subpoena
  attorneys, 120

  criminal cases, 120, 121
  disease index cards, 155
  disobedience of, 125, 126
  fees, 122, 126, 127
  hospital records, 123
  hospital rules and regulations, 155
  incident reports, 80
  malpractice cases, 154
  medical record librarians, 120
  medical staff discussions, 155
  medical witnesses, 126, 127
  mental patient record, 127, 128
  mileage, 122
  photostatic copies, 124
  power to, 120
  quashing of, 156
  records, 84, 87, 105, 123
  rules for, 124, 125
  service, 121, 125
  subpoena duces tecum, 123, 153
  surgical log book, 155
  tissue committee reports, 141, 149,
    154
  witnesses, 120, 122, 125

T

Tissue and Organs
  autologous transplantation, 302
  bone, 302
  burns, 302
  cartilage, 302
  consents, 303, 305
  donation statutes, 305, 306
  eyes, 302, 304
  forms, 303, 304, 305
  homologous transplantation, 302
  kidneys, 302, 304
  legal control, 304
  postmortem homografts, 303
  skin grafts, 302
  statutes, 304, 305
  therapeutic purposes, 304
  transplantation, 304
  wills for, 305

Tissue Reports

as evidence, 151
committees, 143, 244, 315
malpractice claims, 143
medical audit, 143
medicolegal purposes, 143, 151
Organs, *See:* Tissue and Organs
retention, 149, 150
statutes on, 156, 158
subpoena for, 151
surgical review committee, 145
tissue committee functions, 144, 146
tumor and tissue committee, 145
work sheets, 147, 149

Trials,

See: Legal Proceedings
Bill of Rights, 185

clerk of court, 189
common law, 185
court's charge, 193
credibility of witnesses, 187
criminal cases, 186
directed verdict, 193
examination of witnesses, 190, 192
exceptions, 193
exhibits, 192
findings of fact, 189
instructions to jury, 193
motion to dismiss, 191, 192
opening address, 189

powers of court, 185
preliminary motions, 190, 191
prima facie case, 191
qualifications of jurors, 186
questioning witnesses, 185
questions of fact, 186, 187, 188
questions of law, 186, 188
selection of jury, 189
swearing of jury, 189
summing up, 192, 193
trial by jury, 185, 186
verdict by jury, 188, 194
waiver of jury, 186

X

X-Rays

admissibility of, 59
American College of Radiology, 47, 48
best evidence rule, 161
copies of, 161
evidence, 63, 159
identification, 160
ownership, 59, 60–62, 64
photographs, 215
preservation, 47, 58, 62, 65
prints of, 161
reports, 6
specialists, 159, 160
storage of, 62
technicians, 160